INTRODUCTION TO LATTICE THEORY

INTRODUCTION TO LATTICE THEORY

by

GÁBOR SZÁSZ
PROFESSOR OF MATHEMATICS AT SZEGED UNIVERSITY

THIRD REVISED AND ENLARGED EDITION

ACADEMIC PRESS NEW YORK
AND LONDON

The Original
BEVEZETÉS A HÁLÓELMÉLETBE
Akadémiai Kiadó, Budapest

MS revised
by
R. WIEGANDT

Translated
by
DR. B. BALKAY
and
G. TÓTH

Not to be sold in the Soviet Union
or in the countries of the people's democracies

Joint edition published
by
Academic Press, New York and London
and
The Publishing House of the Hungarian Academy of Sciences,
Budapest

Printed in Hungary

PREFACE

About a quarter of a century ago, lattice theory entered the foreground of mathematical interest and its rate of development increased rapidly. Despite the fact that up to now it has yielded less profound theorems than other algebraic fields, today it is already one of the important branches of algebra. Its concepts and methods have found fundamental applications in various areas of mathematics (e.g. diverse disciplines of abstract algebra, mathematical logic, projective and affine geometry, set and measure theory, topology, and ergodic theory) and theoretical physics (e.g. quantum and wave mechanics, and the theory of relativity).

I shall attempt to give a brief sketch of the development of lattice theory. In 1824, in the course of his research in mathematical logic, G. Boole introduced an important class of lattices which were later named Boolean Algebras. In 1890 E. Schröder introduced the lattice concept as it is understood today. A few years later, in 1897, R. Dedekind, through research on groups and ideals, arrived at this same concept. He defined — according to present-day terminology — modular and distributive lattices. These are the classes which have been (up to the present) most important for applications. The development of lattice theory proper commenced around the 1930's. Thereafter it gained so considerable an impetus that Garrett Birkhoff — the major figure thus far in lattice theory — could in his book [19]* give an account not only of its fundamental development but also of its manifold applications.

Most of the pioneer work was done by G. Birkhoff, but beside him must be cited the names of M. H. Stone, Oystein Ore, O. Frink, S. MacLane, R. P. Dilworth, and of Hungarian-born János von Neumann.

In the last decade the scope of lattice-theoretical research also grew wider geographically — some years ago efforts in this direction were initiated in Hungary also.

My book is — as indicated by the title — addressed to those who look for a general orientation within lattice theory or who wish to

* The numbers in brackets refer to the bibliography. With regard to citations, we have adopted in general the practice of mentioning in the text only the bibliography number. However, in the case of theorems occurring in books or longer papers we have also added the original number of the theorem or, lacking such, the original page number.

apply it in mathematical research on topics of different nature. Accordingly, I have attempted on the one hand to introduce the reader to the most important concepts and most generally used simple methods of lattice theory, and on the other hand to point out — as far as possible within the scope of the book — the connections of lattice theory with other branches of mathematics.

In writing my book I have also considered the requirements of the student who regards its study as a first step towards independent lattice-theoretical research. It was in his interest that I have included references to numerous new advances in areas covered by this book, whose detailed discussion would be out of place in such an introductory volume. Those who take a more profound interest in lattice theory should, by all means, study the books of H. Hermes [91], Dubreil-Jacotin—L. Lesieur—R. Croisot [50] and G. Birkhoff [19], which I myself have perused frequently in writing this book. Concerning the principal advances of lattice theory up to 1939, a good summary is found in a report by H. Hermes and G. Köthe [92]. A good survey of the most actual, modern problems of lattice theory is provided by the lectures held at the Symposium of the American Mathematical Society in 1959 (Symposium on Partially Ordered Sets and Lattice Theory) (see [165]).

The study of the lattice-theoretical content of the book — in the stricter sense of the word — requires no more than a rudimentary knowledge of set theory. Nevertheless, it is advantageous if the reader has a good knowledge of abstract algebra.

Although the exercises and applications presume a certain knowledge of diverse disciplines of mathematics, no such knowledge was taken for granted in the further treatment of the theoretical framework.

At the end of each chapter, some exercises are given to help the reader attain the necessary skill for handling the theoretical material. Hints to the solution of the more involved exercises are found at the end of the book.

My book was first published in Hungarian in 1959 followed by a German version in 1962. This German edition was enlarged in so far as it contained references to lattice-theoretical papers that had appeared in the meantime. When preparing the present English version the original manuscript was revised and the most recent developments pertaining to the theme of the book were considered. In writing it, I have received valuable help from Professors L. Fuchs and J. Szendrei, and from Gy. Grätzer, T. E. Schmidt and R. Wiegandt. The text was translated into English by B. Balkay and G. Tóth. I extend to them my sincere thanks for their assistance.

I also wish to thank the Hungarian Academy of Sciences for the commission to write this book and the Publishing House of the Hungarian Academy of Sciences and the Academy Press for their careful work.

Szeged, September 1962.

G. Szász

CONTENTS

CHAPTER I

PARTLY ORDERED SETS

1. Set theoretical notations 11
2. Relations 13
3. Partly ordered sets 15
4. Diagrams 17
5. Special subsets of a partly ordered set 20
6. Length 21
7. Lower and upper bounds 22
8. The minimum and maximum condition 24
9. The Jordan—Dedekind chain condition. Dimension functions 25
Exercises to Chapter I 28

CHAPTER II

LATTICES IN GENERAL

10. Algebras 30
11. Lattices 33
12. The lattice theoretical duality principle 35
13. Semilattices 38
14. Lattices as partly ordered sets 38
15. Diagrams of lattices 42
16. Sublattices. Ideals 43
17. Bound elements of a lattice. Atoms and dual atoms 44
18. Complements, relative complements, semicomplements 45
19. Irreducible and prime elements of a lattice 40
20. The homomorphism of a lattice 51
21. Axiom systems of lattices 53
Exercises to Chapter II 56

CHAPTER III

COMPLETE LATTICES

22. Complete lattices 59
23. Complete sublattices of a complete lattice 63
24. Conditionally complete lattices, σ-lattices 64
25. Compact elements, compactly generated lattices 65
26. Subalgebra lattice of an algebra 67
27. Closure operations 68
28. Galois connections, Dedekind cuts 70
29. Partly ordered sets as topological spaces 74
Exercises to Chapter III 77

CHAPTER IV

DISTRIBUTIVE AND MODULAR LATTICES

30. Distributive lattices 79
31. Infinitely distributive and completely distributive lattices 83
32. Modular lattices 86
33. Characterisation of modular and distributive lattices by their sublattices 88
34. Distributive sublattices of modular lattices 93
35. The isomorphism theorem of modular lattices. Covering conditions 95
36. Meet representations in modular and distributive lattices 97
Exercises to Chapter IV 101

CHAPTER V

SPECIAL SUBCLASSES OF THE CLASS OF MODULAR LATTICES

37. Preliminary theorems 104
38. Modular lattices of locally finite length 107
39. The valuation of a lattice. Metric and quasimetric lattices 108
40. Complemented modular lattices 112
41. Complemented modular lattices and projective spaces 113
Exercises to Chapter V 119

CHAPTER VI

BOOLEAN ALGEBRAS

42. Boolean algebras. De Morgan formulae 122
43. Complete Boolean algebras 124
44. Boolean algebras and Boolean rings 126
45. The algebra of relations 130
46. The lattice of propositions 132
47. Valuations of Boolean algebras 135
Exercises to Chapter VI 138

CHAPTER VII

SEMIMODULAR LATTICES

48. Birkhoff lattices 140
49. Semimodular lattices 142
50. Equivalence lattices 145
51. Linear dependence 149
52. Complemented semimodular lattices 153
Exercises to Chapter VII 157

CHAPTER VIII

IDEALS OF LATTICES

53. Ideals and dual ideals. Ideal chains 159
54. Ideal lattices 161
55. Distributive lattices and rings of sets 165
Exercises to Chapter VIII 168

CHAPTER IX

CONGRUENCE RELATIONS

56. Congruence relations of an algebra 170
57. Permutable equivalence relations 175
58. The Schreier refinement theorem in arbitrary algebras 177
59. Congruence relations of lattices 182
60. Minimal congruence relations of some subsets of a distributive lattice 183
61. The connection between ideals and congruence relations of a lattice 186
Exercises to Chapter IX 189

CHAPTER X

DIRECT AND SUBDIRECT DECOMPOSITIONS

62. Direct unions and decompositions of algebras 191
63. Subdirect unions and decompositions of algebras 194
64. Direct and subdirect union of lattices 196
65. Direct and subdirect decompositions of lattices 199
66. The neutral elements and the centre of a lattice 205
Exercises to Chapter X 208

*

Hints to the solution of the more involved exercises ... 210
Bibliography 216
Index 225

CHAPTER I

PARTLY ORDERED SETS

1. Set Theoretical Notations

In this section we shall describe the notations of set theory to be used in this book. The fundamental concepts of set theory (set, system, subset, union and intersection of sets, function, mapping and power of sets) will be assumed to be known. (Concerning these concepts see e.g. [228], §§ 1—4 and 8.)

The fact that an element x is included in a set M, and an element y is not included in M, will be denoted by $x \in M$ and $y \notin M$, respectively.

A finite set may be given by enumerating its elements in braces; for example, the set consisting of the elements $a_1, \ldots, a_n$ is denoted $\{a_1, \ldots, a_n\}$. This mode of notation can, with a slight modification, be used on sets M of any power. Consider, namely, a set Γ whose power equals that of M and assign one, and only one, element of M to each element γ of Γ (this being feasible because of the equal powers of the sets) and denote this element by a_γ. In this way, the elements of M are provided with the elements of Γ as indices. Hence, Γ is called the "index set". Hereafter, the elements of M will be spoken of as "all elements $a_\gamma(\gamma \in \Gamma)$", and for M itself let us introduce the notation

$$M = \{a_\gamma\}_{\gamma \in \Gamma} \tag{1}$$

If the emphasizing of the index set is inessential for some reason, for example, if M denotes a set of arbitrary power, then instead of (1) we write simply $M = \{a_\gamma\}$.

The fact that R is a subset of the set M is symbolized by $R \subseteq M$. If R is a proper subset of M (that is, if $R \subseteq M$ but $R \neq M$) we write $R \subset M$.

The empty set will be frequently encountered: it is denoted O.

Let now $M_1, \ldots, M_n$ be arbitrary sets. Their union or intersection is denoted respectively by

$$M_1 \cup \ldots \cup M_n \text{ or } M_1 \cap \ldots \cap M_n$$

or by

$$\bigcup_{j=1}^{n} M_j \quad \text{or} \quad \bigcap_{j=1}^{n} M_j \tag{2}$$

Besides brevity, the latter notation has also the advantage that it can be immediately generalised to denote the union or intersection of a set of any power of sets to be symbolised. Analogous to (2), the union and intersection of a countably infinite number of sets M_j ($j = 1, 2, \ldots$) is denoted by the symbols

$$\bigcup_{j=1}^{\infty} M_j \quad \text{or} \quad \bigcap_{j=1}^{\infty} M_j$$

If we wish to denote the intersection or the union of a family of any cardinal number of sets $\{M_\gamma\}_{\gamma \in \Gamma}$ we use the notation

$$\bigcap_{\gamma \in \Gamma} M_\gamma \quad \text{or} \quad \bigcup_{\gamma \in \Gamma} M_\gamma$$

As usual, we shall mean by the *difference of the sets* A and B, denoted $A - B$, the set of all elements of A which are not included in B (see Fig. 1). The set $(A - B) \cup (B - A)$ is termed the *symmetrical difference* of the sets A and B.

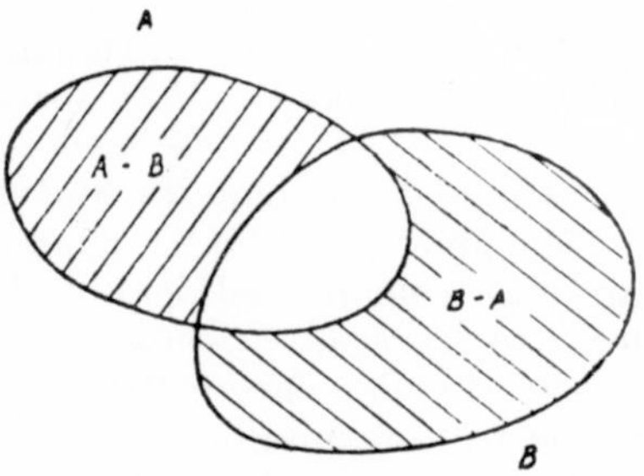

Fig. 1

Let φ be a mapping of a set H onto (or into) the set K. The element which is assigned by φ to x ($\in H$) is denoted $\varphi(x)$. Hence, φ assigns to every element x of H one, and only one, element $\varphi(x)$ of K. This is symbolized as follows:

$$\varphi : x \to \varphi(x) \qquad (x \in H\,;\ \varphi(x) \in K)$$

Instead of this detailed way of writing we sometimes use the shorter notation $x \to \varphi(x)$.

Furthermore, we mean by the *image set* of the subset R ($R \subseteq H$), denoted by $\varphi(R)$, that subset of K consisting of all elements of the form $\varphi(x)$ ($x \in R$).

By the *inverse* of the mapping φ we mean (following [228], § 3) that function, generally many-valued, which assigns to each element y of K every element x of H such that $\varphi(x) = y$. This function is denoted φ^{-1}.

If φ is a one-to-one mapping of H onto K, then φ^{-1} is also a one-to-one mapping of K onto H, namely:

$$\varphi^{-1}\colon \varphi(x) \to x \qquad (\varphi(x) \in K\,;\ x \in H)$$

Let H, K, L be arbitrary sets and φ a mapping of H into K and ψ a mapping of K into L. Then the correspondence $x \to \psi\big(\varphi(x)\big)$ ($x \in H$) is a mapping of H into L, which is called the *product of the mappings* φ and ψ and is denoted by $\psi\varphi$. Accordingly, instead of $\psi(\varphi(x))$ we write for short $\psi\varphi(x)$.

2. Relations

In mathematics — as in everyday life — there are sets containing certain elements (pairs, triples, etc.) connected to each other by having a special property which other elements of the set do not have.

Examples:

(1) Similarity of triangles: In the set of all triangles for a pair of triangles $\mathfrak{A}$, $\mathfrak{B}$ it is either true or not true that $\mathfrak{A}$ is similar to $\mathfrak{B}$.

(2) Divisibility of positive integers: In the set of all positive integers it is either true or false that a divides b.

(3) Betweenness of points of an affine straight line (i.e. a straight line whose points at infinity are disregarded): For a triple of points A, B, C on the line it is either true or false that C lies between A and B.

Frequently, a certain property expresses a connection between the elements of two or more different sets; e.g. orthogonality of straight lines and planes.

Connections of this kind are usually called "relations", an exact definition (one of several possible ones) follows.*

The *product* or *product set* $M_1 \times \ldots \times M_r$ of the (not necessarily distinct) sets $M_1, \ldots, M_r$ ($r \geq 2$) is defined as the set of all sequences of the form

$$(1) \qquad (x_1, \ldots, x_r) \; (x_j \in M_j;\ j = 1, \ldots, r)$$

Now, by a *relation defined on the product set* $M_1 \times \ldots \times M_r$ (or among the sets $M_1, \ldots, M_r$) we will understand a function Φ of r variables which relates to each element of the form (1) of $M_1 \times \ldots \times M_r$ one of the logical values "true" or "false" (= "not true"). Or, expressing the logical values "true" and "false" by the symbols (current in mathematical logic) $\uparrow$ and $\downarrow$, respectively, then for each of the elements of the form (1) either

$$\Phi(x_1, \ldots, x_r) = \uparrow \quad \text{or} \quad \Phi(x_1, \ldots, x_r) = \downarrow$$

Two relations are said to be equal if both are defined on the same set and if they are equal on that set considered as logical functions. In other words, for the relations Φ_1, Φ_2 defined on the set $M_1 \times \ldots \times M_r$ the fact that $\Phi_1 = \Phi_2$ signifies that for any element of the form (1) $\Phi_1(x_1, \ldots, x_r) = \uparrow$ if, and only if, $\Phi_2(x_1, \ldots, x_r) = \uparrow$.

In the following, we shall deal exclusively with the case $r = 2$, and primarily with the special case of $M_1 = M_2$. Accordingly we agree that by a "relation on the set M" we will understand throughout a relation defined on the product set $M \times M$. Furthermore, if Φ is a relation defined on $M_1 \times M_2$ and $\Phi(x_1, x_2) = \uparrow$ ($x_1 \in M_1$; $x_2 \in M_2$), then we write $x_1 \Phi x_2$; and if $\Phi(x_1, x_2) = \downarrow$, we shall write $x_1 \Phi' x_2$. The use of the latter symbol is indicated by the fact that the function Φ' defined by the formula $\Phi'(x_1, x_2) = \uparrow \Longleftrightarrow \Phi(x_1, x_2) = \downarrow$ ($x_1 \in M_1$, $x_2 \in M_2$) is itself a relation on $M_1 \times M_2$.*

* Another, more frequently used but less intuitive definition is found in § 5 of [228].

** The symbols $\Longrightarrow$ and $\Longleftrightarrow$, frequently used later have the meaning "implies" and "if, and only if", respectively.

In the subsequent part of this section we shall only deal with the case $M_1 = M_2 = M$.

A relation Φ defined on the set M is termed
1. *reflexive*, if for all elements x of M, $x\Phi x$ holds;
2. *symmetric*, if for all pairs of elements x, y of M, $x\Phi y$ and $y\Phi x$ hold, or do not hold, simultaneously;
3. antisymmetric, if for all pairs of elements x, y of M, $x\Phi y$ and $y\Phi x$ hold simultaneously only in case of $x = y$;
4. *transitive*, if for any triplet of elements x, y, z of M, $x\Phi y$ and $y\Phi z$ imply $x\Phi z$.

Of the examples cited at the beginning of the paragraph, the first relation is reflexive, symmetric and transitive, the second one is reflexive, antisymmetric and transitive. An example of a non-reflexive, non-transitive but symmetric relation is orthogonality of straight lines. Among sets, the symbol "$\subset$" establishes a transitive relation, the symbol "$\subseteq$", on the other hand, a reflexive, antisymmetric and transitive relation.

The relation Θ defined on the set M is called an *equivalence relation*, or simply an *equivalence*, if Θ is reflexive, symmetric and transitive. A relation Π defined on the set M is called an *ordering relation* or simply an *ordering* if Π is reflexive, antisymmetric and transitive. It is obvious that the relation E defined by

$$x\mathsf{E}y \Longleftrightarrow x = y$$

and called the *equality relation* is the only relation which is both an equivalence and an ordering at the same time.

Relations which are reflexive and transitive are called *quasiorderings*. Examples of such relations are: Let M be a family of topological spaces and let $a\Phi b (a, b \in M)$ mean that b is homeomorphic with a subset of a. Or let M be the set of all real functions of two variables and let $f\Phi g (f, g \in M)$ mean that $f(x, y) \leq g(x, y)$ except on a set of measure zero.

Since equivalence and ordering relations are exceedingly frequent in every branch of mathematics, it is expedient to introduce for these two types of relation a special notation differing from the general one. This will be done as follows. If Θ is a relation of equivalence, we will put $x \equiv y(\Theta)$ instead of $x\Theta y$; and if Π is a relation of ordering, we shall write $x \leq y(\Pi)$ instead of $x\Pi y$. Accordingly, instead of $x\Theta' y$ and $x\Pi' y$, the notations $x \not\equiv y(\Theta)$ and $x \not\leq y(\Pi)$ will be employed.

When only a single equivalence relation or ordering is considered, besides the equality relation, it is permissible to omit indication of the relation (i.e. to use the shorter notations $x \equiv y$, $x \leq y$, $x \not\equiv y$, $x \not\leq y$ respectively).

From the definition of the relation Φ it sometimes may not be immediately apparent whether Φ is an ordering or an equivalence, but this will subsequently be determined. In such cases, to avoid changes in symbols, we will usually use the notations introduced above immediately after defining Φ.

3. Partly Ordered Sets

In this paragraph, a rather ancient concept (Peirce [156]) will be introduced which is of profound significance for all our following considerations.

If on the set P there is defined an ordering, Π, then P will be called a *partly ordered* set with respect to Π. If, however, at least one of the relations $x \leq y(\Pi)$ and $y \leq x(\Pi)$ holds for any pair of elements x, y belonging to P, then P will be termed a *completely ordered* set or *chain* with respect to Π (in lattice theory the latter term is used almost exclusively). Another frequently used expression is: "The relation Π partly orders (or completely orders) the set P."

Obviously each set P is partly ordered by the equality relation. If no other ordering relation is considered on P, then P will be called a completely unordered set.

In the theory of partly ordered sets, terminology is not uniform. Thus, it is also usual to speak of "partially ordered sets" instead of "partly ordered sets" and of "linearly ordered sets" or simply "ordered sets" instead of "completely ordered sets".

Before commencing the study of partly ordered sets, let us consider some examples of sets of this kind.

Example 1. A simple and well-known example is the set V of real numbers; this is completely ordered by the relation "$\leq$" defined by $x \leq y$ if, and only if, $y - x$ is not negative. This relation will be called the *natural ordering of real numbers*, and we shall speak in the same sense of the natural ordering of subsets of V.

This example is to be kept constantly in mind throughout the remainder of this chapter, because most of the concepts to be introduced (e.g. the concept of the partly ordered set itself) are appropriate generalizations of the familiar concept of the natural ordering of real numbers.

Example 2. In the set N of positive integers let $x \leq y$ if, and only if, x is a divisor of y. It is clear that this relation partly orders the set N.

At the same time N, being a subset of the real numbers, V, is completely ordered with respect to the natural ordering.

Example 3. For an arbitrary set M, let $\mathscr{P}(M)$ be the set of all subsets of M. The set $\mathscr{P}(M)$ is partly ordered with respect to the relation

$$(1) \qquad A \leq B \leftrightarrow A \subseteq B\,(A, B \in \mathscr{P}(M)).$$

Example 4. Let S denote the usual three-dimensional space, and $\mathscr{L}(S)$ the set of all linear subspaces of S, the void set also being considered as a linear subspace. Evidently, by writing $\mathscr{L}(S)$ instead of $\mathscr{P}(M)$ in (1), an ordering of $\mathscr{L}(S)$ is obtained.

Example 5. In the set K of all circles of a plane, let $k_1 \leqq k_2$ denote the fact that the circle k_1 is contained by the circle k_2. It is at once apparent that the relation $\leqq$ thus defined partly orders the set K.

Example 6. Consider a set M and the set $\mathcal{R}(M)$ of all relations on M. The set $\mathcal{R}(M)$ may be partly ordered in the following way: let $\Phi \leqq \Psi (\Phi, \Psi \in \mathcal{R}(M))$ if, and only if, for any pair of elements x, y of M, $x\Phi y \Rightarrow x\Psi y$.

Obviously, a relation Φ on M is reflexive if, and only if, with respect to the ordering introduced above, $\Phi \geqq \mathrm{E}$.

In the general case, as in the case of the relation of ordering in Example 1. "$b \geqq a$" is frequently written instead of "$a \leqq b$". The first expression is read "b is greater than or equal to a" ("than" and "to" can eventually be neglected), and the second one "a is smaller than or equal to b". Further symbols used are $<$ and $>$, signifying $a < b$ or $b > a$, if $a \leqq b$ but $a \neq b$.

Let a and b be two arbitrary elements of the partly ordered set P. If $a \leqq b$ or $a \geqq b$, a and b are said to be *comparable*; in the opposite case, a and b are said to be *incomparable* (or non-comparable) elements, which fact is expressed by $a \parallel b$.

Let P be a partly-ordered set with respect to the relation Π and let $\mathfrak{D}(\Pi)$ denote the relation for which

$$a \leqq b(\mathfrak{D}(\Pi)) \Longleftrightarrow a \geqq b\,(\Pi) \quad (a, b \in P)$$

It is easy to see — wherefore the proof is left to the reader — that $\mathfrak{D}(\Pi)$ also partly orders P. $\mathfrak{D}(\Pi)$ is termed the *dual of the ordering relation Π*. Clearly, the dual of $\mathfrak{D}(\Pi)$ is the original relation Π.

Let P_1 be a set partly-ordered with respect to the relation Π_1, and P_2 with respect to Π_2. A single-valued mapping φ of P_1 into P_2 (especially onto P_2)

$$\varphi : x \to \varphi(x) \quad (x \in P_1; \varphi(x) \in P_2)$$

is called an *order preserving mapping*, an *order homomorphic mapping* or an *order homomorphism* of the set P_1 into (or onto) P_2, if

$$(2) \qquad x \leqq y(\Pi_1) \Longleftrightarrow \varphi(x) \leqq \varphi(y)\,(\Pi_2) \quad (x, y \in P_1)$$

If φ^{-1} is an order homomorphism also, then φ is called an order isomorphism. In other words, an order isomorphism of P_1 onto P_2 is a one-to-one mapping of P_1 onto P_2 such that

$$(3) \qquad x \leqq y(\Pi_1) \Longleftrightarrow \varphi(x) \leqq \varphi(y)\,(\Pi_2) \qquad (x, y \in P_1)$$

holds.

If there is an order isomorphic mapping of P_1 onto P_2, then P_1 is said to be *order isomorphic* to P_2 and this fact is expressed symbolically by $P_1 \overset{o}{\approx} P_2$. It can be shown by simple considerations (e.g. [228], § 26) that order isomorphism is an equivalence relation on the set of partly ordered sets. Thus, since $P_1 \approx P_2$ implies $P_2 \approx P_1$, the expression "P_1 and P_2 are order isomorphic" is also used here.

Consider the sets $A = \{a_1, a_2, a_3, a_4\}$, $B = \{b_1, b_2, b_3, b_4\}$ and $C = \{c_1, c_2, c_3, c_4\}$ and define ordering relations one for each, as follows:

$$a_1 < a_2,\ a_1 < a_3,\ a_1 < a_4,\ a_3 < a_4$$

$$b_1 < b_2,\ b_1 < b_3,\ b_1 < b_4,\ b_3 < b_4$$

$$c_1 < c_2 < c_3 < c_4$$

Then define upon A the mappings φ, ψ and σ by the following:

$$\varphi(a_j) = b_j \ (j = 1, 2, 3, 4)$$

$$\psi(a_j) = \begin{cases} b_2, & \text{if } j = 2, \\ b_1, & \text{if } j = 1, 3, 4 \end{cases}$$

$$\sigma(a_j) = c_j \ (j = 1, 2, 3, 4)$$

φ is an order isomorphism, ψ an order homomorphism of A into B and σ an order homomorphism. Although σ is one-to-one, it is not an order isomorphism since the inverse mapping does not preserve the ordering defined on C.

4. Diagrams

The ordering of finite sets can be very clearly illustrated with the aid of diagrams. Before describing the method, we need to introduce some preliminary concepts.

If for a pair of elements a, b of a partly ordered set $a < b$ holds and there is no element x such that $a < x < b$, then it is said that the element a is *covered* by b (or b covers a). This situation will be expressed by the symbol $a \prec b$ (or $b \succ a$). Accordingly, $a \preceq b$ will symbolize that "b either covers or equals a"; for short, "b at most covers a". The latter symbol will, however, be infrequently used.

In Example 3. Section 3, $A \prec B$ if, and only if, $B = A \cup \{b\}$, where b is any element of the set $B - A$. In Example 4, $A \prec B$ means that the linear subspace A is included in the linear subspace B, the latter having one dimension more. In Examples 1 and 5, there occur no elements of which one would cover the other.

An element a of a partly ordered set P is called a *minimal element* of P if P has no element x for which $x < a$ would hold. Similarly, a is a *maximal element* of P if the relation $x > a$ is fulfilled by no element x of P. In other words, an element a of P is a minimal (maximal) element of P if the relations $x \in P$ and $x \leq a$ ($x \geq a$) necessarily imply $x = a$. Clearly, every finite partly ordered set possesses at least one minimal and one maximal element.

A partly ordered set may have more than one maximal and minimal element, but infinite sets may also happen to have none. Let us review the examples of Section 3 from this point of view. In Example 5, every point of the plane (being a circle of zero radius) is a minimal element of the set K; on the other hand, K has no maximal element. The set V of Example 1 has neither maximal, nor minimal elements. The set $\mathscr{P}(M)$ of Example 3 has one maximal and one minimal element — the minimal element is the set O, the maximal element the set M.

Consider now a finite set P with an ordering defined on it and construct the following figure. Represent each element by a circle K_a in the plane of the drawing (denoted by the letter a), such that if $a < b$ $(a, b \in P)$, K_b is above K_a; the relative lateral position of the two circles is of no importance. (Particular examples will be given immediately). Now consider each pair of elements x, y of P for which $x \prec y$ and connect the circles K_x, K_y representing such (and only such) pairs of elements by segments. The resulting figure is the *diagram* of the set P with respect to the considered ordering.

As an illustration, consider the eight-element set $P = \{a, b, c, d, e, f, g, h\}$ for which

$$a < c,\ a < d,\ b < c,\ b < d,\ c < d,\ e < f,\ e < g$$

the remaining pairs of different elements being incomparable. Let us prepare the corresponding diagram. Following the definition of ordering we must place the circle K_c above K_a and K_b, and K_d even higher than K_c. (The circles K_a and K_b may be placed at the same level or at different levels; for reasons of symmetry, the first alternative is adopted.) The positions of the circles K_e, K_f and K_g are independent of those of the former circles, but their relative positions must be such that K_f and K_g are above K_e. Finally, the circle K_h can be placed anywhere, the element h being incomparable to any of the other elements. Since

$$a \prec c,\ b \prec c,\ c \prec d,\ e \prec f,\ e \prec g$$

and since there exist no other relations of covering between the pairs of elements of P, let us connect the circles K_a and K_c, K_b and K_c, K_c and K_d, K_e and K_f, K_e and K_g. The resulting diagram is the one shown as Fig. 2a.

Turning the diagram of Fig. 2a upside down, we obtain the diagram representing the dual ordering (Fig. 2b).

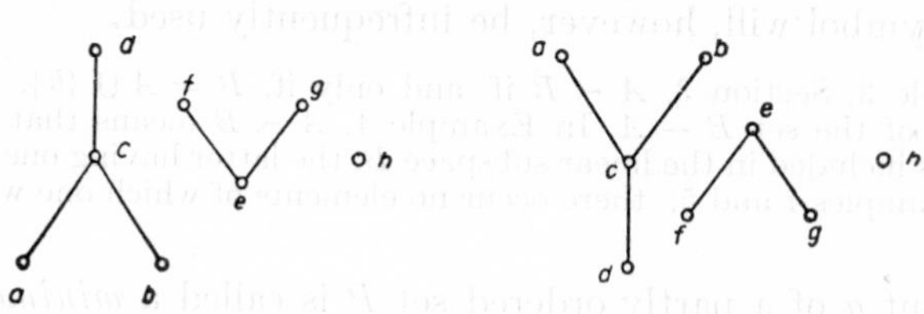

Fig. 2/a *Fig. 2/b*

THEOREM 1. *Every (non-void) finite partly-ordered set can be represented by a diagram* [Birkhoff [12], Theorem 4].

This Theorem will be proved by induction.

PROOF. To begin with, the only ordering of the one-element set $\{a\}$ (defined by $a \leq a$) can be illustrated by drawing a single circle.

Assume now that the statement holds for any partly ordered set consisting of at most $(n-1)$ elements and let P be a partly ordered set of n elements. Since P consists of a finite number of elements, it has at least one maximal element, m. Omitting m, we obtain a subset R of $(n-1)$ elements, which is also partly ordered with respect to the ordering in P. By the induction hypothesis R has a diagram. Thus, placing the circle K_m above the circles of all elements of R, and connecting it with all circles K_x $(x \in R)$ for which $x \prec m$, the figure obtained is the required diagram of P.

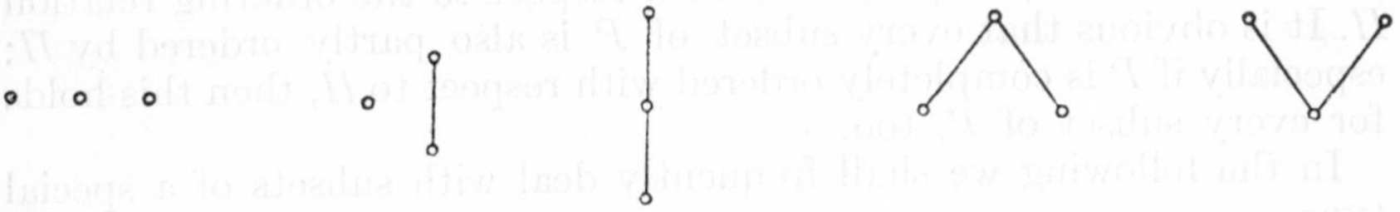

a) b) c) d) e)

Fig. 3

Obviously, if the diagrams of two (finite) partly ordered sets disregarding the notation of the circles, coincide, the two sets are order-isomorphic with respect to the ordering relations considered.

Conversely, let $A = \{a_1, \ldots, a_n\}$ $(n \geqq 1$ being finite) be a set partly ordered by the relation Π_A and $B = \{b_1, \ldots, b_n\}$ a set partly ordered by the relation Π_B and let

$$(1) \qquad a_j \leqq a_k(\Pi_A) \longleftrightarrow b_j \leqq b_k(\Pi_B) \ (j, k = 1, \ldots, n)$$

i.e. let the mapping $a_j \to b_j$ $(j = 1, \ldots, n)$ be an order isomorphism of A onto B. We now show that the two sets — disregarding the notation of the circles — can be represented by the same diagram. As proof, consider the diagram of A and put b_j in the place of each a_j. If $b_j < b_k$, then also $a_j < a_k$ by (1), and consequently, in the re-lettered diagram the circle K_{b_k}. will be above the circle K_{b_j}. Furthermore, also by (1), $b_j \prec b_k$ if, and only if, $a_j \prec a_k$. Hence, in the diagram obtained by re-lettering the circles, K_{b_j} and K_{b_k}, the latter being above, will be immediately connected (meaning that there is no other circle between them along the connecting segment) if and only if $b_j \prec b_k$. Consequently, the re-lettered diagram exactly represents the ordering Π_B of the set B.

Fig. 4

Summarizing: *Two partly ordered sets can be represented by the same diagram if, and only if, they are order isomorphic.*

Hence if for a finite partly ordered set, the structure of the set as a whole is the chief point of concern, the diagram of the set will frequently be constructed without lettering the circles. For example, all essentially different (i.e. mutually non-order-isomorphic) three-element partly ordered sets can be represented by the diagrams 3a — 3e.

By appropriate conventions, some infinite partly ordered sets can be illustrated by diagrams of a similar nature but of generalized meaning. Thus, the natural ordering of positive integers can be very clearly illustrated by the (generalized) diagram of Fig. 4.

5. Special Subsets of a Partly Ordered Set

Let P be a set partly ordered with respect to the ordering relation Π. It is obvious that every subset of P is also partly ordered by Π; especially if P is completely ordered with respect to Π, then this holds for every subset of P, too.

In the following we shall frequently deal with subsets of a special type.

Let a be an arbitrary element of a partly ordered set. We denote the set of all the elements x in P satisfying the inequality $x \leq a$ by $(a]$ and the set of all x in P satisfying $x \geq a$ by $[a)$.

Let further a and b be a pair of elements of P such that $a \leq b$. Then we define as the *interval* bounded by the elements a and b and denote by $[a, b]$ the set of all the elements x of P for which $a \leq x \leq b$ holds.

All the preceding concepts are contained as special cases in the following: A subset R of P will be said to be *convex* if it contains with any pair of elements a, b $(a < b)$ every element of the interval $[a, b]$; i.e. if $a, b \in R$ and $x \in [a, b]$ imply $x \in R$.

A subset R of P is called a *completely unordered subset* if any two elements of R are incomparable with respect to the ordering Π.

On the other hand, a subset C of P is called a *subchain* of P if C is a chain (meaning that any two elements of C are comparable) with respect to the ordering on P.

Note: Any completely unordered subset of a partly ordered set is convex. However, a subchain is not convex in general. (See, for example, the subchain consisting of the elements a and d in Fig. 2a.)

Consider the set $\mathfrak{C}$ of all subchains of P. This set can itself be ordered in the following way: let $C_1 \leq C_2$ $(C_1, C_2 \in \mathfrak{C})$ if, and only if, $C_1 \subseteq C_2$. On this basis, a subchain C of P is termed a *maximal chain* (in P) if C is a maximal element of the partly ordered set $\mathfrak{C}$, i.e. if there exists no subchain $\overline{C}$ in P which would properly include C.

In the set K of Example 5., any subset consisting of concentric circles is a subchain; the simplest way to obtain a completely unordered subset in K is, on the other hand, by considering an (arbitrary) set of circles, no two of which have a common interior point.

Let M denote the set of all pairs of real numbers (x, y), and Π_V the natural ordering of the set of real numbers. Then, the relation defined by the prescription

$$(x_1, y_1) \leq (x_2, y_2)\ (\Pi_M) \Longleftrightarrow x_1 \leq x_2(\Pi_V) \text{ and } y_1 \leq y_2(\Pi_V)$$

is an ordering of M with respect to which the sets

$$C_1\colon \ \ldots, (-2, -2), (-1, -1), (0, 0), (1, 1), (2, 2), \ldots$$

$$C_2\colon \ \ldots, \left(\frac{3}{2}, -\frac{3}{2}\right), (-1, -1), \left(\frac{1}{2}, -\frac{1}{2}\right), (0, 0), \left(\frac{1}{2}, \frac{1}{2}\right), \ldots$$

C_3: the set of all number pairs of the form (x, x)

are subchains, with $C_1 \subset C_2 \subset C_3$. In particular C_3 is a maximal chain in M.

We will consider as an axiom the following intuitive statement:

CHAIN AXIOM. *For any subchain C of a partly ordered set P there exists at least one maximal chain $\bar{C}$ such that $\bar{C} \supseteq C$.*

This statement is generally cited in the literature under the name "Hausdorff–Birkhoff Theorem" and is derived from the axiom of choice (see Hausdorff, [223], p. 140). Its being considered an axiom is justified by the circumstance that, besides being a corollary of the axiom of choice, it is also equivalent to it (see e.g. [228], pp. 23–28, or [19], pp. 42–44); moreover, it is at least as obvious as the latter.

The chain axiom implies the

KURATOWSKI-ZORN LEMMA. *If every subchain of a non-empty partly ordered set P has an upper bound, then P contains a maximal element* (Kuratowski [226], Theorem 1, and Zorn [232]).

This Lemma is frequently used in abstract algebras.

As a matter of fact, the Kuratowski–Zorn Lemma is likewise equivalent to the chain axiom; for a proof, we refer the reader again to [228] and [19].

PROOF. By the chain axiom, P has at least one maximal subchain C. We shall prove that if C has an upper bound m, then m is at the same time a maximal element of P. Indeed, should there be an $s (s \in P)$ such that $s > m$, then $s > m \geqq c$ would hold for any element c of C and hence the set $C \cup \{s\}$ would be a chain properly containing C. This, however, is in contradiction to the assumption that C is maximal. Thus, by making use of the chain axiom, we have proved the lemma.

6. Length

By the *length of a chain* consisting of r elements (that is, being of the form $x_0 < x_1 < \ldots < x_{r-1}$) we shall mean the non-negative integer $r - 1$, and the length of a chain consisting of an infinite number of elements will be symbolized by ∞. Then, the *length of the partly ordered set P* will be defined as the length of the least upper bound of the lengths of all subchains in P.

Consequently, if the length of the subchains in P is within a finite bound and if the least of these bounds is n, the length of P will be considered to be n; on the other hand, if the length of the subchains in P increases beyond all finite bounds, it will be said that the length of P is ∞. Depending on the above considerations, P is said to be either *of finite* or *of infinite length.* (In the special case when P itself is a chain, the adjectives "finite" and "of finite length" on the one hand, and "infinite" and "of infinite length" on the other, will mean the same thing).

An immediate practical consequence of the chain axiom is that, to obtain the length of a partly ordered set it is sufficient to consider the length of its maximal subchains.

The partly ordered set P will be said to be of *locally finite length* if every one of its intervals (considered as partly ordered sets) is of finite length.

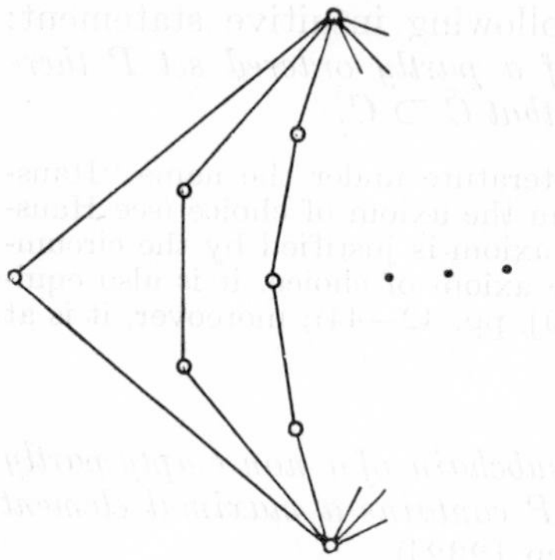

Fig. 5

Every finite partly ordered set is, a fortiori, of finite length. A partly ordered set of finite length, consisting of an infinite number of elements is the set $\mathscr{L}(S)$ of Example 4; its length is 4, because each maximal chain consists of exactly one point, one line and one plane of S, in addition to the void set and S itself. A set of infinite length is the set M discussed in Section 5 prior to the chain axiom.

A set of locally finite length which is, however, not of finite length is, for example the set N of positive integers with respect to the ordering given in Example 2.

The reader's attention is especially directed to the fact that partly ordered sets occur in which the length of all subchains is finite, whereas the length of the set as a whole is nevertheless infinite. This situation is illustrated by Fig. 5: the partly-ordered set represented by that diagram, of generalized meaning, is formed by "hitching up" of chains of the length 2, 3, 4, . . ., n, . . . one of each length. It is immediately apparent that the partly ordered set so constructed is still not of locally finite length.

7. Lower and Upper Bounds

Let R be an arbitrary non-void subset of a partly ordered set P (the case $R = P$ not excluded). An element a is called the *upper (lower) bound* of R, if $x \leq a$ $(x \geq a)$ holds for any element x of R. If R has at least one upper (lower) bound, R is called a *subset bounded above (bounded below)* of P; a subset which is bounded both above and below is called a *bounded subset*. If $R = P$, we shall speak of a *set bounded above* or *bounded below*, respectively.

Especially $(a]$ $(a \in P)$ is the set of all lower bounds, and $[a)$ the set of all upper bounds of a in P.

In the partly ordered set of Fig. 6 the only lower bound of the subset $\{c, e, f, g\}$ is b; the subset $\{c, d\}$ has two lower bounds, a and b; but neither of the sets has an upper bound. In the set V of Example 1, the subset of all positive numbers has an infinite number of lower bounds, namely zero and all negative numbers (whereas the entire set V has no lower bound). Consider also Example 5: all the circles of the plane tangent to a given line form a subset of K which has neither an upper nor a lower bound. The set of Example 2 is bounded below, but unbounded above whereas the sets of Examples 3, and 4 are bounded ones.

It is easily shown that there exists at most one lower bound of the subset R, which is included by R, for if a, b $(\in R)$ are both lower bounds of R, then, by definition, $a \leqq b$ and $b \leqq a$ at the same time and, therefore, by the antisymmetry property of ordering relations, $a = b$. The same consideration is valid for the upper bounds. If there exists a lower, resp. upper bound of a subset R of a partly ordered set P contained by the subset R itself (this will be unique according to what was said above) then this will be termed the *least*, resp. *greatest element* of R. The least and greatest elements together will be called the *bound elements* and every other element of R is called an *inner element*.

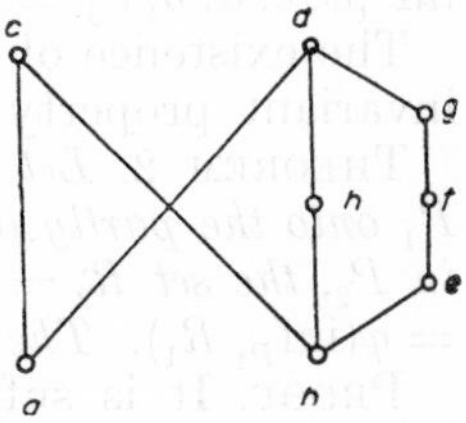

Fig. 6

Clearly, if P itself has a least (greatest) element, it is the only minimal (maximal) element of P.

On the other hand, a minimal (maximal) element m of a set R is not necessarily the least (greatest) element in R, even if R has no minimal (maximal) element besides m. Consider e.g. that subset R of the set N of positive integers which consists of all odd positive integers and of the even numbers 2 and 4. If N is ordered — as in Example 2. — by divisibility, 4 is the only maximal element of R, and there exists no greatest element within this subset.

Let us decide to denote the least and the greatest elements of the partly ordered set in question by the letters o and i respectively. In dealing simultaneously with more than one partly ordered set bounded at least on one side, the least and greatest elements of each will be distinguished by subscripts.

Let R be again an arbitrary subset of the partly ordered set P. The sets of the upper and/or lower bounds of R are themselves subsets of P; consequently, the above definitions can also be applied to these two subsets. Accordingly, we shall introduce the following terms: by the greatest lower (least upper) bound or infimum (supremum) of the subset R within P we will mean the greatest (least) element of the set of the lower (upper) bounds of R, provided there exists such an element. In the following, the names "infimum" and "supremum" will usually be used.

From the above considerations it follows that any subset R of P can have at most one infimum and one supremum; these are to be denoted by $\inf_P R$ and $\sup_P R$. When no confusion can arise, we will simply write "inf R" and "sup R".

The supremum of the subset $\{a, b\}$ of the partly ordered set of Fig. 2a (page 18) is the element c; on the other hand, in the partly ordered set of

Fig. 6 $\{a, b\}$ has no supremum, since the set of the upper bounds of $\{a, b\}$ — the set $\{c, d\}$ — has no least element.

The concepts of the upper and lower bound as well as of the infimum and supremum may be extended to any subsystem* of the partly ordered set P. The natural way of performing this extension is the following: By the upper or lower bound, infimum or supremum of a subsystem R^+ of P we shall mean the lower or upper bound etc. of that subset R which is derived from R^+ by retaining only one element from each complex of identical elements. In this sense e.g. $\inf \{a, c, a, b, c\} = \inf \{a, b, c\}$.

The existence of the infimum and/or supremum is an isomorphism-invariant property in the following sense:

THEOREM 2. *Let φ be an order isomorphism of the partly ordered set P_1 onto the partly ordered set P_2. If a subset R_1 of P_1 has an infimum in P_2, the set $R_2 = \{\varphi(x)\}_{x \in R_1}$ will have an infimum in P_2, $\inf_{P_2} R_2 = \varphi(\inf_{P_1} R_1)$. The corresponding statement for suprema also holds.*

PROOF. It is sufficient to consider the statement concerning the infimum, because for the supremum the proof is similar. Assume that $\inf_{P_1} R_1 = u$ exists. Consider an arbitrary element y of R_2: then $\varphi^{-1}(y) \in R_1$. However, u is a lower bound of R_1, so that $u \leqq \varphi^{-1}(y)$. Since $P_1 \overset{o}{\approx} P_2$, it follows that $\varphi(u) \leqq \varphi(\varphi^{-1}(y)) = y$; hence $\varphi(u)$ is a lower bound of R_2. Now let t be an arbitrary lower bound of R_2 in P_2. Then, by order isomorphism of the two sets, $\varphi^{-1}(t)$ is a lower bound of R_1 in P_1; hence $\varphi^{-1}(t) \leqq u$. Consequently, $t = \varphi(\varphi^{-1}(t)) \leqq \leqq \varphi(u)$. Thereby, the statement $\varphi(u) = \inf_{P_2} R_2$ is proved.

8. The Minimum and Maximum Condition

Let c_0 be an arbitrary element of a partly ordered set S. Let us form a subchain of P in the following way: let the $\left\{\begin{matrix}\text{greatest}\\ \text{least}\end{matrix}\right\}$ element of the subchain be c_0; otherwise, let c_k $(k \geqq 1)$ be an element of P such that $\left\{\begin{matrix}c_k < c_{k-1}\\ c_k > c_{k-1}\end{matrix}\right\}$ be true. If each of the chains so formed, commencing at any c_0, is finite, P is said to satisfy the $\left\{\begin{matrix}\textit{minimum}\\ \textit{maximum}\end{matrix}\right\}$ *condition.***

This terminology is justified by

THEOREM 3. *If a partly ordered set P satisfies the minimum condition (maximum condition), then to any $x \in P$. there exists at least one minimal (maximal) element m of P such that $x \geqq m$ $(x \leqq m)$*

COROLLARY. *Every subchain of a partly ordered subset satisfying the maximum (minimum) condition has a greatest (least) element.*

* It will be remembered that (according to [228], p. 10) a subsystem of a set M means a complex of the elements of M in which an element may occur more than once, as in $\{a, c, a, b, c, c\}$.

** In Birkhoff's work [19] these are termed "descending chain condition" and "ascending chain condition".

PROOF. Consider a partly ordered set P satisfying the minimum condition. For a minimal element x of P, the statement of the theorem is true with $m = x$. If x is not a minimal element, it is possible to choose an element x_1 of P such that $x > x_1$. If x_1 is still not a minimal element, it is possible to choose an element $x_2 (x_2 \in P)$ so that $x > x_1 > x_2$ and so forth. Since P satisfies the minimum condition, in a finite number of steps we will attain an element x_r such that $x > x_1 > x_2, \ldots, > x_r$ and no element of P will be less than x_r. Thus, the statement of the theorem regarding the minimum condition is proved (with $m = x_r$).

The statement regarding the maximum condition can be proved in the same way, by interchanging the symbols $>$ and $<$. The corollary is, on the other hand, trivial. If the maximum (minimum) condition is satisfied by a given partly ordered set, it will be likewise satisfied by all its subsets; furthermore, a chain can have no more than one maximal (minimal) element, and that is at the same time the greatest (least) element of the chain.

The partly ordered sets satisfying both the maximum and minimum conditions have the following property:

THEOREM 4. *A partly ordered set can satisfy both the maximum and minimum conditions if, and only if, every one of its subchains is finite.*

PROOF. Only the necessity of the condition needs proof. Let P be a partly ordered set satisfying the minimum condition. According to the Corollary to Theorem 3, each subchain of P has a least element. Let C_0 be a subchain of P. Let us form a sequence

$$C_0 \supset C_1 \supset \ldots \supset C_j \supset C_{j+1} \supset \cdots$$

of subchains of P in the following way: each C_{j+1} is derived from the preceding C_j $(j = 0, 1, \ldots)$ by omitting the least element c_j of C_j. If C_0 is infinite, the sequence of the C_j's is infinite. Hence, also, the sequence of their least elements

$$c_0 < c_1 < \ldots < c_j < c_{j+1} < \cdots$$

is infinite. In that case, however, P does not satisfy the maximum condition. Thus the theorem is proved by contradiction.

The set of the positive integers — in its natural order — is a simple example of a set satisfying the minimum condition but failing to satisfy the maximum condition.

9. The Jordan—Dedekind Chain Condition Dimension Functions

Let P be a partly ordered set, a and b two elements of P such that $a < b$ and finally C a subchain of P having a as the least and b as the greatest element, then it will be said that the chain C is "situated between the element a and b", or that C "connects the elements a and b". If, in addition, C is a maximal chain of $[a, b]$ then it is called "a maximal chain between a and b", or "a maximal chain connecting a and b".

By the Chain Axiom, in any partly ordered set there is at least one maximal chain between any pair of elements a and b ($a \leq b$). Usually, however, the number of maximal chains between such a pair of elements a, b is greater than one and these maximal chains are generally of different lengths.

For example, in Fig. 6. (page 23) the length of one maximal chain ($b < e < f < g < d$) between the elements b and d is 4; whereas the length of the other ($b < h < d$) is 2.

If for every pair of elements a, b ($a \leq b$) of a partly ordered set, it is true that all maximal chains connecting the elements a and b are of the same length (i.e., if either all chains between a and b are infinite, or the length of all chains equals the same finite number), the set is said to satisfy the *Jordan—Dedekind chain condition.*

Some necessary and sufficient conditions for the Jordan—Dedekind chain condition to be satisfied by a partly ordered set are given in papers by Ore [154] and Croisot [31]. The proof of Ore's principal result was essentially simplified by MacLane [128].

By the *height* or *dimension* $h(a)$ of the element a of a partly ordered set P a bounded below is meant the length of the interval $[o, a]$.* Evidently, the domain of values for the function h consists of non-negative integers and, eventually, of the symbol $+\infty$, with $h(x) = 0$ if, and only if, $x = o$. If P is of locally finite length and satisfies the Jordan—Dedekind chain condition, then each of its elements is of finite height; i.e. $h(a)$ equals the (common) length of the maximal chains between o and a. In this case, $x \prec y$ ($x, y \in P$) if, and only if, $x \leq y$ and $h(x) + 1 = h(y)$.

More generally, let d be a function defined on the partly ordered set P (not necessarily bounded below) such that the domain of values of d consists of (arbitrary) integers and, eventually, of one or both of the symbols $\pm\infty$. The d is called a *dimension function* of P if

$$(1) \qquad x \prec y \Longleftrightarrow x \leq y \text{ and } d(x) + 1 = d(y) \quad (x, y \in P)$$

Now let P be a partly ordered set of locally finite length satisfying the Jordan—Dedekind chain condition. If P contains an element u such that inf $\{u, x\}$ exists for all elements x of P, then a dimension function can be defined upon P, in the following way. To begin with, let us assign to the element u an arbitrary integer $d(u) = d_0$. Subsequently, if the lengths of the maximal chains connecting inf $\{u, x\}$ with u and x are r_{1x} and r_{2x}, respectively, let $d(x) = d_0 - r_{1x} + r_{2x}$. We must prove that the function d thus defined satisfies (1).

* This concept is derived from the dimension for the linear subspaces of a projective space. In projective geometry, the dimension of a linear subspace A ($\neq O$) of a projective space is, however, one less than the dimension $h(A)$ defined within the partly ordered set of all linear subspaces.

Let $x, y \in P$ and $x < y$. In this case, $\inf\{u, x\} \leqq \inf\{u, y\}$ and there evidently exists a maximal chain between $\inf\{u, x\}$ and u which includes $\inf\{u, y\}$, too. (See Fig. 7, where the symbols written beside the segments connecting the circles denote the length of the considered maximal chain between the respective elements). Consequently, the length of the maximal chains between $\inf\{u, x\}$ and $\inf\{u, y\}$ is $r_{1x} - r_{2y}$. Let us denote the length of the maximal chains between x and y by t. Then by definition,

$$d(y) = d_0 - r_{1y} + r_{2y}$$

$$d(x) = d_0 - r_{1x} + r_{2x}$$

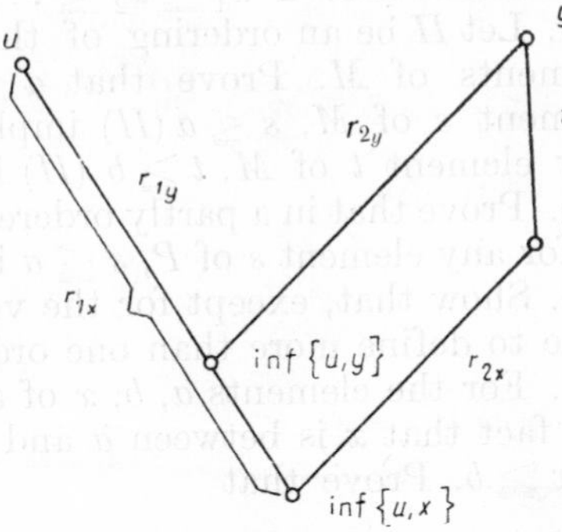

Fig. 7

From these two equations,

$$d(y) - d(x) = (r_{1x} - r_{1y}) + (r_{2y} - r_{2x})$$

Since by the Jordan—Dedekind chain condition, the lengths of all maximal chains between $\inf\{u, x\}$ and y are equal, we have

$$(r_{1x} - r_{1y}) + r_{2y} = r_{2x} + t$$

Substituting into the foregoing equation and rearranging, we obtain $d(y) = d(x) + t$. Thus (1) has been proved, since $x \prec y$ holds if, and only if, $x \leqq y$ and $t = 1$.

Remark 1. If P is bounded below and u is chosen to be o, with $d_0 = 0$, then $d(x)$ will equal the above $h(x)$ for every element x of P.

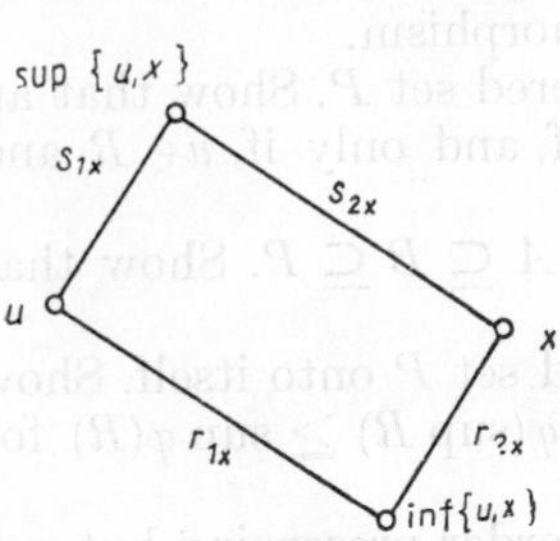

Fig. 8

Remark 2. If $\sup\{u, x\}$ exists for every x, it is possible to define a dimension function d by the aid of the suprema as follows: We assign to u an integer $\bar{d}(u) = \bar{d}_0$ and if the length of the maximal chains between $\sup\{u, x\}$ and u, and $\sup\{u, x\}$ and x, is s_{1x} and s_{2x}, respectively, we assign to x the number $\bar{d}(x) = d_0 + s_{1x} - s_{2x}$.

It is directly apparent that if $\inf\{u, x\}$ and also $\sup\{u, x\}$ exists for any x, the same dimension function is obtained both ways when starting from $d_0 = \bar{d}_0$. Namely, by the Jordan-Dedekind chain condition, $r_{1x} + s_{1x} = r_{2x} + s_{2x}$ (see Fig. 8) and it follows by simple calculation that $\bar{d}(x) = d(x)$, for every x.

Exercises to Chapter I

1. Show that in a partly ordered set $x < x$ is not true for any x and that if $x < y$ and $y < z$, then $x < z$.

2. Show that if in a set M there is defined a relation $<$, satisfying the conditions figuring in the above exercise, the relation $\leq$, defined by "$x \leq y$ means that either $x < y$ or $x = y$", partly orders M.

3. Show that if $x_1 \leq x_2 \leq \ldots \leq x_n \leq x_1$ then $x_1 = x_2 \ldots = x_n$.

4. Let Π be an ordering of the set M, and a, b any pair of the elements of M. Prove that $a \leq b$ (Π) if, and only if, for every element s of M, $s \leq a$ (Π) implies $s \leq b$ (Π) or equivalently if for any element t of M, $t \geq b$ (Π) implies $t \geq a$ (Π).

5. Prove that in a partly ordered set P, a and b are equal if, and only if, for any element s of P, $s \leq a$ implies $s \leq b$ and conversely.

6. Show that, except for the void and single-element set, it is possible to define more than one ordering relation in any set.

7. For the elements a, b, x of a partly ordered set let (axb) denote the fact that x is between a and b, that is, either $a \leq x \leq b$ or $a \geq \geq x \geq b$. Prove that

a) (axb) and (bxa) are equivalent,
b) (abc) and (acb) imply $b = c$,
c) (axb) and (ayx) imply (ayb),
d) (abc) and (acd) imply (bcd),
e) (axb), (xby) and $x \neq b$ imply (aby).

8. Let $K(P)$ denote the set of all pairs of elements (a, b) of the set P, partly ordered with respect to the relation Π_P, for which $a \prec b$. Introduce in the set $K(P)$ a relation Π_K such that $(a, b) \leq (c, d)(\Pi_k)$ if and only if either $a = c$ and $b = d$, or $b \leq c$ (Π_P). Show that Π_K partly orders the set $K(P)$.

9. Let φ be a single-valued mapping of a partly ordered set P_1 onto a partly ordered set P_2, answering the requirements of condition (3) of Section 3. Show that φ is an order isomorphism.

10. Let R be any subset of the partly ordered set P. Show that an element u of P is the least element in R if, and only if, $u \in R$ and $u = \inf_P R$.

11. Let P be any partly ordered set and $A \subseteq B \subseteq P$. Show that $\sup_P B \in A$ implies $\sup_P B = \sup_P A$.

12. Let φ be a mapping of a partly ordered set P onto itself. Show that φ is order preserving if, and only if, $\varphi(\sup R) \geq \sup \varphi(R)$ for every subset R having a supremum in P.

13. Find an example to prove that for an order preserving but not order isomorphic mapping φ the statement of Theorem 2 does not generally hold.

14. Prove that for a triplet of elements a, b, c the existence of $\inf \{\inf \{a, b\}, c\}$ implies the existence of $\inf \{a, b, c\}$, the two infima being equal. Simultaneously, demonstrate by the partly ordered sets given in Figs. 9a and 9b that

a) $\inf\{a, b, c\}$ may exist even if neither $\inf\{\inf\{a, b\}, c\}$ nor $\inf\{a, \inf\{b, c\}\}$ does,
b) $\inf\{\inf\{a, b\}, c\}$ may exist even if $\inf\{a, \inf\{b, c\}\}$ does not.

15. Show that if every two-element subset of a partly ordered set has an infimum, then every finite subset also has one. Show that the statement fails for infinite subsets.

16. Show that a subchain $x_0 < x_1 < \ldots < x_r$ of a partly ordered set P is maximal if, and only if, x_0 is a minimal, x_r a maximal element of P and $x_{j-1} \prec x_j$ $(j = 1, \ldots, r)$.

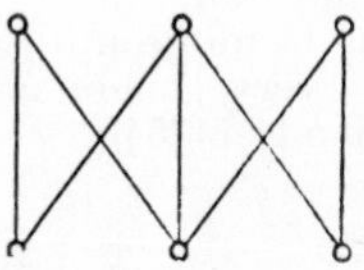

Fig. 9/a

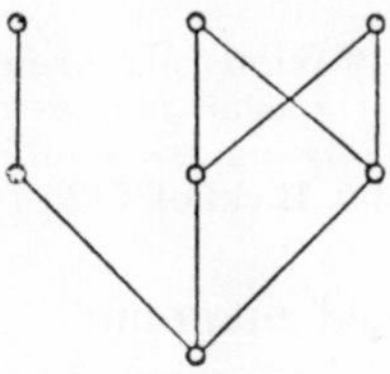

Fig. 9/b

17. Prove that if every subchain and every completely unordered subset of a partly ordered set P is finite, P itself is also finite.

18. Show that for a partly ordered set P the following conditions (A) and (B) are equivalent:
(A) P satisfies the minimum condition and contains no infinite completely unordered subset,
(B) there is no infinite subset of P which would satisfy the maximum condition.

19. Let V_n denote the set of all n-tuples of positive integers and for the elements $(a_1, \ldots, a_n)$ and $(b_1, \ldots, b_n)$ of V_n let $(a_1, \ldots, a_n) \leqq (b_1, \ldots, b_n)$ mean that $a_j \leqq b_j$ $(j = 1, \ldots, n)$. Show that this relation is an ordering of V_n with respect to which no infinite subset of V_n is completely unordered.

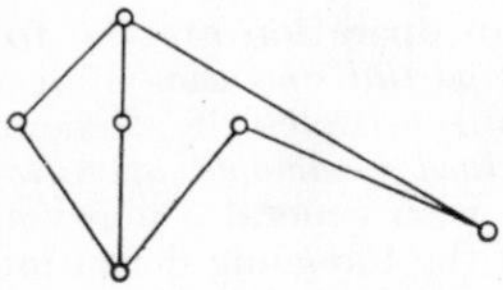

Fig. 10

20. Let S denote the set of all finite sequences formed by the positive integers and let a relation $\leqq$ be defined on S by the following prescription: For a pair of elements $\alpha = (a_1, \ldots, a_n)$, and $\beta = (b_1, \ldots, b_n)$ of S, $\alpha \leqq \beta$ if, and only if, (in the natural order of positive integers) $m \leqq n$ and β has a subsequence $(b_{\bar{1}}, \ldots, b_{\bar{m}})$ for which $a_k \leqq b_{\bar{k}}$ $(k = 1, \ldots, m)$. Show that this relation $\leqq$ partly orders S and that the minimum condition is satisfied with respect to this ordering.

21. Consider the partly ordered set shown in Fig. 10 and show that it is not possible to define a dimension function on it (in spite of its being finite and satisfying the Jordan—Dedekind chain condition).

CHAPTER II

LATTICES IN GENERAL

10. Algebras

In the course of previous algebraic studies, the reader has becomo acquainted with a number of special classes of algebras (semi-groups, grnups, rings and fields). In the following, we shall introduce a very general coocept of "algebras" elaborated by Birkhof [12] (see also Shoda [175]),

A single-valued mapping

$$(1) \qquad f: x_1, \ldots, x_n \to f(x_1, \ldots, x_n)$$

of a non-empty set A into itself is termed an *n-variable operation* defined in A. Of course, it is possible to define several operations in a set A. If A is infinite, then even an infinity of different operations may be defined in A and the number of variables may be different with each operation.

For example, consider the set of all points of a plane denoted by $\mathcal{A}$, while $f_1(P, Q)$ and $f_2(P, Q, R)$ denote the centre of gravity of the segment $\overline{PQ}$ and of the triangle PQR, respectively. f_1 and f_2 are both operations defined in $\mathcal{A}$, f_1 being a two-variable, f_2 a three-variable operation.

In the theory of algebras even functions with an infinite number of variables are often regarded as operations (see e.g. Slominski [229]).

Other generalizations of the above definition of an operation are the following: A function of form (1) is called *an n-variable partial operation* if it is defined (only) for certain (i.e. not necessarily for all) n-tuples of elements $x_1, \ldots, x_n$; a function of form (1) is called a *multi-valued n-variable operation* if $f(x_1, \ldots, x_n)$ is not necessarily a single element but is in general a non-void subset of A. If we cancel the word "non-void" out of the foregoing definition, we come to the concept of the *multi-valued n-variable partial operation.*

Let us remark that Birkhoff's definition of algebras comprises the so-called operator algebras as well, since operators can be regarded as one-variable operations.

If in the set A there are defined the operations

$$f_\gamma: x_1, \ldots, x_{n(\gamma)} \to f(x_1, \ldots, x_{n(\gamma)}) \ (\gamma \in \Gamma)$$

where Γ denotes the appropriate index set, and $n(\gamma)$ is a positive integer depending on γ then A is said to be an *algebra** with respect to the operations $\{f_\gamma\}_{\gamma\in\Gamma}$. If for some reason not all operations $\{f_\gamma\}_{\gamma\in\Gamma}$ are considered, but only a subset $\{f_\delta\}_{\delta\in\Delta}$ $(\Delta \subseteq \Gamma)$ of them then it can be said that "A is an algebra with respect to the operations $\{f_\delta\}_{\delta\in\Delta}$". If the operations considered in A are to be indicated, the symbols $A(\{f_\gamma\}_{\gamma\in\Gamma})$, or $A(\{f_\delta\}_{\delta\in\Delta})$ will be employed, according to the two preceding cases.

By a *subalgebra* of an algebra $A = A(\{f_\gamma\}_{\gamma\in\Gamma})$ we mean all non-empty** subsets R of the elements of A which are "closed" with respect to all operations defined in A, that is, in which for every index $\gamma(\gamma \in \Gamma)$ the following condition is satisfied: if $x_1, \ldots x_{n(\gamma)}$ are elements of R, then $f_\gamma(x_1, \ldots, x_{n(\gamma)})$ is also contained in R.

Let us point out immediately that in applying this definition of subalgebra to familiar cases, some caution is recommended. For, e.g. considering a group G in the usual way as a single-operation algebra, the definition just outlined yields all subsemigroups of G as the subalgebras of G. If we intend to obtain only the subgroups as subalgebras in the sense of the above definition it is also necessary to include the formation of the inverse as a (unary) operation.

Difficulties of a different kind arise in connection with fields. Division by 0 being undefined, division is not an operation, and thus only addition, multiplication and subtraction (or, instead of the latter, the formation of the additive inverse) can be considered as field operations. In this case, however, we obtain all subrings of the fields as algebras. This difficulty can be overcome by making division an operation, for example, by the convention***

$$x \div 0 = \begin{cases} 0 \text{ if } x \neq 0 \\ 1 \text{ if } x = 0 \end{cases}$$

Division, "generalized" in this way, can also be regarded as a field operation and by this consideration, the subalgebras of a field turn out to be the subfields, as was required.

Of course, by such an artificial definition of division by zero, some of the familiar identities of division are lost; for example, with the exception of the cases $x = 0$ and $x = 1$, $(x \div 0) \div (1 \div 0) \neq x \div 1$.

It is appropriate to point out the advantages of the above subalgebra definition as well. Let G be a multiplicative group. If in this group,

* If we assume that these f'_γ 's are only partial operations then we call A a *partial algebra* with respect to $\{f_\gamma\}_{\gamma\in\Gamma}$.

** Birkhoff also counts the void set among the subalgebras. This point of view undoubtedly has some advantages (e.g. the discussion of Section 26 would be simpler that way); it has, however, the disadvantage that it disagrees with generally accepted conventions concerning the most frequently occurring special algebras.

*** Also using the definition $x \div 0 = 0$ in the case when $x = 0$, the single element set $\{0\}$ would also become a subfield, contrary to the accepted convention.

all inner automorphisms, in addition to multiplication and inverse formation, are considered as operations, then the "subalgebras" of G will all be the normal subgroups of the group. Of course, with other kinds of functions (mappings) as operations, other kinds of subsets will result as the subalgebras of G.

The following table is a summary representation of the subalgebras of groups, rings and fields resulting from different operations.

Algebra	Operations considered	Subalgebras
Group	multiplication, inverse formation	subgroups
Group	multiplication, inverse formation, inner automorphisms	normal subgroups
Group	multiplication, inverse formation, all automorphisms	characteristic subgroups
Ring	addition, subtraction, multiplication	subrings
Ring	addition, subtraction, all mapping of the type $f_a(x) = ax$	left ideals
Field	addition, subtraction, multiplication, "generalized" division	subfields

$A = A(\{f_\gamma\}_{\gamma\in\Gamma})$ and $B = B(\{g_\delta\}_{\delta\in\Delta})$ are said to be *similar algebras*, if there exists a one-to-one mapping σ of the set Γ onto the set Δ such that for each $\gamma \in \Gamma$, the operations f_γ and the corresponding $g_{\sigma(\gamma)}$ are of the same number of variables. Clearly, the similarity of algebras is a relation of equivalence.

Let us agree to denote the corresponding operations of similar algebras by the same symbol.

Let $A = A(\{f_\gamma\}_{\gamma\in\Gamma})$ and $B = B(\{f_\gamma\}_{\gamma\in\Gamma})$ be two similar algebras. A single-valued mapping φ is said to be a *homomorphism of A onto (or into) B* if it maps A onto (or into) B, and if for any index $\gamma (\gamma \in \Gamma)$ and any system of elements $x_1, \ldots, x_{n(\gamma)} (\in A)$ we have

$$\varphi\big(f_\gamma(x_1, \ldots, x_{n(\gamma)})\big) = f_\gamma\big(\varphi(x_1), \ldots, \varphi(x_{\gamma(n)})\big) \tag{2}$$

If a mapping φ of this nature is not only single-valued, but one-to-one it is called an *isomorphism*.

In the special case $B = A$ it is usual to speak of an *endomorphism* instead of a homomorphism and of an *automorphism* instead of an isomorphism.

If the algebra A has a homomorphism φ onto the (similar) algebra B, B is said to be the *homomorphic image* of A under the homomorphism φ. This fact is expressed by

$$\varphi: A \sim B$$

If this φ is an isomorphism, we write

$$\varphi: A \approx B$$

and (as φ^{-1}: $B \approx A$ is also true) we say "A and B are isomorphic". Where it is of no importance to explicitly indicate the mapping generating the homomorphism or isomorphism, the shorter notations "$A \sim B$" and "$A \approx B$" are employed.

Isomorphic algebras are not considered, in general, as being essentially different from one another. An important exception is represented by the case, when we are dealing with isomorphic subalgebras of an algebra.

It is to be emphasized that the two sides of a relation $A \sim B$ are not interchangeable in general.

11. Lattices

A set L is called a *lattice* if there are defined in L two binary operations, *meet* and *join*, which assign to every pair a, b of the elements of L, uniquely an element $a \cap b$ (the meet of a and b) as well as an element $a \cup b$ (the join of a and b) in such a way that the following *lattice axioms* $\mathsf{L}_1 - \mathsf{L}_6$ are fulfilled:

L_1. For any elements a, b, c, of L, $(a \cap b) \cap c = a \cap (b \cap c)$

L_2. For any elements a, b, c of L, $(a \cup b) \cup c = a \cup (b \cup c)$

L_3. For any elements a, b of L, $a \cap b = b \cap a$

L_4. For any elements a, b of L, $a \cup b = b \cup a$

L_5. For any elements a, b of L, $a \cap (a \cup b) = a$

L_6. For any elements a, b of L, $a \cup (a \cap b) = a$

In other words, in a lattice both operations are commutative and associative; moreover, they have the properties expressed by L_5 and L_6 respectively, which will be referred to as the *absorption identity of the meet and join*, respectively.

The definition of lattices as a separate class of algebras is due to Schröder ([174], pp. 191–281). The above system of axioms was set up by Dedekind ([38], p. 109); as for other systems of axioms concerning lattices see Section 21.

An important generalization of the lattice concept developed in the course of physical applications is the skew lattice. The theory of skew lattices is not yet sufficiently elaborated; as to the foundations see Jordan [106]–[109], Jordan–Witt [111], Jordan–Böge [110] and Matsushita [135], [136].

The meet $a_1 \cap \ldots \cap a_n$ and join $a_1 \cup \ldots \cup a_n$ of the elements $a_1, \ldots, a_n$ is defined in the usual recursive manner (see for example [228], p. 49). This multi-term meet and join is denoted by

$$\bigcap_{j=1}^{n} a_j \quad \text{and} \quad \bigcup_{j=1}^{n} a_j$$

respectively. By the associativity of the lattice operations, these operations can be performed with any bracketing (not only the one corresponding to the definition).*

For example, according to the definition, $a \frown b \frown c \frown d = ((a \frown b) \frown c) \frown d$ but $a \frown b \frown c \frown d = a \frown (b \frown (c \frown d))$ or $a \frown b \frown c \frown d = (a \frown (b \frown c)) \frown d$ also hold.

It is to be noted that the literature of lattice theory shows no uniform symbolism. Thus for the meet there occur the operational symbols $\cap$, $\wedge$ and $\cdot$; whereas for the join there occur the corresponding operational symbols $\cup$, $\wedge$ and $+$.

An immediate consequence of the absorption identities is

THEOREM 5. *Every lattice has the following properties* (Dedekind [38], p. 109):

L_7. *The operation of meet is idempotent*, i.e. $a \frown a = a$ for any element a of L.

L_8. *The operation of join is idempotent*, i.e. $a \smile a = a$ for any element a of L.

COROLLARY. *For any elements a, b of a lattice $a \frown b = a \smile b$ if, and only if, $a = b$.*

PROOF. The statements L_7 and L_8 may be derived from the axioms L_5 and L_6 as follows:

By L_6, for any pair of elements a, x of L
$a \frown a = a \frown (a \smile (a \frown x))$.

On the other hand, applying L_5 to the case $b = a \frown x$, we get
$a \frown (a \smile (a \frown x)) = a$.

By L_5, for any pair of elements a, x of L
$a \smile a = a \smile (a \frown (a \smile x))$.

On the other hand, applying L_6 to the case $b = a \smile x$, we get
$a \smile (a \frown (a \smile x)) = a$.

Thus the theorem is proved.

The corollary remains to be proved. By the just proved L_7 and L_8, $a = b$ implies $a \frown b = a = a \smile b$. Conversely, if $a \frown b = a \smile b$, then by the axioms L_3 and L_4 we also have $b \frown a = b \smile a$, and thus, by the axioms L_6, L_2 and by the statement L_8 of the theorem

$$a = a \smile (a \frown b) = a \smile (a \smile b) = (a \smile a) \smile b = a \smile b$$

$$b = b \smile (b \frown a) = b \smile (b \smile a) = (b \smile b) \smile a = b \smile a$$

and hence by L_4, $a = b$.

Let us now present some examples of lattices from diverse branches of mathematics.

Example 7. As in Example 3, let $\mathscr{P}(M)$ denote the set of all subsets of M (the void set included). It is easy to see, that $\mathscr{P}(M)$ is a lattice with respect to the operations of set union and set intersection. This lattice is called the *subset lattice* of M.

* For proof, see e.g. [228], Theorem 23.

Example 8. It is known that the set union and set intersection of any two closed subsets of a plane are likewise closed. Hence, the closed sets of the plane form a lattice with respect to these set operations. For similar reasons, the corresponding statement holds for all open sets of the plane.

Example 9. In the set $\mathfrak{K}$ of all convex domains of the plane let $A \frown B$ denote the set intersection of the convex domains A and B, and $A \smile B$ the convex envelope of $A \cup B$. The set $\mathfrak{K}$ is a lattice with respect to these two operations.

Example 10. Consider the set $\mathscr{L}(S)$ of all linear subspaces of the three-dimensional space S (the void set included). Define on $\mathscr{L}(S)$ two operations so that the symbol $X \frown Y (X, Y \in \mathscr{L}(S))$ denotes the set intersection of the subspaces X, Y and $X \smile Y$ the smallest subspace including the subspaces X, Y. With respect to these two operations, $\mathscr{L}(S)$ forms a lattice, called the *subspace lattice* of S.

Example 11. In the set N of positive integers let $a \frown b$ and $a \smile b$ $(a, b \in N)$ denote the greatest common divisor and the least common multiple, respectively, of the numbers a and b. With respect to these two operations, N is a lattice.

Example 12. Let H and K be two arbitrary subgroups of a group G. Let $H \frown K$ denote the set intersection of the subgroups H, K (which is itself a subgroup of G), and $H \smile K$ the subgroup generated by H and K. With respect to these two operations, the set of all subgroups of G is a lattice, the *subgroup lattice* of G.

Example 13. In the set of real functions, defined on the interval $[0, 1]$ of real numbers, let $f \frown g$ denote the function which assumes the smaller and $f \smile g$ denote the function which assumes the greater of the values $f(x)$ and $g(x)$ for every x in $[0, 1]$. (The former function is usually called the lower, the latter the upper envelope of the two functions.) It is easy to see that the lattice axioms are fulfilled by these two operations.

12. The Lattice Theoretical Duality Principle

On inspection of the axiom system $\mathsf{L}_1 - \mathsf{L}_6$ of lattices it is at once apparent that the axioms of even index differ from those of odd index only in that the symbol of meet in the former ones is substituted by the symbol of join in the latter, and conversely. An important consequence of this is the lattice theoretical "duality principle", which will be formulated below, after the appropriate preliminary definitions.

By a *lattice theoretical proposition* we mean a statement A (no matter whether true or false) in which in addition to certain expressions of logic ("equal" "for every element of L... holds"... there exists an element of L such that, "if and only if,..." etc.) and variables, only the operational symbols $\frown$ and $\smile$ occur. On interchanging the symbols $\frown$ and $\smile$ in A, we again obtain a lattice theoretical proposition; this latter is termed *the dual of the statement* A and denoted by $\mathfrak{D}(\mathsf{A})$. Clearly, the dual of the statement $\mathfrak{D}(\mathsf{A})$ is A

itself. Symbolically: $\mathfrak{D}(\mathfrak{D}(\mathsf{A})) = \mathsf{A}$. Consequently, the duality of two statements is mutual, whence it is frequently said of two such statements that they are "duals of each other".

The procedure by which one of two dual statements can be derived from the other — that is, the interchanging of the operational symbols $\frown$, $\smile$ in the formulation of the statement in question — is called the *dualization of the statement.*

Let us now consider a set $\mathsf{H} = \{\mathsf{A}_\gamma\}$ of lattice theoretical propositions. (The case of H consisting of a single statement is not excluded.) Let us denote by $\mathfrak{D}(\mathsf{H})$ that set of statements (also lattice theoretical propositions) which is obtained by dualizing every statement of H. An H for which $\mathfrak{D}(\mathsf{H}) = \mathsf{H}$ is called a *set of self-dual statements.* (For this to be the case, it is evidently necessary for H to include the dual of every one of its statements.) A single statement A may also be a self-dual set of statements: in that case A is said to be a *self-dual statement.*

A statement B is usually called a corollary of $\mathsf{H} = \{\mathsf{A}_\gamma\}$ if B can be proved by utilizing the A_γ's.* Dualizing every statement utilized to justify the individual steps of the proof — this is called the *dualization* of the proof (this method has already been applied in the proof of Theorem 5) — we obtain a proof of the statement $\mathfrak{D}(\mathsf{B})$ by the statements $\mathfrak{D}(\mathsf{A})$. Hence, if B is a corollary to H, $\mathfrak{D}(\mathsf{B})$ is also a corollary to $\mathfrak{D}(\mathsf{H})$ and conversely.

Applying this result to the case $\mathsf{H} = \mathfrak{D}(\mathsf{H})$ it follows immediately that if H is self-dual, and a statement B is implied by H, then the dual $\mathfrak{D}(\mathsf{B})$ of B is also implied by H.

The duals of the lattice axioms L_1, L_3, L_5 are the lattice axioms L_2, L_4, L_6 (and conversely); thus, the axiom system $\mathsf{L}_1 - \mathsf{L}_6$ is self-dual. Hence there prevails the

LATTICE THEORETICAL DUALITY PRINCIPLE. *The dual of any true lattice theoretical proposition is itself a true lattice theoretical proposition.*

As a matter of course, "a true lattice theoretical proposition" means a statement implied by the lattice axioms.

This duality principle was first proposed by Schröder ([174], Theorem 35, p. 315).

If a statement or proof of lattice theory contains, besides the symbols $\frown$, $\smile$ and certain expressions of logic, other symbols or expressions derived from them by appropriate definitions, dualization may be performed by first transcribing the "derived" symbols and expressions — in accordance with their definitions — into the original form containing the symbols $\frown$, $\smile$.

An application of the duality principle will be demonstrated in the course of proving:

THEOREM 6. *Every lattice has the following property*:

L_9. *For any elements* a, b *of the lattice,* $a \frown b = b$ *if, and only if,* $b \smile a = a$

(Bergmann [9], p. 271).

* This of course, does not mean that B is necessarily true, because among the A_γ's false statements may also occur.

PROOF. L_9 comprises two statements:

L_9'. For a given pair of elements a, b of a lattice $a \frown b = b$ implies $b \smile a = a$;

L_9''. For a given pair of elements a, b of a lattice $b \smile a = a$ implies $a \frown b = b$.

In this form, L_9' and L_9'' are seemingly non-dual, as they differ not only in that the operational symbols $\frown$ and $\smile$ but also the letters a and b are interchanged. But, since a and b are arbitrary elements of L, it is legitimate to write a instead of b — for example in L_9'', — leaving L_9' unchanged. In this way we obtain the statement

L_9^*. For a given pair of elements a, b of a lattice, $a \smile b = b$ implies $b \frown a = a$.

This is even formally dual to L_9', moreover L_9'' and L_9^* together are equivalent to L_9. (This also means that L_9 is self-dual.) Thus, by the duality principle it suffices to prove only L_9'.

Let a, b be a pair of elements of a lattice for which $b = a \frown b$. Then $b \smile a = (a \frown b) \smile a$. But by L_4 and L_6, $(a \frown b) \smile a = a \smile (a \frown b) = a$. Thus, L_9' (and consequently also L_9) is proved.

An interesting consequence of the lattice theoretical duality principle is the following: If we have a lattice L with the operational symbols $\frown$ and $\smile$, then the operations $\wedge$ and $\vee$ defined by the equalities

$$a \wedge b = a \smile b, \ a \vee b = a \frown b \quad (a, b \in L)$$

define a new lattice. This new lattice is called the *dual of the lattice* L and is denoted $\mathfrak{D}(L)$. Clearly $\mathfrak{D}(\mathfrak{D}(L)) = L$. It can happen that* $\mathfrak{D}(L) \approx L$ in which case it is said that L is *self-dual*. In other words, a lattice L is self-dual if, and only if, it has a one-to-one mapping onto itself such that $\varphi(a \frown b) = \varphi(a) \wedge \varphi(b)$ and $\varphi(a \smile b) = \varphi(a) \vee \varphi(b)$, that is,

$$\varphi(a \frown b) = \varphi(a) \smile \varphi(b) \tag{1}$$

$$\varphi(a \smile b) = \varphi(a) \frown \varphi(b) \tag{2}$$

The subset lattice $\mathscr{P}(M)$ of any set M is self-dual. Namely, $\varphi(X) = M - X$ $(X \subseteq M)$ is a one-to-one mapping of $\mathscr{P}(M)$ onto itself and, for arbitrary elements A, B of $\mathscr{P}(M)$

$$\varphi(A \frown B) = M - (A \cap B) = (M - A) \cup (M - B) = \varphi(A) \smile \varphi(B)$$

$$\varphi(A \smile B) = M - (A \cup B) = (M - A) \cap (M - B) = \varphi(A) \frown \varphi(B)$$

The subspace lattice of the three-dimensional projective space T is also self-dual. To prove this, introduce in T a system of homogeneous co-ordinates and define upon the subspace lattice of T a mapping φ in the following way: Let $\varphi(O) = T$ and $\varphi(T) = O$, moreover, let φ assign to a point with the co-ordinates (x_1, x_2, x_3, x_4) that plane with the co-ordinates (u_1, u_2, u_3, u_4) for which $u_j = \varrho x_j$ $(j = 1, 2, 3, 4;\ \varrho \neq 0$ and real), and conversely. Finally, let φ assign to a line e the (common) line of intersection of the planes assigned to the points

* By the definition of isomorphism between two algebras, the lattices L_1 and L^2 are said to be isomorphic, if there exists a one-to-one mapping φ of L_1 onto L_2 such that $\varphi(a \frown b) = \varphi(a) \frown \varphi(b)$, $\varphi(a \smile b) = \varphi(a) \smile \varphi(b)$ for every pair of elements a, b of L_1.

of e (the existence of such a common line is not evident, but it is proved in projective geometry). It can be shown that for the mapping defined in this way, (1) and (2) hold.

Contrary to the above two examples, the lattice given as Example 11 is not self-dual. By the definitions of the operations in N, $1 \frown x = 1$ holds for every element x of N, that is, the number 1 is the zero element of the meet operation and hence the isomorphism $N \approx \mathfrak{D}(N)$ could hold only if (see for example [228], Theorem 54) the join operation would also have a zero element. However, for an element u of N, $u \smile x = u$ holds if, and only if, u is a multiple of x and there is no positive integer which would be a multiple of all positive integers.

13. Semilattices

For every algebra of two operations it is an important and interesting question as to what algebra would result if one of the operations were discarded. (For example, it is usual in ring theory to call attention to the fact that a ring is a group with respect to addition and a semigroup with respect to multiplication.)

In the case of a lattice L, let $L^{\frown}$ and $L^{\smile}$, respectively, denote those one-operation algebras, the elements of which are the same as the elements of L, but only the meet operation of L is considered in $L^{\frown}$ and only the join operation of L in $L^{\smile}$. According to L_1, L_3, L_7 and L_2, L_4, L_8, respectively, the operation defined on both structures $L^{\frown}$ and $L^{\smile}$ is associative, commutative and idempotent.

In general, a set H is called (after Klein–Barmen [115]) a *semilattice* if there is defined in it an operation which assigns to each pair of elements a, b an element $a \circ b$ so that the following *semilattice axioms* are satisfied:

H_1. *The operation* $\circ$ *is associative,* that is, $(a \circ b) \circ c = a \circ (b \circ c)$ for any triplet of elements a, b, c of H.

H_2. *The operation* $\circ$ *is commutative,* that is, $a \circ b = b \circ a$ for any pair of elements of H.

H_3. *The operation* $\circ$ *is idempotent*, that is, $a \circ a = a$ for any element a of H.

Accordingly, if L is a lattice, both $L^{\frown}$ and $L^{\smile}$ are semilattices; the former is called the *meet-semilattice*, the latter the *join-semilattice* of L. Between these two semilattices a connection (and a very close one, as will be seen in the next section) is established by L_5 and L_6, and L_9, respectively.

14. Lattices as Partly Ordered Sets

In every lattice, an order relation may be defined in a natural way, by utilizing the lattice operations:

THEOREM 7. *In a lattice L the prescription*

$$a \leqq b \iff a \frown b = a \qquad (a, b \in L) \tag{1}$$

defines an ordering relation.

The theorem was first stated by Huntington (although only for a special class of lattices, the Boolean algebras); see [93], p. 294.

Observe that the ordering relations of the lattices occurring in Examples 7, 10 and 11 are the relations defined in Examples 3, 4 and 2, in that order.

Before beginning the proof there are two remarks to be made.

Remark 1. In the case of a lattice L, only the relation (1) will be considered as an ordering of L. Accordingly it will be called the *ordering relation* or simply the *ordering of the lattice* L. (Hence, for lattices, all concepts introduced in Chapter I are understood to refer to this ordering relation.) By the commutativity of the lattice operations and by the property L_9, the definition

$$(2) \qquad a \leqq b \longleftrightarrow a \cup b = b \qquad (a, b \in L)$$

is equivalent to (1). Hence, if it is more convenient, (2) can be used instead of (1).

Remark 2. It will often be necessary to dualize lattice theoretical propositions involving, in addition to the lattice operations, the ordering of the lattice as well. Therefore it will be useful to find out beforehand the dual statement of "$a \leqq b$". By the definition (1) $a \leqq b$ means that $a \cap b = a$. The dual of the latter statement is the statement "$a \cup b = a$" which by L_4 and (2) means that $a \geqq b$. Hence, in *lattice-theoretical duality the dual of the statement "$a \leqq b$" is the statement "$a \geqq b$"*. Hence, we have at once the special case (which is, however, directly apparent from the definition) that the dual of the ordering of the lattice L is the ordering of the lattice $\mathfrak{D}(L)$.

Now let us proceed to the proof of Theorem 7. The relation defined by (1) is reflexive. For any element a of L there follows $a \cap a = a$ by L_7, and therefore, by (1) $a \leqq a$. Moreover, the relation is antisymmetric. By its definition, for any pair of elements a, b of L, $a \leqq b$ and $b \leqq a$ hold simultaneously if, and only if, $a \cap b = a$ and $b \cap a = b$ whence by L_3, $a = a \cap b = b \cap a = b$. Finally, in order to show the transitivity of the relation, consider a triplet of elements a, b, c of L such that $a \leqq b$ and $b \leqq c$, i.e. $a \cap b = a$ and $b \cap c = b$. Then, applying L_1,

$$a \cap c = (a \cap b) \cap c = a \cap (b \cap c) = a \cap b = a$$

which implies $a \leqq c$.

In the course of the proof, we have only made use of the properties of $L^{\cap}$. The statement of the theorem is therefore valid for every semilattice, too, if the sign "$\cap$" is the sign of the operation in the semilattice.

THEOREM 8. *With respect to the ordering* (1), *every finite subset* $\{a_1, \ldots, a_n\}$ *of the lattice L has an infimum and a supremum, namely,*

$$(3) \qquad \inf_L \{a_1, \ldots, a_n\} = \bigcap_{j=1}^{n} a_j, \qquad \sup_L \{a_1, \ldots, a_n\} = \bigcup_{j=1}^{n} a_j$$

PROOF. The proposition of the theorem can be expressed in more detail as follows: *For any elements* $a_1, \ldots, a_n$ *of* L,

$$(4) \qquad \bigcap_{j=1}^{n} a_j \leqq a_1, \ldots, a_n \leqq \bigcup_{j=1}^{n} a_j$$

$$(5) \qquad u \leqq a_1, \ldots, a_n \Longrightarrow u \leqq \bigcap_{j=1}^{n} a_j$$

$$(6) \qquad u \geqq a_1, \ldots, a_n \Longrightarrow u \geqq \bigcup_{j=1}^{n} a_j$$

The two statements comprised by (4) being mutually dual, and (6) being the dual of (5), it is sufficient to prove (5) and the first half of (4). The latter is obtained as follows: For any a_k $(k = 1, \ldots, n)$

$$(\bigcap_{j=1}^{n} a_j) \frown a_k = a_1 \frown \ldots \frown a_{k-1} \frown (a_k \frown a_k) \frown$$
$$\frown a_{k+1} \frown \ldots \frown a_n = \bigcap_{j=1}^{n} a_j$$

by the subsequent application of L_3 and L_7.

As for (5), by the conditions regarding u we have $u \frown a_k = u$ $(k = 1, \ldots, n)$ and hence by L_1

$$u \frown (a_1 \frown \ldots \frown a_n) = (u \frown a_1) \frown (a_2 \frown \ldots \frown a_n) =$$
$$= u \frown (a_2 \frown \ldots \frown a_n) = (u \frown a_2) \frown (a_3 \frown \ldots \frown a_n) =$$
$$= u \frown (a_3 \frown \ldots \frown a_n) = \ldots = u$$

This step completes the proof of Theorem 8.

(3) also implies the following connection between the operations and the ordering in lattices:

For any elements $a_1, \ldots, a_n, b_1, \ldots b_n, a, b$ *of a lattice* L

$$(7) \quad a_j \leqq b_j \, (j = 1, \ldots, n) \Longrightarrow \begin{cases} a_1 \frown \ldots \frown a_n \leqq b_1 \frown \ldots \frown b_n \text{ and} \\ a_1 \smile \ldots \smile a_n \leqq b_1 \smile \ldots \smile b_n \end{cases}$$

Especially,

$$(8) \qquad a_j \leqq b \, (j = 1, \ldots, n) \Longrightarrow a_1 \smile \ldots \smile a_n \leqq b$$

$$(9) \qquad b_j \geqq a \, (j = 1, \ldots, n) \Longrightarrow b_1 \frown \ldots \frown b_n \geqq a$$

By these it follows immediately:

$$(10) \qquad a_j \leqq b_k \, (j = 1, \ldots, m; \; k = 1, \ldots, n) \Longrightarrow$$
$$\Longrightarrow a_1 \smile \ldots \smile a_m \leqq b_1 \frown \ldots \frown b_n$$

In fact, if the condition is satisfied, then, by (8), $a_1 \cup \ldots \cup a_n \leq b_k$ prevails for any k and hence, by (9), the statement is true.

The reader is advised to bear well in mind, the relations listed under (1)—(10) because these will be employed in the following without further reference.

By Theorem 7 every lattice — though a two-operation algebra by definition — can also be considered as a partly ordered set. Because of this "double nature" of the lattices, the following theorem is of considerable importance.

THEOREM 9. *If two lattices are isomorphic, they are also order isomorphic and conversely.**

SUPPLEMENT. *For two lattices L_1 and L_2 the following three statements are equivalent*:

$$1.\ L_1^{\cap} \approx L_2^{\cap}, \quad 2.\ L_1^{\cup} \approx L_2^{\cup}, \quad 3.\ L_1 \approx L_2$$

Consequently, *in a lattice the operations of meet and join mutually determine each other.*

PROOF. Let L_1 and L_2 be arbitrary lattices. By Remark 2 above, $\mathfrak{D}(L_1) \overset{o}{\approx} \mathfrak{D}(L_2)$ if, and only if, $L_1 \overset{o}{\approx} L_2$. Thus, by the duality principle it is sufficient to prove $L_1^{\cap} \approx L_2^{\cap} \Rightarrow L_1 \overset{o}{\approx} L_2 \Rightarrow L_1 \approx L_2$.** Therefore, suppose that $L_1^{\cap} \approx L_2^{\cap}$. Then there is a one-to-one mapping φ of L_1 onto L_2 such that

$$\varphi(a \cap b) = \varphi(a) \cap \varphi(b) \qquad (a, b \in L_1)$$

is satisfied. Let the ordering relations of L_1 and L_2 be denoted by Π_1 and Π_2, respectively. Then

$$a \leq b\ (\Pi_1) \Longleftrightarrow a \cap b = a \Longleftrightarrow \varphi(a \cap b) = \varphi(a) \Longleftrightarrow$$
$$\Longleftrightarrow \varphi(a) \cap \varphi(b) = \varphi(a) \Longleftrightarrow \varphi(a) \leq \varphi(b)\ (\Pi_2)$$

Hence, $L_1 \overset{o}{\approx} L_2$.

Suppose $L_1 \overset{o}{\approx} L_2$. Then there exists a one-to-one mapping ψ of L_1 onto L_2 such that the condition

$$a \leq b(\Pi_1) \Longleftrightarrow \psi(a) \leq \psi(b)\ (\Pi_2)$$

is satisfied. So, by Theorems 8 and 2

$$\psi(a) \cap \psi(b) = \inf_{L_2} \{\psi(a), \psi(b)\} = \psi(\inf_{L_1} \{a, b\}) = \psi(a \cap b)$$
$$\psi(a) \cup \psi(b) = \sup_{L_2} \{\psi(a), \psi(b)\} = \psi(\sup_{L_1} \{a, b\}) = \psi(a \cup b)$$

Together these two equations imply that $L_1 \approx L_2$

* Formulated in more detail, the theorem states the following: If two lattices (as algebras) are isomorphic, then the partly ordered sets derived from them by (1) are order isomorphic. Conversely, if two lattices have the property that the partly ordered sets derived from them are isomorphic, the two lattices are isomorphic.

** Indeed by dualising the statement $L_1^{\cap} \approx L_2^{\cap} \Longrightarrow L_1 \overset{o}{\approx} L_2$ we obtain $L_1^{\cup} \approx L_2^{\cup} \Longrightarrow \mathfrak{D}(L_1) \overset{o}{\approx} \mathfrak{D}(L_2)$.

By Theorem 8, the ordering of lattices generates partly ordered sets, in which any finite subset has both an infimum and a supremum. Conversely, if a partly ordered set P has this property, the operations

$$(11) \qquad a \frown b = \inf \{a, b\}, \ a \smile b = \sup \{a, b\}$$

make P a lattice (Peirce [156], I, p. 33). To begin with, the operations thus defined are evidently commutative. The absorption identities are also valid, since for any a, b we have

$$\inf \{a, b\} \leqq a \leqq \sup \{a, b\},$$

whence

$$\inf \{a, \sup \{a, b\}\} = a = \sup \{a, \inf \{a, b\}\}$$

It remains to prove that these operations are associative. Let a, b, c be arbitrary elements of P and introduce, for the sake of brevity, the notations $u = \inf \{\inf \{a, b\}, c\}$, $v = \inf \{a, b, c\}$. By the definition of the infimum, $u \leqq \inf \{a, b\} \leqq a, b$ and $u \leqq c$, consequently $u \leqq \inf \{a, b, c\} = v$. At the same time, not only is $v \leqq a, b$, so that $v \leqq \inf \{a, b\}$ but also, $v \leqq c$; hence, $v \leqq \inf \{\inf \{a, b\}, c\} = u$. Consequently,

$$(12) \qquad \inf \{\inf \{a, b\}, c\} = \inf \{a, b, c\}$$

Similarly,

$$(13) \qquad \inf \{a, \inf \{b, c\}\} = \inf \{a, b, c\}$$

and (12) and (13) remain true also if "sup" is written instead of "inf". Hence, the operations under (11) are indeed associative.

It is expressly pointed out that the lattice defined by (11) is order isomorphic to P. Indeed, if Π denotes the ordering in P, and Π^* the ordering of the lattice defined by (11), we have

$$a \leqq b \ (\Pi^*) \Longleftrightarrow \inf \{a, b\} = a \Longleftrightarrow a \leqq b \ (\Pi)$$

Accordingly, if in a set P partly ordered by a relation Π each two-element subset has an infimum and supremum, it is usually said that "ordered by Π (or with respect to the ordering relation Π) P forms a lattice".

15. Diagrams of Lattices

Any finite lattice—being a finite partly ordered set—can be represented by a diagram called the *diagram of the lattice*. It was found in Section 4 that different finite partly ordered sets can be represented by the same diagram if, and only if, they are order isomorphic. Thus by Theorem 9, *any finite lattice is uniquely determined by its diagram, up to isomorphism.* Finite lattices are usually given only by their diagrams. The handling of the diagram is as simple as that of operation tables, with the added advantage that the diagram gives the definitions of both operations at once.

From the diagram of a lattice, the meet and join of two elements, say a and b, can be found by bearing in mind that (see Theorem 8) $a \cap b = \inf\{a, b\}$ and $a \cup b = \sup\{a, b\}$. Hence:

If $a \leqq b$, we have $a \cap b = a$, $a \cup b = b$; if $a \geqq b$, we have $a \cap b = b$, $a \cup b = a$. Finally, if $a \parallel b$, then $a \cap b$ is that element situated highest among the elements (under both a and b) from which it is possible to move along line segments connecting circles of the diagram upward to both a and b. The element $a \cup b$ is found by duality considerations.

For example, the diagram of Fig. 11 represents a lattice in which the operations are defined as follows: For any element x of the lattice, $o \cap x = o$, $o \cup x = x$ $i \cap x = x$, $i \cup x = i$, and

$\cap$	a	b	c	d	e
a	a	o	a	a	o
b	o	b	o	b	b
c	a	o	c	a	o
d	a	b	a	d	b
e	o	b	o	b	e

$\cup$	a	b	c	d	e
a	a	d	c	d	i
b	d	b	i	d	e
c	c	i	c	i	i
d	d	d	i	d	i
e	i	e	i	i	e

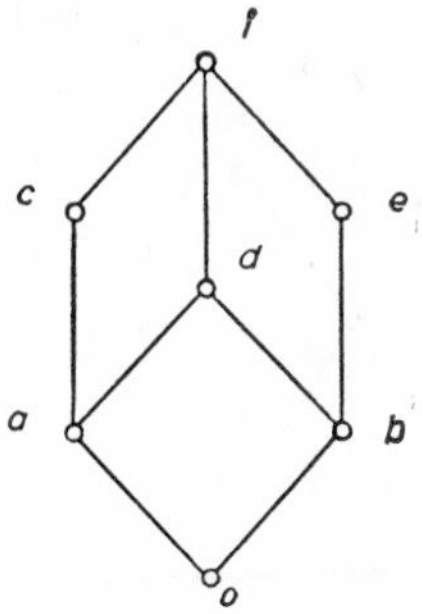

Fig. 11

16. Sublattices. Ideals

According to the definition of "subalgebras" of an algebra, we call every non-empty subset R of L such that

$$(1) \qquad a, b \in R \Longrightarrow a \cap b,\ a \cup b \in R$$

a *sublattice* of the lattice L. Clearly, the axioms $\mathsf{L}_1 - \mathsf{L}_6$ are then satisfied by any triplet a, b, c of the elements of R. Hence, as should be expected of a subalgebra, any sublattice of a lattice L forms a lattice with respect to the operations defined in L.

Concrete examples for sublattices are:

1. Let H be an arbitrary set and $K \subseteq H$. Then, the subset lattice of K is a sublattice of the subset lattice of H.
2. In the set of Example 11, the sets of all divisors or all multiples of any integer form sublattices.

Any subchain C of a lattice L is a sublattice of L: In fact, for any pair of elements a, b of C, either $a \leqq b$, whence $a \cap b = a$ and $a \cup b = b$, or $a \geqq b$, whence $a \cap b = b$ and $a \cup b = a$; the proof that (1) holds is trivial in both cases.

As a consequence of the inequalities proposed in Section 13, every $(u]$ and $[u)$ $(u \in L)$, as well as every interval of the lattice L, is a sublattice of L.

Since any single-element subset $\{a\}$ of the lattice L can be regarded as a zero-length chain or as an interval $[a, a]$, every $\{a\}$ is a sublattice of L. (This statement can also be directly verified by considering L_7 and L_8.) Furthermore, L is also a sublattice of itself.

The sublattices of the lattice L other than L itself are called the *proper sublattices* of L. The proper sublattices consisting of more than one element are called *non-trivial sublattices.* If a proper (non-trivial) sublattice is a chain, it is also called a proper (non-trivial) subchain of L. Any lattice of at least three elements has non-trivial subchains.

The non-trivial sublattices of the lattice shown in Fig. 12 are the non-trivial subchains and the subset $\{a, b, c, i\}$. The set $M = \{o, b, c, i\}$ is likewise a lattice with respect to the ordering of the given lattice, but in M the meet of the elements b, c equals o. This, however, contradicts the meet definition shown by the diagram so that M is not a sublattice of the given lattice.

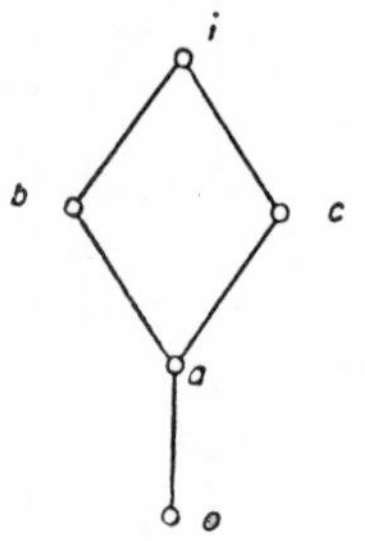

Fig. 12

We also introduce the following very important concept. A subset I of a lattice L is called an *ideal* of L if I satisfies the two following conditions:

I_1. *$a, b \in I$ implies $a \cup b \in I$*);

I_2. *for any element x of the lattice, $a \in I$ implies $a \cap x \in I$.*

By this definition, every ideal of a lattice L is a sublattice of L.

Ideals will be discussed in more detail in Chapter VIII.

17. Bound Elements of a Lattice Atoms and Dual Atoms

In conformity with the nomenclature introduced in Section 7, if a lattice L has an element $\begin{Bmatrix} o \\ i \end{Bmatrix}$ such that any element x of L satisfies the inequality $\begin{Bmatrix} o \leq x \\ i \geq x \end{Bmatrix}$, then $\begin{Bmatrix} o \\ i \end{Bmatrix}$ is called the $\begin{Bmatrix} \text{least} \\ \text{greatest} \end{Bmatrix}$ element of L. These elements will also be called the bound elements of L.

By the definition of the ordering of lattices, the least element o and the greatest element i of the lattice L satisfy the identities

$$(1) \qquad o \cap x = o, \quad o \cup x = x \quad (x \in L)$$

$$(2) \qquad i \cup x = i \quad i \cap x = x \quad (x \in L)$$

These can be verbally stated as follows: *The* $\begin{Bmatrix} \textit{least} \\ \textit{greatest} \end{Bmatrix}$ *element* $\begin{Bmatrix} o \\ i \end{Bmatrix}$ *of the lattice L (provided it exists) is the* $\begin{Bmatrix} \textit{zero} \\ \textit{unity} \end{Bmatrix}$ *element of the meet sublattice $L^{\cap}$ and the* $\begin{Bmatrix} \textit{unity} \\ \textit{zero} \end{Bmatrix}$ *element of the join sublattice $L^{\cup}$.*

Each of the lattices in Examples 7, 8, 10 and 13 has a least as well as a greatest element. These are, in that order, O and M, O and the plane itself, O and S, and finally the one-element subgroup (consisting of the unity element) and G. The least element of the lattice N of Example 11 is the number 1; that lattice has no greatest element.

Concerning the existence of bound elements, the following will be shown:

THEOREM 10. *Every lattice has at most one minimal and one maximal element; these elements are at the same time the least and greatest element of that lattice.*

That is to say, in a lattice the terms "minimal element" and "least element" (similarly "maximal element" and "greatest element") mean the same thing.

COROLLARY. *A lattice satisfying the* $\begin{Bmatrix} \textit{minimum} \\ \textit{maximum} \end{Bmatrix}$ *condition has a* $\begin{Bmatrix} \textit{least} \\ \textit{greatest} \end{Bmatrix}$ *element. In particular every lattice of finite length is bounded.*

PROOF. It is known that for arbitrary elements m, x of a lattice, $m \cap x \leqq m$. If, however, m is minimal, $m \cap x < m$ is impossible and thus, $m \cap x = x$ i.e., $m \leqq x$ for any x. Thus the proposition of the theorem concerning the minimal elements is proved; the other proposition is dual to this one. The corollary follows by applying Theorem 3.

An element p of a lattice bounded below is called an *atom* if $p \succ o$. If there can be found for each element a $(\neq o)$ of L an atom p such that $a \geqq p$, L is called an *atomic lattice.*

Dually, an element m of a lattice L bounded above is called a *dual atom* if $m \prec i$. L is called a *dually atomic lattice* if there can be found for any element a $(\neq i)$ a dual atom m such that $a \leqq m$.

In the literature on lattice theory, the term "point" is also used instead of "atom".

18. Complements, Relative Complements, Semicomplements

In Example 7, there may be found for each set A a set B such that $A \cap B = O$, $A \cup B = M$; in fact $B = M - A$ is such a set. The set $M - A$ is usually called "complementary" to A. By analogy, let us introduce the following terminology.

Let L be a bounded lattice and u any element of L. By a *complement* of u is meant any x of L satisfying the equations

$$u \cap x = o \tag{1}$$

$$u \cup x = i \tag{2}$$

By the commutativity of the meet and join operations, and by definition, the property of complementarity is symmetrical: if x is a complement of u, so is u a complement of x.

From Equation (1) of the preceeding section by the substitution $x = i$ we obtain $o \cap i = o$ and $o \cup i = i$ respectively. Hence, i is the complement of o. Since by the same equations $o \cup x = i$ is valid only for $x = i$ it follows that i is the only complement of o. By duality o is the only complement of i.

The boundedness of a lattice does not at all imply that every element has a complement; nor does it mean that every element has at most one complement (examples will be given below). If an element u of a bounded lattice L has at least one complement, u is called a *complemented element* of L. If u has exactly one complement, it is called a *uniquely complemented element* of L. If all elements of L are complemented (uniquely complemented) L is said to be a *complemented (uniquely complemented) lattice*.

In the lattice of Fig. 11 (p. 43), a is a uniquely complemented element; its unique complement is e. On the other hand, e is not uniquely complemented since c, as well as a, is a complement of e. The element d is not complemented.

The lattice $\mathscr{P}(M)$ mentioned at the beginning of the section is a uniquely complemented lattice.

The subspace lattice $\mathscr{L}(S)$ of the three-dimensional space S is complemented but not uniquely complemented. Moreover, every element of $\mathscr{L}(S)$ other than S and O has an infinite number of complements: any point of S in $\mathscr{L}(S)$ has for complements every plane of S which does not include the point in question, and any line of S has as complements every line skew to the given line.

The simplest examples of non-complemented bounded lattices are bounded chains.

According as to whether the lattice in question is bounded, complemented or uniquely complemented, the complementation in it may be considered as a partial operation, many-valued operation, or an operation.

Now let L be an arbitrary lattice (that is, one which is not necessarily bounded either below or above). Let $[a, b]$ be some interval of L and u an element of $[a, b]$. If some element x of L satisfies the equations

$$u \cap x = a \tag{3}$$

$$u \cup x = b \tag{4}$$

then x is included in the sublattice $[a, b]$. Moreover it is a complement of u in that sublattice. On this basis, an element x of L for which (3) and (4) hold is called a *relative complement of* u in $[a, b]$. The adjective "relative" indicates that the complement is considered relative to a sublattice. It is also usual to say that x is a *relative complement of u with respect to the pair of elements a, b*. Clearly, if x is a relative complement of u in $[a, b]$, u is a relative complement of x in the same interval.

A lattice L is said to be *relatively complemented* if, for any triplet of its elements a, b, u ($a \leqq u \leqq b$), there can be found at least one complement of u in $[a, b]$, in other words, if every interval of L is a complemented sublattice.

In the case of a bounded lattice, the relative complements of an element u with respect to the pair of elements o, i are, by equations (1)—(4), themselves, the complements of u. Hence, if a bounded lattice is relatively complemented, it is also complemented.

On the contrary, the lattice seen in Fig. 13 is complemented (the common complement of a and c being b), but not relatively complemented: a has no relative complement in $[o, c]$. Consequently, complemented lattices are not necessarily relatively complemented.

Consider the set $\mathscr{F}(M)$ of all finite subsets of an infinite set M (including the void set). This set is a sublattice of the subset lattice $\mathscr{P}(M)$. The lattice $\mathscr{F}(M)$ is not bounded (above), but it is relatively complemented. If A, B and U are finite subsets of M and $A \subseteq U \subseteq B$, the (unique) relative complement of U in $[A, B]$ is the set $B - (U - A) = (B - U) \cup A$.

In the rest of this section we shall consider only lattices bounded below. Such a lattice L is called *section complemented* if each interval of the form $[o, a]$ $(a \in L)$ of L is a complemented sublattice of L, that is, if to each pair a, u $(u \leqq a)$ of elements of L, there exists an element x $(\in L)$ such that $u \frown x = o$ and $u \smile x = a$.

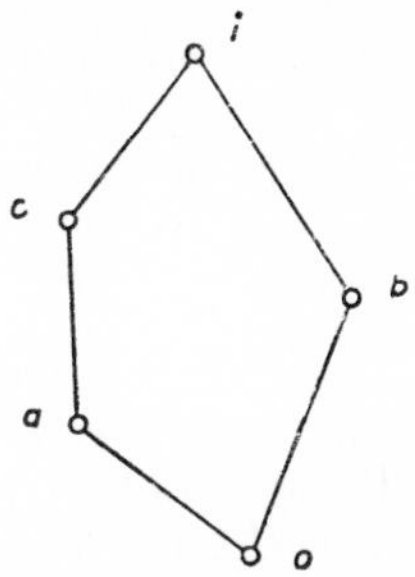

Fig. 13

For lattices bounded below, the complement concept may also be generalized as follows: By the *semicomplement* of an element u of a lattice L bounded below we mean every element x of L satisfying (1). Evidently, at the same time u is also the semicomplement of x; if we want to emphasize the symmetricity of this connection, we say that u and x are *disjoint* elements.

All the semicomplements of an element u form a partly ordered set U. A semicomplement x_0 of u is called a *maximal semicomplement* if it is a maximal element of U, i.e. if

$$u \frown x = o \text{ and } x \geqq x_0 \text{ imply } x = x_0$$

If, in particular, U has a greatest element, this will be termed the *pseudo-complement* of u. This concept has an importance chiefly in the topological applications of lattice theory.

Let x be a semicomplement of u, and let y be any element of L such that $y \leqq x$. Then, $u \frown y \leqq u \frown x = o$, that is, $u \frown y \leqq o$. On the other hand, o being the least element of L, $u \frown y \geqq o$. This, together with the former relation, means that $u \frown y = o$. In other words, *if x be a semicomplement of u, so is every element of* $(x]$. A fortiori, the set U of all semicomplements of u forms a convex subset of L.

It is apparent from the definition that o is a semicomplement of every element. The semicomplements other than o of an element u are termed the *proper semicomplements* of u. If M is a proper semicomplement of u and at the same time a maximal semicomplement of the same element then it is called a *maximal proper semicomplement* of u.

Equations (1) and (2) of the preceding section directly imply that every element other than o is a proper semicomplement of o, whereas the element i, even if it exists, has no proper semicomplement. The bound elements of the lattice are thus seen to behave peculiarly regarding the existence of proper semicomplements.

A lattice L bounded below is called a *semicomplemented lattice* if every inner element of L has at least one proper semicomplement.

Clearly, every complemented lattice is, a fortiori, semicomplemented.

The lattice N of Example 11 is a semicomplemented lattice not bounded above.

Let us add — as maximal element — the set M itself to the lattice $\mathscr{F}(M)$ mentioned above. In this way we obtain a bounded semicomplemented lattice; if, however, M is infinite, the lattice is nevertheless non-complemented.

A lattice L bounded below is called *weakly complemented* if for any pair a, b $(a < b)$ of elements of L, a has a semicomplement that is, however, not a semicomplement of b i.e.

$$(5) \qquad a \cap x = o\,, \qquad b \cap x \neq o$$

The definition directly implies

THEOREM 11. *Every weakly complemented lattice is semicomplemented.*

PROOF. Let a be any inner element of a weakly complemented lattice L. By Theorem 10, a cannot be a maximal element, hence there exists an element $b\,(\in L)$ such that $a < b$. Then there exists at least one x which satisfies (5). Clearly, x is a proper semicomplement of a.

On the other hand, we have

THEOREM 12. *Every section complemented lattice bounded below is weakly complemented.*

PROOF. Let a, b $(a < b)$ be any pair of elements of a section complemented lattice L bounded below, and let x be a relative complement of a in $[o, b]$. Then, $a \cap x = o$ and $a \cup x = b$. Hence, on the one hand, x is a semicomplement of a, and on the other, $b \cap x = (a \cup x) \cap x = x$. Thus it is sufficient to prove that $x \neq o$. However, were $x = o$ true, then, by the equations (1) of the preceding chapter, we should have $b = a \cup x = a \cup o = a$, which contradicts the assumption $a < b$.

Finally we prove

THEOREM 13. *Every uniquely complemented lattice is weakly complemented.*

PROOF. Let a and b be elements of a uniquely complemented lattice with $a < b$. We denote by a' the (unique) complement of a. Then we have, on the one hand

$$(6) \qquad a \cap a' = o\,,$$

and on the other hand $b \cup a' \geqq a \cup a' = i$, i.e. $b \cup a' = i$. Hence it follows that

$$(7) \qquad b \cap a' \neq o\,,$$

unless we had two different complements a and b for a', contrary to the assumption. Yet it follows from (6) and (7) that the lattice is indeed weakly complemented.

It is to be noted that the term "weakly complemented lattice" is not at all expressive, since the name suggests that the concept is derived by weakening the condition for the lattice to be complemented, whereas in reality many complemented lattices are not weakly complemented (e.g. the lattice of Fig. 13, in which a and c have only common semicomplements, namely o and b).

A special class of weakly complemented lattices is discussed by Balachandran [5].

19. Irreducible and Prime Elements of a Lattice

Any element a of a lattice can be represented in the form $a = x \cap y$: For example, by choosing x equal to a, and y greater than or equal to a. However, a "decomposition" of this kind of a presents no new information about a; only the representations of the forms $a = x \cap y$ with $x, y > a$ are of interest.

Accordingly, an element a of a lattice L is said to be *meet-reducible* if there exist in L elements a_1, a_2 such that

$$a = a_1 \cap a_2 \quad (a_1, a_2 > a) \tag{1}$$

If some a has no decomposition at all of the form (1), it is said to be *meet-irreducible*.

Dually, some element a of L is said to be *join-reducible* or *join-irreducible*, depending on whether or not it can be represented in the form

$$a = a_1 \cup a_2 \quad (a_1, a_2 < a) \tag{2}$$

Clearly, the least element and every atom of a lattice bounded below is join-irreducible, while the greatest element and every dual atom of a lattice bounded above is meet-irreducible.

In the lattice N of Example 11, further join-irreducible elements are all elements of the form p^a, where p is prime and a an integer greater than 1.

Every element of a chain is meet-irreducible as well as join-irreducible.

Conversely, it may happen that every element of a lattice is meet- as well as join-reducible. A lattice of this kind is presented in the following example. Let I denote the set of integers and let us form the product set $I \times I$. Now define in $I \times I$ two operations, a meet and a join, as follows:*

$$\left.\begin{array}{ll} (3) & (x_1, x_2) \cap (y_1, y_2) = \big(\min(x_1, y_1), \min(x_2, y_2)\big) \\ (4) & (x_1, x_2) \cup (y_1, y_2) = \big(\max(x_1, y_1), \max(x_2, y_2)\big) \end{array}\right\} \ (x_1, x_2, y_1, y_2 \in I)$$

It is easy to see that $I \times I$ is a lattice with respect to these operations (part of its diagram in the generalized sense is shown as Fig. 14 on the next page). Consider an arbitrary element (a_1, a_2) of $I \times I$. If p_j $(j = 1, 2)$ is an (arbitrary) integer greater than a_j and q_j another less than a_j, then

$$(a_1, a_2) = (a_1, p_2) \cap (p_1, a_2)$$

$$(a_1, a_2) = (a_1, q_2) \cup (q_1, a_2)$$

* In the case of arbitrary integers x and y, min (x, y) denotes the lesser one of x and y, while max (x, y) denotes the greater one. — Incidentally, the algebra defined by (3) and (4) is — by the terminology to be introduced in Section 62 — the direct union of the chain I with itself.

and in the lattice $I \times I$

$$(a_1, q_2),\ (q_1, a_2) < (a_1, a_2) < (a_1, p_2),\ (p_1, a_2)$$

THEOREM 14. *In a lattice satisfying the maximum condition, every one of its elements can be represented as the meet of a finite number of meet-irreducible elements.*

The formulation of the dual statement is left to the reader.

PROOF. Let L be a lattice satisfying the maximum condition, and let H denote the set of all elements of L which cannot be represented as postulated by the theorem. Then we have to show that H is void.

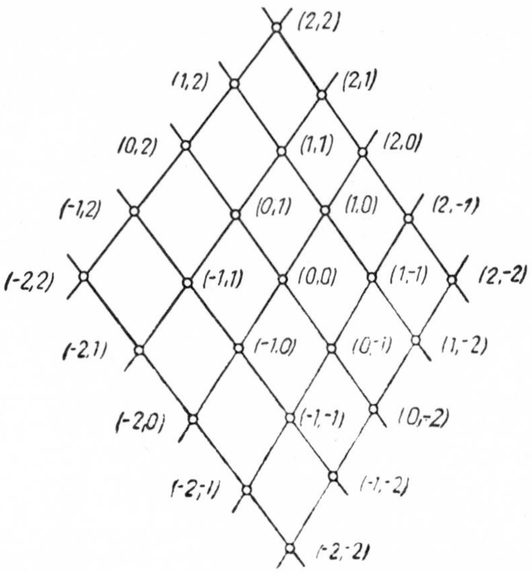

Fig. 14

Clearly, H contains no meet-irreducible element, since if a is such an element, then $a = a \frown a$ or $a = a \frown i$ are easily found representations of the required form. (By the corollary of Theorem 10, L has a greatest element.)

Assume that — contrary to our statement — H is non-void. Since the maximum condition is also valid in H, the set H has at least one maximal element m. From the above statement it follows that m is meet-reducible. Hence, elements m_1, m_2 occur in L such that

$$(5) \qquad m = m_1 \frown m_2 \quad (m_1, m_2 > m)$$

Since m is a maximal element of H, the elements m_1, m_2 are not contained by H. Hence, m_1 and m_2 can be represented in the form $m_1 = q_1 \frown \ldots \frown q_s$ and $m_2 = r_1 \frown \ldots \frown r_t$ respectively, where all the q_j and r_k are meet-irreducible and $q_j > m_1$, $r_k > m_2$. But then, by (5), $m = \bigcap_{j=1}^{s} q_j \frown \bigcap_{j=1}^{t} r_k$, in contradiction to $m \in H$. This contradiction means that the assumption $H \neq O$ was incorrect, and thus furnishes the required proof.

A generalization of the concept of an irreducible element is as follows: An element a of a lattice L is called *meet-prime* if $a_1 \frown a_2 \leqq a$ implies that either $a_1 \leqq a$ or $a_2 \leqq a$ (or both) hold; the dual definition is valid for the case of *join-prime* elements.

It is obvious that *every meet-(join-)prime element is a fortiori meet-(join-)irreducible.** Moreover the least element of a lattice bounded below is obviously join-prime, while the greatest element of a lattice bounded above is meet-prime.

THEOREM 15. *In a complemented lattice every* $\left\{\begin{matrix}\textit{join-}\\ \textit{meet-}\end{matrix}\right\}$ *prime element except the* $\left\{\begin{matrix}\textit{least}\\ \textit{greatest}\end{matrix}\right\}$ *one is an* $\left\{\begin{matrix}\textit{atom}\\ \textit{dual atom}\end{matrix}\right\}$ *of the lattice.*

PROOF. Owing to the lattice theoretical duality principle it is sufficient to prove the first statement of the theorem.

Let L be a complemented lattice and p a join-prime element of it other than o. Let us suppose that for an element q of L we have $o \leqq q < p$. Denoting by q' one of the complements of q we have

$$p \leqq q \smile q' (= i)$$

Because p is prime and $p \nleqq q$, hence it follows $p \leqq q'$. In this case, however, we have

$$q = p \frown q \leqq q' \frown q = o$$

i.e. $q = o$.

Some further interesting results concerning prime elements can be found in the paper [6] of Balachandran, which, however, should be read only after the study of Chapter III.

20. The Homomorphism of a Lattice

In Section 14 it was shown that every lattice can also be regarded as a partly ordered set. Moreover, lattices were seen to be partly ordered sets in which any finite subset has an infimum and a supremum. Conversely, from every partly ordered set having this property a lattice can be formed. It was also shown (Theorem 9) that as regards the isomorphism of two lattices it is of no importance whether they are regarded as two-operation algebras or as partly ordered sets. Nevertheless, a lattice L and the partly ordered set formed therefrom behave differently in a number of important particulars. For example, with respect to an ordering in L, every subset of L is also partly ordered, whereas not every subset of L is a lattice with respect to the operations defined in L. The difference in the behaviour of the lattice and of the partly ordered set derived therefrom is also apparent in their homomorphisms.

* As to the converse statement see Exercise 26 to Chapter IV.

A single-valued (but not necessarily one-to-one) mapping φ of a lattice L_1 into — or, especially, onto — a lattice L_2 is termed a *homomorphism* (or *homomorphic mapping)* if for every pair of elements a, b of L_1

$$\varphi(a \frown b) = \varphi(a) \frown \varphi(b) \tag{1}$$

and

$$\varphi(a \smile b) = \varphi(a) \smile \varphi(b) \tag{2}$$

If the single-valued mapping φ of L_1 into (especially, onto) L_2 is such that $\begin{Bmatrix}\text{only (1)}\\ \text{only (2)}\end{Bmatrix}$ is satisfied for every pair of elements a, b of L_1, φ is called a $\begin{Bmatrix}\textit{meet}\\ \textit{join}\end{Bmatrix}$ *homomorphism* or $\begin{Bmatrix}\textit{meet-}\\ \textit{join-}\end{Bmatrix}$ *homomorphic mapping*. Finally, by the definition introduced in Section 3, a single valued mapping φ of L_1 into (or onto) L_2 is called an *order homomorphism* or an *order homomorphic* (or else an *order preserving)* mapping, if for every pair of elements a, b of L_1, $a \leqq b$ implies $\varphi(a) \leqq \varphi(b)$.

It is seen that a meet-homomorphic (join-homomorphic) mapping of L_1 into L_2 is, as a matter of fact, a homomorphism of $L_1^{\frown}$ into $L_2^{\frown}$ ($L_1^{\smile}$ into $L_2^{\smile}$).

Evidently, an isomorphism of a lattice is, a fortiori, a homomorphism, and every homomorphism of a lattice is simultaneously a meet and join homomorphism. Furthermore, every meet- and join homomorphism is at the same time an order preserving mapping. Indeed, if φ is a meet-homomorphism of L_1 onto L_2 and $a \leqq b$ $(a, b \in L)$, we have $\varphi(a) \frown \varphi(b) = \varphi(a \frown b) = \varphi(a)$, whence $\varphi(a) \leqq \varphi(b)$. By duality, it follows that every join homomorphism is also order preserving.

The relations between isomorphisms and the classes of mappings defined above can be schematically illustrated as follows:

isomorphism

⇓

homomorphism

⇙ ⇘

meet-homomorphism join-homomorphism

⇘ ⇙

order preserving mapping
(order homomorphism)

It was first observed by Ore ([150], I, p. 416) that these concepts are all distinct. This fact will be illustrated by using the lattices L_1, L_2, L_3 of Fig. 15 and by the following mappings of L_1 onto L_2 and L_3, respectively:

$$\varphi\colon \varphi(o_1) = \varphi(p) = \varphi(q) = o_2,\ \varphi(i_1) = i_2$$

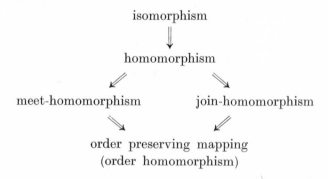

$$\psi: \psi(i_1) = \psi(p) = \psi(q) = i_2, \ \psi(o_1) = o_2$$

$$\sigma: \sigma(o_2) = o_3, \ \sigma(p) = r, \ \sigma(q) = s, \ \sigma(i_1) = i_3$$

It is obvious that every one of these three mappings is order-preserving. However, $\varphi(p \frown q) = \varphi(o_1) = o_2 = \varphi(p) \frown \varphi(q)$, and hence φ is a meet homorphism; but, it is not a homomorphism since $\varphi(p \smile q) = \varphi(i_1) = i_2$ and $\varphi(p) \smile \varphi(q) = o_2$. By the dual consideration, it follows that ψ is a join-homomorphism but not a homomorphism. Finally, the (order preserving) mapping σ is neither a meet-, nor a join homomorphism, since

$$\sigma(p \frown q) = \sigma(o_1) = o_3 \text{ and } \sigma(p) \frown \sigma(q) = r \frown s = r$$

$$\sigma(p \smile q) = \sigma(i_1) = i_3 \text{ and } \sigma(p) \smile \sigma(q) = r \smile s = s$$

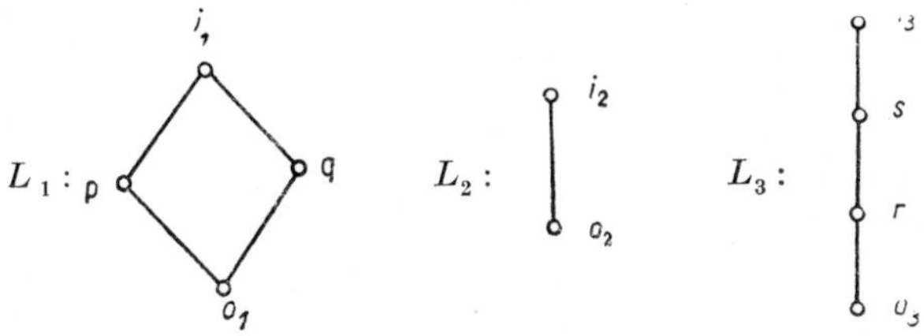

Fig. 15

Let L_1 and L_2 be two lattices and let the homomorphism $\varphi : L_1 \sim L_2$ hold. If L_2 has a least element o_2, the set of the elements x satisfying the equation $\varphi(x) = o_2$ is called the *kernel of the homomorphism* φ and denoted K_φ. If, on the other hand, L_2 is not bounded below, the homorphism φ is said to have no kernel.

THEOREM 16. *If a homomorphism of a lattice has a kernel, this kernel is then an ideal of the lattice.*

Indeed, if $a \in K_\varphi$, we have by (1)

$$\varphi(a \frown b) = \varphi(a) \frown \varphi(b) = o_2 \frown \varphi(b) = o_2$$

If b is also an element of K_φ, we have by (2)

$$\varphi(a \smile b) = \varphi(a) \smile \varphi(b) = o_2 \smile o_2 = o_2$$

Thus the kernel K_φ of φ has the properties I_2 and I_1 occurring in the definition of ideals.

21. Axiom Systems of Lattices

In the first part of this section it will be shown that the set $\mathsf{L}_1 - \mathsf{L}_6$ of the lattice axioms represents an independent axiom system (Kimura [113]), that is, to any axiom L_j ($j = 1, \ldots, 6$) it is possible to find a two-operation algebra for which (using the symbols $\frown$, $\smile$ as operational symbols), every L_k ($k = 1, \ldots, 6$) $k \neq j$) holds except L_j.

1. *Demonstration of the independence of L_3.* Let us define upon the set $\{a, b\}$ a two-operation algebra S by the following tables of operation:

$\cap$	a	b
a	a	a
b	b	b

$\cup$	a	b
a	a	a
b	a	b

Then, with the symbols x, y, z denoting any of the elements a, b, the following equations hold:

$$(x \cap y) \cap z = x \cap z = x = x \cap (y \cap z)$$

$$x \cap (x \cup y) = x$$

$$x \cup (x \cap y) = x \cup x = x$$

which show that L_1, L_5 and L_6 are valid. L_4 is also satisfied, since the table of the operation $\cup$ is symmetrical with respect to the principal diagonal. Finally, L_2 is also satisfied: if one of x, y, z equals a, we have $(x \cup y) \cup z = a = x \cup \cup (y \cup z)$ and, by L_4, already proved, $(b \cup b) \cup b = b \cup (b \cup b)$.

Consequently, L_1, L_2, $L_4 - L_6$ are satisfied in S. On the contrary, L_3 is not satisfied, since the table of operations of $\cap$ is not symmetrical with respect to the principal diagonal ($a \cap b = a$, but $b \cap a = b$).

2. *Demonstration of the independence of* L_5. Let us consider again the set $\{a, b\}$, and let us define thereupon a two-operation algebra T in the following way: The "meet" of any two elements of T is equal to b, and $\cup$ is defined in the same way as in the preceding S. Then, L_1 and L_3 are evidently satisfied; furthermore, by the results of concerning $S^{\cap}$ in 1., L_2 and L_4 also hold. Finally, L_6 is also valid, since for any elements x, y of T, $x \cup (x \cap y) = x \cup b = x$.

On the other hand, L_5 is not satisfied in T: for example, $a \cap (a \cup a) = a \cap a = b$.

3. *Demonstration of the independence of* L_1. Let us consider the five-element lattice — denoted for short by L — defined by the diagram shown in Fig. 12 (p. 44). By modifying — as it were, "ruining" — L, let us define an algebra V as follows: let the operation $\cup$ in V be defined exactly as $\cup$ in the lattice L and, except for the elements b, c, also the operation $\cap$; whereas in V let $b \cap \cup c = c \cap b = o$.

Since $V^{\cup}$ is identical with the semilattice $L^{\cup}$, L_2 and L_4 are also valid in V. It is also obvious that the modification of the definition of $\cap$ has not disturbed the validity of L_3.

The satisfying of L_5 can be seen as follows. By the definition of $\cap$, except for the cases $x = b$, $x \cup y = c$, and $x = c$, $x \cup y = b$, the value of $x \cap (x \cup y)$ is the same as in L — that is equal to x. However, the "excepted cases" cannot occur, since $b \cup y = c$ and $c \cup y = b$ can be true for no element y of V.

L_6 can be proved by similar considerations. Disregarding the cases $x = b$, $y = c$ and $x = c$, $y = b$, the value of $x \cup (x \cap y)$ in V is necessarily the same as in L — that is, equal to x. On the other hand, for the exceptional cases it follows by direct computation that

$$b \cup (b \cap c) = b \cup o = b$$

$$c \cup (c \cap b) = c \cup o = c$$

Hence, each of $L_2 - L_6$ is satisfied in V. However, L_1 is not satisfied since $b \cap (c \cap a) = b \cap a = a$ and $(b \cap c) \cap a = o \cap a = o$.

4. *Demonstration of the independence of* L_4, L_6, and L_2. It is sufficient to interchange the symbols $\cap$ and $\cup$ in the previous examples.

In 1—4 we have proved the independence of the axiom system $L_1 - L_6$. In the independency examples dealt with thus far some disproportionality is to be seen. When proving the independence of L_1 and L_2 we have used algebras consisting of five elements, while in the other cases only two-element algebras were needed. This, however, turns out to be inevitable, as we can prove (Szász [197]), that for an algebra of not more than four elements, satisfying the axioms $L_3 - L_6$, either both of the axioms L_1 and L_2 hold or neither of them do.

It was shown (in Theorems 5 and 6) that every lattice has the properties L_7 and L_9. The following converse of this statement is also true:

If for some two-variable operations $\frown$, $\smile$ *defined on a set* L, *the axioms* $L_1 - L_4$, L_6 *and* L_9 *hold, then* L_5 *and* L_6 *are also satisfield.*

For any elements a, b of L we have by L_1 and L_7 $a \frown (a \frown b) = (a \frown a) \frown b = a \frown b$, and thus by L_9, $(a \frown b) \smile a = a$; and the latter implies L_6 because of L_4. The satisfying of L_5 can now be proved by „dualization": because — as the reader may well convinve himself — what has been said concerning the lattice theoretical duality principle can be transferred to any algebra in which two two-variable operations are defined.

Theorems 5 and 6, together with this proved converse statement mean that lattices can be characterised (in addition to the axiom system $L_1 - L_6$) by the axiom system consisting of $L_1 - L_4$, L_6 and L_9 (Klein-Barmen [114]). This second axiom system is again independent as was first shown by Kobayasi [118]. In order to prove this point only appropriate examples of independence will be enumerated. The detailed computation is left to the reader.

The independence of L_1 and L_2 can be proved by the above algebra V but one can now give independence examples consisting of three elements as follows:

$\frown$	a	b	c
a	a	b	c
b	b	b	a
c	c	a	c

$\smile$	a	b	c
a	a	a	a
b	a	b	a
c	a	a	c

and its dual, respectively. The independence of L_3 and L_4 is proved by the two-operation algebra given by

$\frown$	a	b	c
a	a	a	a
b	b	b	b
c	a	b	c

$\smile$	a	b	c
a	a	c	c
b	c	b	c
c	c	c	c

and by its dual, respectively. To prove the independence of L_6, consider the two-operation algebra defined by the operation tables

$\frown$	a	b
a	a	a
b	a	a

$\smile$	a	b
a	a	b
b	b	a

Finally to prove the independence of L_9, consider the two-operation algebra defined by the operation tables

$\frown$	a	b
a	a	a
b	a	b

$\smile$	a	b
a	a	a
b	a	a

It can be demonstrated that the independence examples given above are all of a minimal number of elements (see Szász [197]).

Besides the two systems of lattice axioms dealt with thus far many other systems are also well known. It is not our aim to review all these in detail. We would mention only that, among others, Felscher [60] and Sorkin [182] conducted investigations in that direction, while Rudeanu [169] determined all the independent systems of axioms for lattices that may be formed from the axioms $L_1 - L_9$.

It can be proved that the system of axioms $H_1 - H_3$ for semilattices is independent, too; as independence examples, e.g. the following one operational algebras might be used:

for H_1:

	a	b
a	a	a
b	a	a

for H_2:

	a	b
a	a	b
b	a	b

for H_3:

	a	b	c
a	a	a	b
b	a	b	b
c	b	b	c

Exercises to Chapter II

1. Find all lattices of at most six elements and draw their diagrams.
2. Prove that for arbitrary elements x, y of a lattice

a) $x \parallel y \Longleftrightarrow x \cap y < x, y < x \cup y$;

b) $x \cap y < x \Longleftrightarrow x \cup y < y$

3. Prove for arbitrary elements a, b, c, d of a lattice, the inequalities

$$(a \cap b) \cup (b \cap c) \cup (c \cap a) \leq (a \cup b) \cap (b \cup c) \cap (c \cup a)$$

and

$$(a \cap c) \cup (b \cap d) \leq (a \cup b) \cap (c \cup d)$$

4. Show that if for the elements a, b, c of a lattice $a, b \prec c$ and $a \neq b$, then $a \cup b = c$.
5. Without utilizing the ordering of the lattice, prove that every finite lattice has a least and a greatest element.
6. Prove that if a lattice satisfies the minimum condition, it is also atomic.
7. Find the lattices all subsets of which are sublattices.
8. Show that the set-intersection of two intervals of a lattice is either void or an interval.
9. Show that a sublattice R of a lattice L is convex if, and only if, $a, b \in R \Rightarrow [a \cap b, a \cup b] \subseteq R$.
10. Show that any lattice is isomorphic to a sublattice of one (moreover, of an infinite number of) complemented lattice(s).
11. Show that an element p of a lattice L is an atom of L if, and only if, for each element x of L either $x \geq p$ or $x \cap p = o$.

12. Let L be a uniquely complemented lattice and let x' denote the complement of $x(\in L)$. Prove that if p is an atom of L, p' is a dual atom, and that if p, q are distinct atoms of L, then $q \leqq p'$.

13. Prove that a lattice bounded below is weakly complemented if, and only if, there exists for every pair of elements u, v $(u \neq v)$ of the lattice an element x such that $(u \frown v) \frown x = o$, $(u \smile v) \frown x \neq o$.

14. Find the join and meet-irreducible elements of the lattice shown in Fig. 11 (p. 43). Find in this lattice a join-reducible element which, in a suitably chosen sublattice, is no more join-reducible.

15. Prove that a lattice is a chain if, and only if, every one of its elements is meet-irreducible.

16. Let $a_0 \prec a_1 \prec \ldots a_r$ and $b_0 \prec b_1 \prec \ldots b_s$ be two chains of a finite lattice, both consisting of join-irreducible elements. Show that $a_j \frown b_k = a_0 \frown b_0$ for each pair of indices j, k $(j = 0, 1, \ldots, r;$ $k = 0, 1, \ldots, s)$.

17. Prove that every homomorphic image of a lattice bounded (below) is likewise bounded (below).

18. Prove that every order preserving mapping of a chain is a homomomorphism.

19. Prove that if every order preserving mapping of a lattice is a homorphism, the lattice is a chain.

20. Let φ be a homomorphism of a lattice L_1 onto a lattice L_2. Prove that $x \prec y (x, y \in L_1)$ implies $\varphi(x) \preceq \varphi(y)$. Show by some example that if φ is only a meet- or only a join homomorphism the above proposition is false.

21. Show that the length of a homomorphic mapping of a lattice is at most equal to the length of the original lattice. Find out if the same is true for meet-, join- and order homomorphisms of lattices.

22. Let L_1 and L_2 be arbitrary lattices and $\varphi\colon L_1 \sim L_2$. Show that if a subset $R \subset L_2$ is an ideal of L_2, then the set of elements x of L_1 with $\varphi(x) \in R$ (the so called "complete inverse of R") is an ideal of L_1.

23. Show that every join-homomorphic image of a lattice satisfying the maximum condition also satisfies the maximum condition.

24. Let φ be a single-valued mapping of a lattice L onto another lattice such that $x < y$ implies $\varphi(x) < \varphi(y)$ for each pair x, y of L. Show that if φ is a meet homomorphism it is also an isomorphism but if φ is only order preserving it is not necessarily an isomorphism.

25. Let a, b be two arbitrary but fixed elements of a lattice L. Prove that

$$\varphi\colon \varphi(x) = ((a \frown b) \smile x) \frown (a \smile b)$$

is an order preserving mapping of L onto $[a \frown b, a \smile b]$.

26. On a lattice L define the mappings φ and ψ as follows: let $\varphi(a) = (a]$ $(a \in L)$ and let $\psi(a)$ denote the set of all atoms of L included in $(a]$. Show that both these are meet-homomorphic mappings of L into the subset lattice of L.

27. Let H be a semilattice with the operation symbol $\circ$ and for any mappings φ and ψ of H into itself let $\varphi \circ \psi$ denote the mapping defined by

$$\varphi \circ \psi(x) = \varphi(x) \circ \psi(x) \quad (x \in H)$$

Finally let Γ denote the set of all single-valued mappings of H into itself. Show that a $\gamma \in \Gamma$ is a homomorphism if, and only if, for each element α, β of Γ and each element x of H, $\gamma(\alpha \circ \beta)(x) = \gamma\alpha(x) \circ \circ\, \gamma\beta(x)$.

CHAPTER III

COMPLETE LATTICES

22. Complete Lattices

By Theorem 8, for any finite sublattice $R=\{a_1, \ldots, a_n\}$ of a lattice L, $\inf_L R = \bigcap_{j=1}^{n} a_j$, $\sup_L R = \bigcup_{j=1}^{n} a_j$. These formulae enable us to define (for infinite lattices) the meets and joins of certain infinite sets of elements.

For a non-void subset $R = \{a_\gamma\}_{\gamma\in\Gamma}$, of any power, of a lattice L, we understand by the meet of the elements a_γ $(\gamma \in \Gamma)$ the element $\inf_L R$, by their join, the element $\sup_L R$ — provided these elements exist — and we shall symbolize them by

$$\bigcap_{\varphi\in\Gamma} a_\gamma \quad \text{and} \quad \bigcup_{\varphi\in\Gamma} a_\gamma$$

or, even more briefly, by

$$\bigcap R \text{ and } \bigcup R$$

If $\inf_L R$ ($\sup_L R$) does not exist, then it is said that the meet (join) of the elements of R does not exist.

This definition and notation conforms to the definition and notation previously applied to finite subsets.

Let $\{a_\gamma\}_{\gamma\in\Gamma}$, $\{b_\gamma\}_{\gamma\in\Gamma}$ and $\{c_\delta\}_{\delta\in\Delta}$ be subsets of a lattice L, which has both infima and suprema. It follows at once from the above definition that

$$(1) \qquad a_\gamma \leqq b_\gamma \, (\gamma \in \Gamma) \Longrightarrow \begin{cases} \bigcap_{\gamma\in\Gamma} a_\gamma \leqq \bigcap_{\gamma\in\Gamma} b_\gamma, \\ \bigcup_{\gamma\in\Gamma} a_\gamma \leqq \bigcup_{\gamma\in\Gamma} b_\gamma, \end{cases}$$

and

$$a_\gamma \leqq b_\delta \text{ (for each pair } \gamma, \delta) \Longrightarrow \bigcup_{\gamma\in\Gamma} a_\gamma \leqq \bigcap_{\delta\in\Delta} c_\delta$$

Sometimes it is necessary to form the meet or join of an element of the form $a = \bigcap_{\lambda} a_\lambda$ or $b = \bigcup_{\mu} b_\mu$ with other elements. In such cases, the symbols $\bigcap$, $\bigcup$ will be taken to represent parentheses, too. As typical examples, let us cite the following:

1. $x \cup \bigcap_{\lambda} a_\lambda$ denotes the join of x and a;

2. $\bigcup_\lambda b_\mu \cap y$ denotes the meet of b and y;

3. $\bigcap_\lambda a_\mu \cap \bigcup_\mu b_\mu$ denotes the meet of a and b.

Instead of the second it is, however, more usual to write $y \cap \bigcup_\mu b_\mu$. On the other hand, the join of all elements $b_\mu \cap y$ is denoted with brackets i.e. $\bigcup_\mu (b_\mu \cap y)$.

If for any non-void subset R of a lattice L, $\left\{\begin{array}{l}\text{the meet } \bigcap R \\ \text{the join } \bigcup R\end{array}\right\}$ exists L is said to be a *lattice complete with respect to the* $\left\{\begin{array}{l}\textit{meet} \\ \textit{join}\end{array}\right\}$; if L is complete with respect to both operations, the lattice is said to be *complete*. In particular, if a complete lattice is a chain, it is called a *complete chain*.

The concept of a complete lattice was introduced — although under a different name — by Birkhoff ([10], p. 44).

It is apparent from the definition that *every finite lattice is complete*. Some non-trivial examples will be given after the proof of Theorem 17.

If L is a complete lattice, then in particular, both $\bigcap L = \inf_L L$ and $\bigcup L = \sup_L L$ must exist. But by the definition of the infima $\bigcap L \leq x$ for all x in L thus $\bigcap L$ is the least element of L. Similarly, $\bigcup L$ is the greatest element of L. Hence, *every complete lattice is bounded*.

Further, it follows at once by the definition that *the dual of a complete lattice is likewise a complete lattice*. Consequently, *the dual to every true proposition concerning complete lattices is also true*. This may be expressed as "the duality principle of the complete lattices". In other words, the method of dualizing proofs can also be utilized in verifying statements particularly restricted to complete lattices.

In the case of a complete lattice the forming of the infimum and supremum may be considered to be a (generalized) operation the number of variables of which equals the number of elements of the lattice. Therefore from this aspect the following definitions may be introduced:

A single-valued mapping φ of a complete lattice L_1 into another complete lattice L_2 is called a *complete homomorphism* if for an arbitrary subset $\{a_\gamma\}_{\gamma \in \Gamma}$ of L_1

$$\varphi(\bigcap_{\gamma \in \Gamma} a_\gamma) = \bigcap_{\gamma \in \Gamma} \varphi(a_\gamma) \tag{2}$$

and

$$\varphi(\bigcup_{\gamma \in \Gamma} a_\gamma) = \bigcup_{\gamma \in \Gamma} \varphi(a_\gamma) \tag{3}$$

are valid. If, in addition, φ is one-to-one and $\varphi(L_1) = L_2$, then we say that φ is a *complete isomorphism* of L_1 onto L_2.

If only (2) or (3) is valid for every subset $\{a_\gamma\}_{\gamma \in \Gamma}$ of L_1, then φ is called a *complete meet-homomorphism*, or a *complete join-homomorphism* respectively.

Obviously every complete homomorphism (resp. complete isomorphism) is especially a homomorphism (resp. isomorphism), too.

The concepts contained in the following section are also connected with the same aspect.

Frequent use will be made of the following:

THEOREM 17. *If P is a partly ordered set bounded above each of whose non-void subsets R has an infimum, then each non-void subset of P will have a supremum, too, and by the definitions* $\bigcap R = \inf R$, $\bigcup R = \sup R$, *then P becomes a complete lattice.*

COROLLARY. *If a bounded lattice is complete with respect to one of the lattice operations, it is also complete with respect to the other.*

PROOF. Only the first part of the theorem — that is, the existence of all suprema in P — needs to be proved, since it has already been shown in Section 14 that the infima and suprema possess the properties postulated by the lattice axioms. The corollary is evident if the theorem is true.

Let R be an arbitrary non-void subset of P, and let U denote the set of all upper bounds of R. Since P has a greatest element, U is non-void, and by the premises of the theorem, $\inf U$ exists. It will be shown that $\inf U$ equals $\sup R$. By the definition of U, every element r of R is a lower bound of U, and thus $r \leqq \inf U$. Hence, $\inf U$ is an upper bound of R. On the other hand, if u is an arbitrary upper bound of R, then $u \in U$, and so $\inf U \leqq u$; that is to say, $\inf U$ is in fact the least upper bound of R.

Now, a sufficient condition for a lattice to be complete will be stated.

THEOREM 18. *If a lattice satisfies both the maximum and the minimum condition (in particular, if it is of finite length), it is complete.*

PROOF. Let L be a lattice satisfying the assumptions of the theorem and consequently, by the corollary of Theorem 10, being bounded. Let R be any non-void subset of L and K denote the set of all lower bounds of R. The set K is certainly non-void (since, at least, $o \in K$), and itself satisfies the maximum condition. Hence, by Theorem 3, K has (at least) one maximal element, m. This m is of course itself a lower bound of R. We shall show that m is the greatest lower bound of R in L. For this purpose, consider an arbitrary element s of K. Then, for every element r of R, $r \geqq s$ and $r \geqq m$, so that $r \geqq s \cup m$; that is, $s \cup m$ is also an element of K. Hence, neither $s > m$ nor $s \parallel m$ is possible, since both would yield $s \cup m > m$, in contradiction to m being maximal. Hence, indeed, $s \leqq m$ $(s \in K)$.

The existence of $\sup_L R$ can be verified either by dualization, or by using Theorem 17.

The interval $[0, 1]$ of real numbers, being a complete chain, is a trivial example of a complete lattice satisfying neither the maximum, nor the minimum condition.

Now let us present some simple examples of complete lattices. Further examples will be discussed in Sections 26—29.

Example 14. The subset lattice of every set is complete. Moreover, for arbitrary subsets R_δ $(\delta \in \Delta)$ of a set M, we have in $\mathscr{P}(M)$

$$\bigcap_\delta R_\delta = \inf \{R_\delta\} = \bigcap_\delta R_\delta, \quad \bigcup_\delta R_\delta = \sup \{R_\delta\} = \bigcup_\delta R_\delta$$

Example 15. The set N_0 of non-negative integers, as ordered by divisibility, is bounded above (its greatest element being the number zero), and for any of its subsets H there exists $\inf_{N_0} H$; this is the greatest common divisor of the elements of H. Hence, by Theorem 17, N_0 is a complete lattice. Moreover, for finite H, $\sup_{N_0} H$ is the least common multiple of the elements in H, whereas for infinite H it is zero (since, from N_0, an infinite set can be selected only by choosing numbers greater than any fixed positive number).

Example 16. Every so-called affine or projective space is essentially a set of points and lines, connected by the relation of incidence. A far-reaching generalization of this type of space will now be introduced.

A set T is called an *incidence space* if there is assigned to T a set $\mathfrak{G}$ which contains none of the elements of T, and a relation $\mid$ which is defined over the product set $T \times \mathfrak{G}$. More precisely, it is said that "T forms a linear space together with $\mathfrak{G}$ and $\mid$". The elements of T are called "points", those of $\mathfrak{G}$ "lines", and $\mid$ the relation of incidence. The fact $\pi \mid \mathfrak{g} (\pi \in T;\ \mathfrak{g} \in \mathfrak{G})$ is stated verbally as follows: "π is situated on (is contained by) $\mathfrak{g}$". The set of all points situated on $\mathfrak{g}$ is denoted by $[\mathfrak{g}]$. Thus, $\pi \mid \mathfrak{g}$ is equivalent to $\pi \in [\mathfrak{g}]$. In the following, the latter notation will be used.

The points $\pi_1, \ldots, \pi_r$ of the incidence space T are said to be *collinear* if there exists a line $\mathfrak{g}$ such that $\pi_1, \ldots, \pi_r \in [\mathfrak{g}]$. By a *linear subspace* of T will be understood to mean a subset R of T satisfying the following condition: if $\pi, \varrho \in R$, $\pi \neq \varrho$ and the points π, ϱ, ξ are collinear, then $\xi \in R$.

Clearly, the meet of a set of arbitrary power of linear subspaces is likewise a linear subspace. However, T itself is also a linear subspace, and hence, by Theorem 17, the set of all linear subspaces of T — to be denoted by $\mathscr{L}(T)$ — is a complete lattice with respect to the relation of set inclusion. The lattice $\mathscr{L}(T)$ is called the *subspace lattice* of the linear space T.

The void set O and the subsets of T consisting of one point each are linear subspaces of T; the latter are just the atoms of $\mathscr{L}(T)$. Since every linear subspace of T except O contains at least one subspace consisting of only one point, *the lattice* $\mathscr{L}(T)$ *is atomic*.

A special subclass of incidence space will be discussed in Section 41.

Let L be an arbitrary lattice and let σ denote some mapping of L into itself. All elements a of L such that $\sigma(a) = a$ are termed *fixelements* of the mapping σ. For a complete lattice, we have

THEOREM 19 (fixelement theorem). *Every order preserving mapping of a complete lattice into itself has a fixelement.*

The theorem is essentially due to Knaster ([117], Lemma).

PROOF. Let L be a complete lattice, σ an order preserving mapping of L into itself and S the set of all the elements $x \in L$ such that $x \leq$

$\leq \sigma(x)$. Clearly, S is non-void, since $o \leq \sigma(o)$. Hence, L being complete, $\sup_L S$ exists. Let it be denoted by u. Then, for any element of S, $u \geq s$ and thus, σ being order preserving, also $\sigma(u) \geq \sigma(s) \geq s$. In other words, $\sigma(u)$ is an upper bound of S, and hence

$$\sigma(u) \geq u. \tag{4}$$

This implies, σ being order preserving, that $\sigma(\sigma(u)) \geq \sigma(u)$; that is, $\sigma(u) \in S$. Hence (by the definition of u), $\sigma(u) \leq u$. This means, however, together with (4), that $\sigma(u) = u$.

The following supplement of Theorem 18 is also true (Tarski [201], Theorem 1): The fixpoints of an order preserving mapping of a complete lattice L into itself themselves form a complete lattice with respect to the ordering in L (This lattice is generally not a sublattice of L).

The converse of the theorem is also true (Davis [37]). If every order preserving mapping of a lattice into itself has a fixpoint, then the lattice is complete.

Both results were extended by Wolk to a special class of partly ordered sets ([217] Theorems 4 and 5 respectively).

For a generalisation of the fixpoint theorem concerning partly ordered sets, see Abian—Brown [1].

23. Complete Sublattices of a Complete Lattice

Consider a complete lattice L and a sublattice R of it. It often happens that $\inf_R H (\sup_R H)$ does not exist for some subset H of R, or that it exists but differs from $\inf_L H$ ($\sup_L H$). (In the latter case it can at least be stated that $\inf_R H \leq \inf_L H \leq \sup_L H \leq \sup_R H$, since $\inf_R H$ ($\sup_R H$) is a lower (upper) bound of H in L also.)

Accordingly, let us introduce the following terms: A subset R of a complete lattice will be called a $\begin{Bmatrix} \textit{meet-} \\ \textit{join-} \end{Bmatrix}$ *complete sublattice* of L if $\begin{Bmatrix} \inf_R H \\ \sup_R H \end{Bmatrix}$ exists for every subset of R and coincides with $\begin{Bmatrix} \inf_L H \\ \sup_R H \end{Bmatrix}$. If R is a sublattice of L which is both meet- and join-complete at the same time R is called a *complete sublattice*.

It is obvious that *any interval of a complete lattice is a complete sublattice*. Indeed if $H \subseteq [a, b] \subseteq L$ and L is a complete lattice, then a is a lower and b an upper bound of H. Hence by the definition of infima and suprema, $a \leq \inf_L H \leq \sup_L H \leq b$. In other words $\inf_L H$ and $\sup_L H$ both belong to $[a, b]$ and consequently $\inf_L H$ is the greatest lower bound and $\sup_L H$ the least upper bound of H in $[a, b]$ too.

We give some examples of sublattices of a complete lattice which are not complete sublattices.

1. Let us consider the subchain C of rational numbers in the interval $[0, 1]$ of real numbers. This is not a complete sublattice of $[0, 1]$ since — for example — if $S = \{a_1, a_2, \ldots\}$ is a strictly increasing infinite sequence of the elements of C which tends to an irrational number, then obviously $\sup_C S$ does not exist.

2. In the lattice N_0 of example 15, the set K consisting of all odd positive integers is a sublattice; however, since K consists of an infinite number of elements and $O \notin K$, $\sup_K K$ (that is, a greatest element in K) does not exist.

3. Consider the set E of all subsets of the points situated on the real number axis e. By what has been stated concerning Example 14, E is a complete lattice with regard to set inclusion. Let Z denote the set of all closed subsets of e; Z is a sublattice of E. However, Z is not a complete sublattice in E, since, for instance, (using the bracket to symbolize the intervals of real number line) for the elements $H_k = \left[\frac{k-1}{k}, \frac{k}{k+1}\right]$ $(k = 1, 2, \ldots)$ of Z, $\sup_E \{H_k\}_{k=1,2\ldots} = \bigcup_{k=1}^{\infty} \left[\frac{k-1}{k}, \frac{k}{k+1}\right] = [0, 1)$ (where $[0,1)$ denotes an interval closed on the left but open on the right) and $\sup_Z \cdot \{H_k\}_k = 1, 2, \ldots = [0,1]$.

By the concepts introduced above so-called topological spaces can be suitably defined.

Let certain subsets Z_λ $(\lambda \in \Lambda)$ of a set T be called the *closed subsets* of T. If $Z = \{Z_\lambda\}_{\lambda \in \Lambda}$ is a meet-complete sublattice of the subset lattice of T, and $Z \ni T, O$, then T is said to be a *topological space* with the topology defined by Z. In this topology, the *open subsets* of T are the sets $N_\lambda = T - Z_\lambda$ $(\lambda \in \Lambda)$. Since*

$$\bigcup_{\mu \in M} (T - Z\mu) = T - \bigcap_{\mu \in M} Z_\mu \; (M \subseteq \Lambda)$$

hence $\mathscr{N} = \{N_\lambda\}_{\lambda \in \Lambda}$ is a join-complete sublattice of the subset lattice of T, and clearly $\mathscr{N} \ni O, T$. Consequently, T and the void set O are simultaneously both open and closed.

A topological space T is called a T_1-space if, and only if, every single-element subset of T is closed. Furthermore, a T_1-space is called a *Hausdorff space*, if for any of its pairs of elements x, y there may be found open sets X, Y such that $x \in X$, $y \in Y$ and $X \cap Y = O$.

In the theory of topological spaces, the methods and concepts of lattice theory have been found to be very useful (see, for example, Vaidyanathaswamy [230]).

24. Conditionally Complete Lattices, σ-Lattices

As mentioned above (in Example 11) the set N of positive integers forms a lattice with respect to the operations of forming greatest common divisors and least a common multiples. The set V of real numbers also forms a lattice (and, moreover, a chain), with respect to its natural ordering. These lattices are not bounded, and hence, they are, a fortiori, not complete; however, each of their bounded subsets has an infimum and a supremum. The lattice discussed in Example 13 is also a lattice of this kind.

A lattice is said to be *conditionally complete* if each of its non-void bounded subsets has an infimum and a supremum.

* If $x \in \bigcup_{\mu \in M} (T - Z_\mu)$, there exists a μ such that $x \in T - Z_\mu$, i.e. $x \notin Z_\mu$; but then $x \notin \bigcap_{\mu \in M} Z_\mu$ and thus $x \in T - \bigcap_{\mu \in M} Z_\mu$. Therefore $\bigcup_{\mu \in M} (T - Z_\mu) \subseteq T - \bigcap_{\mu \in M} Z_\mu$. The "$\supseteq$" can be proved similarly.

Clearly, every complete lattice is, a fortiori, conditionally complete. Conversely, every conditionally complete bounded lattice is also complete. Moreover:

THEOREM 20. *If we affix bound elements to a conditionally complete lattice, we obtain a complete lattice.*

This theorem will be proved in the following more general form.

Let Π be an ordering relation of the set P under which every non-void subset, bounded below, of P has an infimum. Affix to P an element $\bar{o}$ and an element $\bar{i}$, and define on the set $\bar{P}$ thus obtained an ordering relation $\bar{\Pi}$ as follows: For any pair of elements x, y of P let $x \leq y(\bar{\Pi})$ if, and only if, $x \leq y(\Pi)$; furthermore, for every $x \in P$, let $\bar{o} < x < \bar{i}\,(\bar{\Pi})$ be satisfied. Then $\bar{P}$ is a complete lattice under $\bar{\Pi}$.

PROOF. Let $\bar{X}$ be a non-void subset of $\bar{P}$. If $\bar{X} \ni \bar{o}$ or $\bar{X}$ is a subset of P without any lower bound in P, then $\inf_{\bar{P}} \bar{X} = \bar{o}$; if $\bar{X} = \{\bar{i}\}$ then $\inf_{\bar{P}} \bar{X} = \bar{i}$. In every other case the set $X = \bar{X} - \{\bar{i}\}$ is a non-void subset, bounded below, of P; hence, by the assumption, $\inf_P X$ exists. On the other hand, since $\bar{i} > x$ for every element x of X, the (eventual) affixing of $\bar{i}$ to X does not affect the value of the infimum; hence $\inf_{\bar{P}} \bar{X} = \inf_P X$. Hence, every subset $\bar{X}$ of $\bar{P}$ has an infimum in $\bar{P}$. Since $\bar{P}$ is by definition bounded above, every subset $\bar{X}$ also has a supremum in $\bar{P}$ by Theorem 17.

Another generalization of the complete lattice concept — used especially in set theory and measure theory — is the following:

A lattice L is called a *σ-lattice* if every countable subset of it possesses an infimum and supremum in L.

25. Compact Elements, Compactly Generated Lattices

In recent years the class of lattices to be defined in this section has aroused very considerable interest.

By a covering of an element c of the lattice L is meant any subset $\{c_\gamma\}_{\gamma\in\Gamma}$ of L such that $c \leq \bigcup_{\gamma\in\Gamma} c_\gamma$. The element c is called *compact*, if out of every covering $\{c_\gamma\}$ we can select a finite one, i.e. a subset $\{c_{\gamma_1}, \ldots, c_{\gamma_n}\}$ $(\gamma_j \in \Gamma;\ j = 1, \ldots, n)$ so that we have $c \leq \bigcup_{j=1}^{n} c_{\gamma_j}$, too.

A complete lattice is termed *compactly generated*, if every element of it can be represented as a join of a (finite of infinite) number of compact elements.

THEOREM 21. *Every element of a lattice satisfying the maximum condition is compact.*

PROOF. Let $R = \{r_\lambda\}$ be a subset of a lattice satisfying the maximum condition for which $\bigcup_\lambda r_\lambda$ exists. We will show that one can select from R a finite subset $\{r_{\lambda_1}, \ldots, r_{\gamma_n}\}$ so that

$$\bigcup_\lambda r_\lambda = \bigcup_{j=1}^{n} r_{\lambda_j}, \tag{1}$$

from which the statement of the theorem is an immediate consequence.

Let us choose for r_{λ_1} any element of R, and for r_{λ_j} an element of R, for which

$$r_{\lambda_j} \nleq r_{\lambda_1} \cup \ldots \cup r_{\lambda_{j-1}}$$

Then we have

(2) $$r_{\lambda_1} < r_{\lambda_1} \cup r_{\lambda_2} < \ldots < \bigcup_{j=1}^{m-1} r_{\lambda_j} < \bigcup_{j=1}^{m} r_{\lambda_j} < \ldots$$

Owing to the maximum condition the chain (2) is a finite one, i.e. there exists a positive integer n such that the relation $r_\lambda \nleq r_{\lambda_1} \cup \ldots \cup r_{\lambda_n}$ should not hold for any index λ, i.e. that for every λ we should have

$$r_\lambda \leqq r_{\lambda_1} \cup \ldots \cup r_{\lambda_n}$$

Hence we have

$$\bigcup_{\lambda} r_\lambda \leqq \bigcup_{j=1}^{n} r_{\lambda_j}$$

on the other hand the inequality of opposite direction is obviously valid. Therefore (1) must hold.

An element a of a lattice L is called *completely meet-irreducible*, if for every S ($S \subseteq L$) from $a \in \bigcap S$ it follows that $a \in S$.

The most important property of the compactly generated lattices from the point of view of application is the following:

THEOREM 22. *Every element of a compactly generated lattice can be represented as a meet of completely meet-irreducible elements.*

We shall see from the proof that such a representation consists in general of an infinite number of elements.

PROOF. Let a be an arbitrary element of the compactly generated lattice L and let us denote by M the set of all completely meet-irreducible elements greater than or equal to a. We shall demonstrate that $a = \inf_L M$.

First of all, by the definition of M, the element a is a lower bound of M.

Let b be an arbitrary lower bound of M; we prove that $b > a$ can not hold.

Let us suppose that $b > a$. Because L is compactly generated, it follows from this inequality that there is a compact element c in L such that $b \geqq c$ and $a \ngeq c$. Let us take the set Q of all the elements q for which

(3) $$q \geqq a \text{ and } q \ngeq c$$

The set Q is not void, since $Q \ni a$. Let $\{q_\mu\}$ be a subchain of Q and $q^* = \bigcup_\mu q_\mu$. Obviously $q^* \geqq a$. On the other hand, $q^* \ngeq c$, because from $q^* \geqq c$ it would follow that $\{q_\mu\}$ is a covering of c from which no finite covering could be selected, contrary to the compactness of c. Therefore $q^* \in Q$ is also true, i.e. every subchain of Q has an upper bound in Q. Applying to Q the Kuratowski—Zorn lemma we find that there exists an element $q = q_0$ satisfying (3) which is maximal with regard to the property figuring in (3), (i.e. if $x > q_0$, then $x \geqq c$). This q_0 *must be completely meet-irreducible*, because from the existence of a representation $q_0 = \bigcap_{\nu} x_\nu (x_\nu > q_0)$ it would follow $x_0 > c$ for every ν, i.e. $q_0 \geqq c$ (contrary to the fact that $q_0 \in Q$). On the other hand, q_0 *can not be completely meet-irreducible*, as in this case, because of the meaning of b and of $q_0 \geqq a$, we should have $q_0 \geqq b$; this can not be true, however, because we know that $b \geqq c$ and $q_0 \ngeqq c$. So we have two contradictory results for q_0, thus showing the incorrectness of our starting supposition i.e.: $b \not> a$.

Now let us suppose that M has a lower bound d which is not comparable with a. Then the element $b = a \cup d$ is also a lower bound greater than a for M so that we come back to the preceding case.

That means that for every lower bound b of M the inequality $b \leqq a$ is true. Thus the proof is completed.

Regarding other properties of compactly generated lattices the papers of Crawley [29], [30] and Dilworth—Crawley [49] may be consulted.

26. Subalgebra Lattice of an Algebra

Let $\mathscr{S}(A)$ denote the set of all subalgebras of an algebra $A = A(\{f_\gamma\}_{\gamma\in\Gamma})$ and $\{R_\delta\}_{\delta\in\Delta}$ a subsystem of the elements of $\mathscr{S}(A)$. For the set intersection $R = \bigcap_{\delta\in\Delta} R_\delta$ of the subalgebras $R_\delta (\delta \in \Delta)$ we show that two possibilities may arise: either $R = O$, or $R \in \mathscr{S}(A)$. Assume that $R \neq O$, and consider any operation f_γ of A. If $x_1, \ldots, x_{n(\gamma)} \in R$, then $x_1, \ldots, x_{n(\gamma)} \in R_\delta$ for every δ, and consequently, by the definition of subalgebra, $f_\gamma(x_1, \ldots, x_{n(\gamma)}) \in R_\delta (\delta \in \Delta)$. Hence, $f_\gamma(x_1, \ldots, x_{n(\gamma)}) \in \bigcap_{\delta\in\Delta} R_\delta = R$.

Let U be a non-void subset of A and consider the subalgebras of A which include U. Of these, one, the intersection of the subalgebras including U, will be smallest. It is called the *subalgebra generated by U* and denoted (in this book) by $\langle U \rangle$.

For the sake of simplicity of terminology, the meaning of the symbol $\langle\ \rangle$ will also be extended to the case $U = O$ with the convention (following naturally from what has just been stated) that $\langle O \rangle$ shall denote the intersection of all subalgebras of A.

The set $\mathscr{S}(A)$ — being a subset of $\mathscr{P}(A)$ — is partly ordered with respect to set inclusion. It is also immediately apparent that $\mathscr{S}(A)$ is, for all A bounded above. It is, however, bounded below if, and only if, $\langle O \rangle \in \mathscr{S}(A)$ that is, if $\langle O \rangle \neq O$. This is the case, for example, with all subgroups of a group, all subrings or ideals of a ring. On the other hand, if all sublattices of a lattice L are considered, and L consists of at least two elements, $\langle O \rangle = O$, since, taking any two elements a, b $(a \neq b)$ of L, $\{a\}, \{b\} \in \mathscr{S}(L)$ and $\{a\} \cap \{b\} = O$. Hence, $\mathscr{S}(L)$ itself is generally not even a lattice with respect to set inclusion; nevertheless, as will be shown below, if $\langle O \rangle$ is added to $\mathscr{S}(A)$, a complete lattice results.

Let $\overline{\mathscr{S}(A)}$ denote the set obtained from $\mathscr{S}(A)$ by adding $\langle O \rangle$ as a new element to it.* For this set, we have

THEOREM 23. *For any algebra A, the set $\overline{\mathscr{S}(A)}$ is a complete lattice with respect to set inclusion and for any subset* $\{R_\lambda\}_{\lambda \in \Lambda}$ of $\overline{\mathscr{S}(A)}$,

$$\bigcap_{\lambda \in \Lambda} R_\lambda = \bigcap_{\lambda \in \Lambda} R_\lambda, \quad \bigcup_{\lambda \in \Lambda} R_\lambda = \langle \bigcup_{\lambda \in \Lambda} R_\lambda \rangle$$

(Birkhoff [10], Theorem 3.1).

As, according to the first paragraph of this section, $\bigcap_{\lambda \in \Lambda} R_\lambda \in \overline{\mathscr{S}(A)}$ therefore (with respect to the considered ordering), $\inf \{R_\lambda\}_{\lambda \in \Lambda} = \bigcap_{\lambda \in \Lambda} R_\lambda$. However, $A \in \overline{\mathscr{S}(A)}$, too, and hence, by Theorem 17, $\overline{\mathscr{S}(A)}$ is a complete lattice. The formula concerning the join in $\overline{\mathscr{S}(A)}$ follows directly from the definition of the $\langle\ \rangle$ symbol.

The lattice $\overline{\mathscr{S}(A)}$ is termed the *subalgebra lattice* of the algebra A.

27. Closure Operations

By a *closure operation* on a partly ordered set P we mean an order preserving mapping φ of P into P such that, for every element $x \in P$, the extensivity

(1) $$\varphi(x) \geqq x$$

and the *idempotency***

(2) $$\varphi^2(x) = \varphi(x)$$

hold. For a closure operation φ the element $\varphi(x)$ is called the *φ-closure* of x, and, if an element x coincides with its φ-closure, it is said to be *φ-closed*. In other words, the φ-closed elements are the fixelements of φ. If only one closure operation is considered, we shall simply speak of "closure" and "closed elements" instead of "φ-closure" and "φ-closed elements".

It is clear by (1) that *the maximal elements of a partly ordered set P are all closed under any closure operation of P.*

Furthermore *the φ-closed elements of P are precisely all elements of the form $\varphi(x)$ $(x \in P)$*. In fact, by (2), every element of this type of P is φ-closed under φ, and also, if y is a φ-closed element of P, then $y = \varphi(y)$.

THEOREM 24. *Let φ be a closure operation of a partly ordered set P. If some subset R of P consists exlusively of φ-closed elements and if $\inf_P R$ exists, this infimum itself is also φ-closed* (Ward [213]).

* In other words, if $\langle O \rangle \neq O$, then $\overline{\mathscr{S}(A)} = \mathscr{S}(A)$, and if $\langle O \rangle = O$, then $\overline{\mathscr{S}(A)}$ denotes the set formed by adding the void set as a new element to $\mathscr{S}(A)$.

** By the convention of Section 1, $\varphi^2(x)$ is a briefer notation for $\varphi(\varphi(x))$.

PROOF. Let R be a subset of P consisting exclusively of closed elements for which $r = \inf_P R$ exists. By the definition of the infimum, for any element x of R, we have $x \geqq r$, and hence, by the order preserving property of φ, also $\varphi(x) \geqq \varphi(r)$. Furthermore, since R consists exclusively of closed elements, $x = \varphi(x)$. Hence, $\varphi(r)$ is a lower bound of R and, as such, $\varphi(r) \leqq \inf_P R = r$. However, by (1), $\varphi(r) \geqq r$. These two inequalities imply $\varphi(r) = r$.

In applications, the closure operations of complete lattices are mostly considered. For the closed elements of these, there holds the somewhat stronger

THEOREM 25. *Let φ be a closure operation of a complete lattice L. The set Z_φ of the φ-closed elements of L is itself a complete lattice with respect to the ordering in L; that is, for every subset R of Z_φ,*

$$\inf_{Z_\varphi} R = \inf_L R, \qquad \sup_{Z_\varphi} R = \varphi(\sup_L R)$$

(Ward [213]).

PROOF. Let R be an arbitrary subset of Z_φ. By Theorem 24, $\inf_L R \in Z_\varphi$, and hence, $\inf_L R = \inf_{Z_\varphi} R$. Furthermore, by the remark before Theorem 24, the greatest element of L is closed. Thus, in accordance with Theorem 17, Z_φ is a complete lattice.

The formula concerning the suprema remains to be proved. Let us introduce the notation $u = \varphi(\sup_L R)$. By (1), $u \geqq \sup_L R$; that is, u is an upper bound of R in L. However, by the remark before Theorem 24, $u \in Z_\varphi$, and hence u is also an upper bound of R in Z_φ. Let y be any upper bound of R in L. Then $y \geqq \sup_L R$, and so, by the order preserving property of φ, $\varphi(y) \geqq u$. If, particularly, $y \in Z_\varphi$, this yields $y \geqq u$. Thus we have found that u is, in fact, the least upper bound of R in Z_φ.

The importance of closure operations is pointed out by the following examples:

1. A highly important field of application of closure operations is the theory of topological spaces. For example, one efficient method of determining the closed subsets of a set T is to define a closure operation φ on the subset lattice $\mathcal{S}(T)$ which is at the same time an endomorphism of $\mathcal{S}(T)$ and for which $\varphi(O) = O$, then (by Theorem 25) the φ-closed elements define a topology on T. If we require to fulfil the further condition that every single-element subset of T be φ-closed, we obtain a T_1-space.

2. Conversely, let us assign to every subset X of a topological space the intersection of all subsets closed by the definition of the space and containing X and denote it by $\varphi(X)$. Clearly, φ is a closure operation of the subset lattice of the space, and it is also easy to see that the φ-closed elements of the subset lattice are precisely the closed subsets of the space.

3. Let M denote the set of all points of a plane. The subset lattice $\mathcal{S}(M)$ of the set, as was shown earlier, is a complete lattice. Assign to every subset X of M the so-called convex boundary of X (that is,

the smallest convex subset in M containing X), and denote it $\varphi(X)$. The mapping thus defined in $\mathscr{P}(M)$ is clearly a closure operation. The φ-closed elements are the convex subsets of the plane, and with respect to the ordering in $\mathscr{P}(M)$, they indeed form a complete lattice in which

$$\bigcap_{\lambda\in\Lambda} K_\lambda = \bigcap_{\lambda\in\Lambda} K_\lambda, \quad \bigcup_{\lambda\in\Lambda} K_\lambda = \varphi(\bigcup_{\lambda\in\Lambda} K_\lambda)$$

4. Assign to every subset R of an algebra A the subalgebra $\langle R\rangle$ generated by R. It is easily seen that the mapping

$$\varphi : R \to \varphi(R) = \langle R\rangle$$

is a closure operation of the subset lattice of A, and the φ-closed elements are just the subalgebras of A. In this way, another proof of Theorem 23 is arrived at.

A further important type of closure operations will be discussed in the section to follow.

In the investigations concerning closure operations, remarkable results have recently been obtained by Dwinger ([51], [52], [53]). See also Morgado [140].

28. Galois Connections, Dedekind Cuts

Let S and T be a pair of partly ordered sets, σ a single-valued mapping of S into T, and τ a single valued mapping of T into S. We will say that the pair of mappings σ, τ establishes a *Galois connection* between the partly ordered sets S and T, if the following conditions (1)—(4) are satisfied:

(1) $$x_1 \leqq x_2 \Longrightarrow \sigma(x_1) \geqq \sigma(x_2) \quad (x_1, x_2 \in S),$$

(2) $$y_1 \leqq y_2 \Longrightarrow \tau(y_1) \geqq \tau(y_2) \quad (y_1, y_2 \in T),$$

(3) $$x \leqq \tau\sigma(x) \text{ for every element } x \text{ of } S,$$

(4) $$y \leqq \sigma\tau(y) \text{ for every element } y \text{ of } T.$$

Now let us consider the most frequently occurring type of Galois connection.

Let U and V be two lattices and Φ a relation defined between U and V. Let us assign to every non-void subset X of U the set of all elements y of V satisfying the relation $x\Phi y$ for every element x $(\in X)$, and let us denote this set by $X^\vartriangle$. Similarly, let us assign to every non-void subset Y of V the set of all elements x of U which satisfy the relation $x\Phi y$ for every element $y(\in Y)$; let us denote this latter set by $Y^\triangledown$. Let this definition be extended to the void set by putting $O^\vartriangle = V$, $O^\triangledown = U$. It is immediately evident that the pair of mappings.

(5) $$X \to X^\vartriangle (X \subseteq U), \quad Y \to Y^\triangledown (Y \subseteq V)$$

establishes a Galois connection between the subset lattices of U and V. This is called the *Galois connection corresponding to the relation Φ.*

The above fact was recognized by Birkhoff and published by him in the first edition of [19].

By a result of Ore ([155], Theorem 20 and Everett [59], Theorem 5) every Galois connection can be obtained in the above way, by means of an appropriate relation.

A different method of constructing Galois connections is treated by Aumann [3].

Pickert has shown [160] that each of the two mappings establishing a Galois connection will be determined by the other, namely $\tau(y) = \sup_{\sigma(x) \geq y} x$ (and dually). Hence it follows that the Galois connections between complete lattices may be given as the mappings transforming the supremum of an arbitrary subset into the infimum of the image set. A special representation of the Galois connections between complete lattices was given by Raney [168] for cases where at least one of the complete lattices is completely distributive (in the sense of Section 31).

Before stating our next theorem, we must introduce a new concept. A one-to-one mapping φ of a lattice L_1 onto a lattice L_2 is called a *dual isomorphism* if φ is an isomorphism of L_1 onto $\mathfrak{D}(L_2)$, that is, if for every pair of elements a, b of L_1, $\varphi(a \frown b) = \varphi(a) \smile \varphi(b)$, and $\varphi(a \smile b) = \varphi(a) \frown \varphi(b)$. Let us point out immediately that (as the reader will easily convince himself by applying the line of thought used in proving Theorem 9) φ is a dual isomorphism if, and only if, it satisfies the condition

$$a \leq b \Longleftrightarrow \varphi(a) \geq \varphi(b) \qquad (a, b \in L_1)$$

THEOREM 26. *If the pair of mappings σ, τ establishes a Galois connection between the partly ordered sets S, and T, then $\tau\sigma$ is a closure operation of S, and $\sigma\tau$ is a closure operation of T. If S and T are complete lattices, then the set Z_S of the $\sigma\tau$-closed elements of S as well as the set Z_T of the $\sigma\tau$-closed elements of T are likewise complete lattices, and σ is a dual isomorphism of Z_S onto Z_T, while τ is a dual isomorphism of Z_T onto Z_S.* (Ore [155], Theorem 2).

COROLLARY. *Let U and V be any two sets and Φ a relation defined on the product set $U \times V$. Then, the mapping $X \rightarrow X^{\triangle\triangledown} (X \subseteq U)$ is a closure operation of the subset lattice $\mathcal{P}(U)$ of the set U, while $Y \rightarrow Y^{\triangledown\triangle}$ $(Y \subseteq V)$ is a closure operation of the subset lattice $\mathcal{P}(V)$ of the set V. Furthermore, all elements of the form $X^{\triangle\triangledown}$ of $\mathcal{P}(U)$ form a complete lattice, as well as all elements of the form $Y^{\triangle\triangledown}$ of $\mathcal{P}(V)$, and between the two lattices the mappings* (5) *establish dual isomorphisms.*

PROOF. By (1) and (2), the mapping $\tau\sigma$ is order preserving, and by (3) it is extensive. We shall show that it is idempotent as well. By (3), for any element x of S

$$\tau\sigma\tau\sigma(x) = \tau\sigma(\tau\sigma(x)) \geq \tau\sigma(x) \tag{6}$$

But $\sigma(x) \in T$ and so, by (4), the inequality $\sigma(x) \leq \sigma\tau(\sigma(x)) = \sigma\tau\sigma(x)$ also holds. Therefore by applying (2), we obtain

$$(7) \qquad \tau\sigma(x) \geqq \tau\sigma\tau\sigma(x)$$

However, (6) and (7) together just imply $(\tau\sigma)^2 = (\tau\sigma)\ (\tau\sigma) = \tau\sigma$.

Interchanging σ and τ it is found that $\sigma\tau$ is also a closure operation.

Now consider the case when both S and T are complete lattices. Then, by Theorem 25, both Z_S and Z_T are complete lattices with respect to the ordering relation of S and T, respectively. Let us show that σ is a dual isomorphism of Z_S onto Z_T.

First, σ maps Z_S into Z_T, since if $x \in Z_S$, then $\sigma(x) = \sigma(\tau\sigma(x)) = \sigma\tau(\sigma(x))$ and the $\sigma\tau$-images, as $\sigma\tau$-closed elements, belong to Z_T. Further, the mapping is one-to-one, since $x_1, x_2 \in Z_S$ and $\sigma(x_1) = \sigma(x_2)$ imply $x_1 = \tau\sigma(x_1) = \tau\sigma(x_2) = x_2$. Every element y of Z_γ is an image element by σ, since $y = \sigma\tau(y) = \sigma(\tau(y))$, and $\tau(y) \in Z_S$. This last statement may be proved in the same way as the statement $\sigma(x) \in Z_T$ above. Consequently, σ is a one-to-one mapping of Z_S onto Z_T. Finally, for any pair of elements x_1, x_2 of Z_S, the inequality $\sigma(x_1) \leqq \sigma(x_2)$ implies by (2), $x_1 = \tau\sigma(x_1) \geqq \tau\sigma(x_2) = x_2$ and together with (1) this means indeed that σ is a dual isomorphism.

It can be seen by the same consideration that τ is a dual isomorphism of Z_T onto Z_S. The proof of the theorem is thus completed.

To prove the corollary, it is sufficient to bear in mind that, by the remark before Theorem 24, the elements closed under the closure operations in question are all elements of the form $X^{\triangle\triangledown}$ and $Y^{\triangledown\triangle}$, respectively.

Examples

1. Concerning the notations and terms occurring in this example, not define. elsewhere in this book, the reader is referred to paras 112 and 153 of [228] Let $\mathsf{N} \mid \mathsf{K}$ be a Galois field with the Galois group $\mathfrak{G}$. Let us define between N and the subset lattice of $\mathfrak{G}$ a relation Φ such that $a\Phi g$ ($a \in \mathsf{N}$; $g \in \mathfrak{G}$) if and only if $ga = a$. It is not difficult to see that in the Galois connection corresponding to Φ the fixpoints of the mapping $\mathsf{L} \to \mathsf{L}^{\triangle\triangledown}$ ($\mathsf{L} \subseteq \mathsf{N}$) are the subfields of $\mathsf{N} \mid \mathsf{K}$, and the fixelements of $\mathscr{H} \to \mathscr{H}^{\triangledown\triangle}$ ($\mathscr{H} \subseteq \mathfrak{G}$) are the subgroups of $\mathfrak{G}$. Consequently, Theorem 26 yields the basic theorem of Galois theory and — using the notation of [228] — its supplement as corollaries.

2. In a group G let $x\Phi y$ ($x, y \in G$) mean $xy = yx$. Since this relation is symmetric, the two functions defining the Galois connection corresponding to Φ coincide and, hence, for every subset H of G, $H^\triangle = H^\triangledown$. More precisely $H^\triangle$ is the centralizer of the set H in G. The elements closed under the closure operation $H \to H^{\triangle\triangle}$ ($H \subseteq G$) are certain subgroups of G.

3. Consider a projective plane S and a polarity of the same. (For the concepts of projective geometry occurring in this example, see for instance [221] or [224].) Let us define among the points of S a relation Φ such that $a\Phi b$ ($a, b \in S$) holds if, and only if, the points a and b are conjugate with respect to the polarity considered. This is again a symmetric relation. The elements closed under the closure operation $X^{\triangle\triangle}$ ($X \subseteq S$) are the linear subspaces of S, and if Y is any point or line of S, then Y is the polar or pole, respectively, of Y.

As a further application of Galois connections, we shall generalize the concept of the Dedekind cut — known from the analysis of real numbers — to arbitrary partly ordered sets.

Let P be a partly ordered set. In the Galois connection corresponding to the ordering of P, $X^\triangle (X \subseteq P)$ is the set of all upper bounds, $X^\triangledown$ the set of all lower bounds of X. The set $X^{\triangle\triangledown}$ is called the *Dedekind cut* determined by X. Particularly, if $X = \{a\}$ $(a \in P)$, then, writing $a^\triangle$ instead of $\{a\}^\triangle$, $a^\triangle = [a)$ and $a^{\triangle\triangledown} = (a]$.

Let $D(P)$ denote the set of all Dedekind cuts determined by the subsets of the partly ordered set P.

The following theorem will be verified:

THEOREM 27. *For every partly ordered set P, the set $D(P)$, partly ordered by set inclusion, forms a complete lattice and the mapping φ: $x \to (x]$ $(x \in P)$ is an order isomorphism of P onto a subset of $D(P)$. Moreover, if* $\inf_P R$ *or* $\sup_P R$ *exists for some subset R of P, then**

$$\inf_L \varphi(R) = \varphi(\inf_P R), \quad \sup_L \varphi(R) = \varphi(\sup_P R)$$

(MacNeille [127], Theorems 11.7 and 11.9).

COROLLARY. *Every lattice is isomorphic to some sublattice of a complete lattice.*

PROOF. First, by the corollary to Theorem 26 applied to the case when $U = V = P$ and Φ is the ordering relation of P, $D(P)$ is, with respect to set inclusion, a complete lattice. Next we consider the subset consisting of all elements of the form $(x]$ $(x \in P)$ of $D(P)$ and prove that φ maps P order isomorphically onto this subset of $D(P)$. To do this it is sufficient to show that

$$x \leqq y \Longleftrightarrow (x] \subseteq (y]$$

the one-to-one property of the mapping is then a trivial consequence. However, if $x \leqq y$, then

$$t \in (x] \Longrightarrow t \leqq x \Longrightarrow t \leqq y \Longrightarrow t \in (y]$$

and, on the other hand, if $(x] \subseteq (y]$, then $x \in (x] \subseteq (y]$ implies $x \leqq y$.

By the formulae in Theorem 25, the last proposition of the theorem means that whenever $u = \inf_P \{a_\nu\}$ or $v = \sup_P \{a_\nu\}$ exists for a subset $R = \{a_\nu\}$ of P, then

(8) $$\bigcap_\nu (a_\nu] = (u]$$

(9) $$(\bigcup_\nu (a])^{\triangle\triangledown} = (v]$$

Now, these formulae may be verified as follows. For any element t of P,

$$\begin{aligned} t \in \bigcap_\nu (a_\nu] &\Longleftrightarrow t \in (a_\nu] \text{ for every } \nu \Longleftrightarrow \\ &\Longleftrightarrow t \leqq a_\nu \text{ for every } \nu \Longleftrightarrow \\ &\Longleftrightarrow t \leqq \inf_P \{a_\nu\} = u \Longleftrightarrow \\ &\Longleftrightarrow t \in (u] \end{aligned}$$

* It should be remembered that $\varphi(R)$ is the image set of R.

and hence (8) holds. On the other hand, some element t ($\in P$) is contained by the left side of (9) if, and only if, t is a lower bound of the set $(\bigcup_\nu (a_\nu))^\triangle$; in other words, if every upper bound y ($\in P$) of the set $\bigcup_\nu (a_\nu]$ is greater than or equal to t. However, y is an upper bound of the set $\bigcup_\nu (a_\nu]$ if, and only if, it is an upper bound of $\{a_\nu\}$; the latter is equivalent to $y \geqq \sup_P\{a_\nu\} = v$. Summarizing, $t \in (\bigcup_\nu (a_\nu])^{\triangle\nabla}$ precisely if for every y, the inequality $y \geqq v$ implies $y \geqq t$; and this is equivalent to $v \geqq t$. Thus (9), too, has been proved.

The corollary is trivial. It must be pointed out, however, that the lattice $D(P)$ may have properties essentially different from those of P.

For instance, numerous examples prove that the lattice of all Dedekind cuts of a distributive lattice (to be defined in Section 29) is not necessarily distributive itself. In this connection, Funayama has given in [74] a necessary and sufficient condition for the lattice of the Dedekind cuts to be distributive.

29. Partly Ordered Sets as Topological Spaces

A topological space can be defined — as in Section 23 — by setting all the closed subsets of the space. In Example 1 of Section 27 another procedure appeared: as an auxiliary concept the closure operation was introduced there and we established as closed sets the subsets of the space which had been closed with respect to the given closure operation. We shall now describe a third procedure which is used very frequently.

If we wish to introduce a topology on a set T, we consider a subset $\{S_\gamma\}_{\gamma\in\Gamma}$ of the subset lattice $\mathscr{P}(T)$ and form the smallest sublattice $\mathfrak{Z}$ of $\mathscr{P}(T)$ which includes every S_γ, as well as O and T. (Briefly stated, $\mathfrak{Z}$ is the meet-complete sublattice, generated by $\{S_\gamma\} \cup \{O, T\}$ in $\mathscr{P}(T)$). The elements of $\mathfrak{Z}$ will be considered as the closed subsets of T.

The elements of $\mathfrak{Z}$ thus defined can be simply expressed by means of the S_γ. First, since $\mathfrak{Z}$ is a sublattice, it must include every set of the form

$$U_\delta = \bigcup_{j=1}^{n} S_{\gamma_j} \qquad (\gamma_j \in \Gamma) \tag{1}$$

Moreover, $\mathfrak{Z}$ being meet-complete in $\mathscr{P}(T)$, it must also contain every set of the form

$$Z_\gamma = \bigcap_\delta \bigcup_{j(\delta)=1}^{n(\delta)} S_{\gamma_{j(\delta)}} \quad (\gamma_{j(\delta)} \in \Gamma) \tag{2}$$

(where δ may run through an arbitrary index set). However, all the sets of the form (2), together with O and T, exhaust $\mathfrak{Z}$, since, as can be proved by direct computation, these sets form a meet-complete lattice which contains $\{S_\gamma\} \cup \{O, T\}$*

* Only the fact that the join of two sets of the form (2) is also of the same form is non-trivial. This, however, is a special case of the lemma of Section 31 (to be proved later).

The family of the sets U_δ in (1) is usually called the *base* of $\mathfrak{T}$, the set $\{S_\gamma\}_{\gamma\in\Gamma}$ the *sub-base* of $\mathfrak{T}$.

In the case of a partly ordered set P it can be prescribed as a quite matter of fact requirement that the intervals as well as all subsets of the form $(u]$ and $[u)$ $(u \in P)$ of P be closed. Accordingly, one of the natural topologies of partly ordered sets is the *interval topology*, in which the elements of the sub-base (generating the closed sets of the space) are just these subsets. Since every single-element subset of a partly ordered set is an interval, *by introducing an interval topology on a partly ordered set, a T_1-space is obtained.*

For chains, the following somewhat stronger proposition also holds: *By introducing an interval topology on a chain, a Hausdorff space is obtained.** To prove this statement, consider a chain C and an arbitrary pair a, b of its elements with $a < b$. If $a \prec b$, then $(a] = C - [b)$ and $[b) = C - (a]$, whence both $(a]$ and $[b)$ are open sets as well, and $(a] \ni a$, $[b) \ni b$, $(a] \cap [b) = O$. On the other hand, if there exists an x such that $a < x < b$, then $A = C - [x)$ and $B = C - (x]$ are open sets such that $A \ni a$, $B \ni b$ and $A \cap B = O$.

It can be shown that by defining an interval topology on a complete lattice, a compact space is obtained, compact in the sense that to each system $\{G_\nu\}_{\nu\in N}$ of open subsets of the space, a finite number of $G_\nu (\nu \in N', N' \subseteq N)$ may be found such that $\bigcup_{\nu\in N} G_\nu = \bigcup_{\nu\in N'} G_\nu$. ([19], Chapter IV, Theorem 15.)

In complete lattices, a different "natural" topology, the convergence topology can also be introduced. Before defining this concept, we shall make the following preliminary definitions.

A partly ordered set P is called an $\left\{\begin{matrix}\textit{up}\\ \textit{down}\end{matrix}\right\}$ *directed set* if, any two-element subset of P has (at least) one $\left\{\begin{matrix}\text{upper}\\ \text{lower}\end{matrix}\right\}$ bound in P. A partly ordered set up directed and down directed at the same time is called a *directed set*.

Let $\{x_\lambda\}_{\lambda\in\Lambda}$ be a subset of a complete lattice L, with a directed index set Λ. Let us introduce the following notation:

$$\lim\inf\{x_\lambda\} = \bigcup_{\lambda}\bigcap_{\mu\geq\lambda} x_\mu$$

$$\lim\sup\{x_\lambda\} = \bigcap_{\lambda}\bigcup_{\mu\geq\lambda} x_\mu$$

Evidently, $\lim\inf\{x_\lambda\} \leq \lim\sup\{x_\lambda\}$. If, in particular, $\lim\inf\{x_\lambda\} = \lim\sup\{x_\lambda\} = x$, x is said to be the *limit* of $\{x_\lambda\}$, written $\lim\{x_\lambda\} = x$. In this case, it is usual to say that $\{x_\lambda\}$ is *convergent*, or more precisely that it *converges to* x.** It is clear that if $x_\lambda = a$ $(\lambda \in \Lambda)$, then $\lim\{x_\lambda\} = a$.

* For generalisations of this statement, see Wolk [218] and Matshushima [134].

** This convergence is called order convergence and, correspondingly, convergence topology to be defined below, is also termed order topology. For a given order rela-

A subset $\{x_\varrho^*\}_{\varrho \in P}$ ($P \subseteq \Lambda$) of $\{x_\lambda\}_{\lambda \in \Lambda}$ will be called *cofinal* if to every x_λ there exists at least one x_ϱ^* such that $\varrho \geq \lambda$. We will now prove that if $\{x_\varrho^*\}_{\varrho \in P}$ is a cofinal subset of a convergent set $\{x_\lambda\}_{\lambda \in \lambda}$ then $\{x_\varrho\}_{\varrho \in P}$ is also convergent. and

$$\lim \{x_\varrho^*\} = \lim \{x_\lambda\}.$$

Indeed, by the assumption, there exists to every λ a ϱ such that $\{x_\sigma^*\}_{\sigma \geq \varrho} \subseteq \{x_\mu\}_{\mu \geq \lambda}$, and hence $\bigcup_\lambda \bigcap_{\mu \geq \lambda} x_\mu \leq \bigcup_\varrho \bigcap_{\sigma \geq \varrho} x_\sigma^* \leq \bigcap_\varrho \bigcup_{\sigma \geq \varrho} x_\sigma^* \leq \bigcap_\lambda \bigcup_{\mu \geq \lambda} x_\mu$; that is, $\lim \{x_\lambda\} = \lim\inf \{x_\lambda\} \leq \lim\inf \{x_\varrho^*\} \leq \lim\sup \{x_\varrho^*\} \leq$ $\leq \lim\sup \{x_\lambda\} = \lim \{x_\lambda\}$.

In the *convergence topology* of a complete lattice L, a closed subset of L is a subset which contains together with any convergent set, the limit of the set. By this definition, the meet of closed sets of arbitrary power is closed. It is easily shown that if Z_1 and $Z_2 (\subseteq L)$ are closed, then so is $Z_1 \cup Z_2$. Let $\{x_\lambda\}_{\lambda \in \Lambda}$ be a convergent subset of $Z_1 \cup Z_2$. There are two cases to be considered. Let us consider first the case when there is a $\lambda_0 (\in \Lambda)$ such that the x_λ, with indices greater than λ_0, belong either all to Z_1 or all to Z_2; assume that all such x_λ belong to Z_1 (this assumption can be made without loss of generality). Then,

$$\lim \{x_\lambda\}_{\lambda \in \Lambda} = \lim \{x_\lambda\}_{\lambda \geq \lambda_0} \in Z_1 \subseteq Z_1 \cup Z_2$$

There remains the case when no such λ_0 exists. Then, $\{x_\varrho^*\} = \{x_\lambda\} \cap Z_1$ is a cofinal subset of $\{x_\lambda\}$, and hence $\lim \{x_\lambda\} = \lim \{x_\varrho^*\} \in Z_1$.

Thus by *introducing the convergence topology on a complete lattice, a T_1-space is obtained.**

Let a be a lower bound of the subset $\{x_\lambda\}$. Then, $a \leq \lim\inf \{x_\lambda\}$. By this and the dual statement, *in the convergence topology of a complete lattice L, every interval of L as well as all the subsets of the form* $(u]$ and $[u)$ ($u \in L$) are closed. Consequently every subset of L closed with regard to the interval topology is also closed with respect to the convergence topology of L. This is usually expressed by saying that (for complete lattices) convergence topology is "stronger" than interval topology.

Further interesting results concerning topologies definable in partly ordered sets (particularly, in lattices), may be found in papers by Wallmann [209], Frink [67] and Northam [148] as well as in Birkhoff's book [19] (Chapter III, Section 5 and Chapter IV, Sections 8—9).

---

tion, order convergence in general does not agree with the convergence belonging to order topology. (The erroneous argument of Birkhoff [19], Chapter IV, Theorem 13, relies on an assumption of this agreement: according to him, order topology would necessarliy define a Hausdorff space; cf. the next footnote).

* The convergence topology in general does not define a Hausdorff space; see Northam [148], Floyd—Klee [65] and Floyd [64].

Exercises to Chapter III

1. Prove that if some element of a lattice satisfying the maximum condition can be expressed in the form $a = \bigcup_{\gamma \in \Gamma} a_\gamma$, then it is possible to select from the set $R = \{a_\gamma\}_{\gamma \in \Gamma}$ a finite subset $\{a_1, \ldots, a_r\}$, the elements of which already suffice to yield a as their join.

2. Let L be a complete lattice satisfying the minimum condition. For any element a of L, let u_a denote the join of all x ($\in L$) covering a. Show that $u_a \cap y = a$ implies $y = a$ for any element y of L.

3. Find an example for a homomorphism of a complete lattice which is not a complete homomorphism.

4. Let L_1 and L_2 be complete lattices. Show that if φ is a complete homomorphism of L_1 onto L_2, then for any c^*($\in L_2$) the set of all c ($\in L_1$) satisfying the equation $\varphi(c) = c^*$ is an interval of L_1.*

5. For the lattices L_1 and L_2 let $\varphi_1 : L_1 \sim L_2$ and $\varphi_2 : L_2 \sim L_1$ be homomorphisms preserving all infinite joins and meets. Show that if the mapping $\varphi_2 \varphi_1$ is identical on L_1 and the lattice L_2 is complete, then L_1 is complete, too.

6. Let L be a complete lattice and R a subset of L. Show that for any $H \subseteq R$, the inclusion $\inf_L H \in R$ implies $\inf_L H = \inf_L R$.

7. Prove that if σ is an order preserving mapping of a conditionally complete lattice into itself, and for some elements a, b of the lattice $a \leq \sigma(a) \leq \sigma(b) \leq b$, then σ has a fixelement in $[a, b]$.

8. Let L be a complete lattice and σ an order preserving mapping of L into itself. Show that the set of all fixelements of σ in L has a least element.

9. Show that every lattice satisfying either the maximum or the minimum condition is conditionally complete.

10. Prove that any lattice in which every bounded non-void subset has an infimum is conditionally complete.

11. Show that the join of two compact elements of a lattice is itself compact.

12. Find examples for an endomorphism of a complete lattice which are

a) non-extensive but idempotent,

b) non-idempotent but extensive,

c) neither extensive nor idempotent.

13. Show that a mapping φ of a partly ordered set into itself is a closure operation if, and only if, φ is extensive and for any elements x, y of the set, $x \leq \varphi(y) \Rightarrow \varphi(x) \leq \varphi(y)$.

14. Prove that if for a mapping λ of a lattice L into itself, $\lambda(x \cup y) = \lambda(x) \cup y$ ($x, y \in L$), then λ is a closure operation of L.*

* The converse of this statement is also true; see Dwinger [56], Theorem 2.

** A mapping with the property formulated in this exercise is called a translation. By making use of this type of mapping, some special classes of lattices may be characterised (see Szász [195]).

15. Let φ be a closure operation of a complete lattice L, and let Z_φ denote the set of the φ-closed elements of L. Show that $\varphi(x) = \inf_L(Z_\varphi \cap [x))$.

16. Let U be a subset of a complete lattice L such that $i \in U$ and, for any non-void subset H of U, $\inf_L H \in U$. Show that

$$\psi_U(x) = \inf_L(U \cap [x))$$

is a closure operation in L and that the ψ_U-closed elements are the elements of U.

17. Let $C(P)$ denote the set of all closure operations of the partly ordered set P and, for any elements φ and ψ of $C(P)$, let $\varphi \leqq \psi$ mean that $\varphi(x) \leqq \psi(x)$ for every $x \in P$. Show that this relation partly orders $C(P)$ and, moreover, $\varphi \leqq \psi$ if, and only if, $Z_\varphi \supseteq Z_\psi$. (For the meaning of Z_φ, see Exercise 15.)

18. Show that if the mappings σ and τ establish a Galois connection then $\tau(y)$ is the supremum of all x satisfying the inequality $\sigma(x) \geqq y$.

19. Let S and T be two partly ordered sets. Prove that the single-valued mappings σ of S into T and τ of T into S establish a Galois connection between S and T if, and only if, in addition to (1) and (4) of Section 28, the following condition also holds: for any element x ($\in S$) and y ($\in T$), $\sigma(x) \geqq y$ implies $x \leqq \tau(y)$.

20. Let L be a (complete) lattice which contains, beside the bound elements, o, i, a countably infinite number of mutually incomparable elements $x_1, x_2, \ldots$. Show that the set $\{x_1, x_2, \ldots\}$ is closed under the convergence topology of L but not closed under the interval topology of L.

CHAPTER IV

DISTRIBUTIVE AND MODULAR LATTICES

30. Distributive Lattices

The class of lattices investigated in the earliest period of lattice theory consisted of those which satisfy the following conditions in addition to the lattice axioms.

L_{10}. *For any triplet of elements a, b, c of the lattice,*

$$a \frown (b \smile c) = (a \frown b) \smile (a \frown c);$$

L_{11}. *For any triplet of elements a, b, c of the lattice,*

$$a \smile (b \frown c) = (a \smile b) \frown (a \smile c)$$

A lattice for which L_{10} and L_{11} hold is called *distributive*; L_{10} is called the *distributive identity of the meet*, L_{11} that *of the join*.

The complemented distributive lattices are called *Boolean algebras*, after Boole, who was the first to elaborate them (see Boole [22]).

By the inequalities of Section 14, the inequalities

$$a \frown (b \smile c) \geqq (a \frown b) \smile (a \frown c)$$

and

$$a \smile (b \frown c) \leqq (a \smile b) \frown (a \smile c)$$

similar to the distributive identities, hold for any triplet of elements a, b, c of any lattice; the $\left\{\begin{matrix}\text{former}\\ \text{latter}\end{matrix}\right\}$ is called the *distributive inequality of the* $\left\{\begin{matrix}\textit{meet}\\ \textit{join}\end{matrix}\right\}$. By these two inequalities, in order to prove the distributivity of a lattice it is sufficient to show that for any triplet a, b, c of the lattice

(1) $$a \frown (b \smile c) \leqq (a \frown b) \smile (a \frown c)$$

and

(2) $$a \smile (b \frown c) \geqq (a \smile b) \frown (a \smile c)$$

The following theorem and its two corollaries are theoretically important and practically useful:

THEOREM 28. *Whenever a lattice satisfies L_{10}, it also satisfies L_{11} and conversely* (Schröder [174], p. 286).

COROLLARY 1. *A lattice in which* L_{10} *or* L_{11} *is satisfied is distributive.*

COROLLARY 2. *A lattice in which one of the inequalities* (1), (2) *is satisfied without restriction is distributive.*

PROOF. If L_{10} holds for a lattice, then for any triplet a, b, c of the lattice

$$(a \cup b) \cap (a \cup c) = \big((a \cup b) \cap a\big) \cup \big((a \cup b) \cap c\big) =$$
$$= a \cup \big((a \cap c) \cup (b \cap c)\big) =$$
$$= \big(a \cup (a \cap c)\big) \cup (b \cap c) = a \cup (b \cap c)$$

and hence, L_{11} also holds. By the dual consideration, L_{10} can be deduced from L_{11}. The theorem is thus proved; the corollaries are trivial.

By the foregoing, the set of propositions $L_1 - L_6$ and L_{10}, or $L_1 - L_6$ and L_{11} can be considered as systems of axioms of distributive lattices. Other systems of axioms for distributive lattices have been given — among others — by G. D. Birkhoff—G. Birkhoff [21], Croisot [35], Ellis [57], Sholander [176] and Vassiliou [206].

We shall now verify the following theorem:

THEOREM 29. *The dual, every sublattice and every homomorphic image of a distributive lattice is likewise a distributive lattice.*

PROOF. The first proposition of the theorem is trivial, since L_{10} and L_{11} are mutually dual.

If R is a sublattice of a distributive lattice L, then L_{10} and L_{11} hold, particularly, for the triplets of elements of R as well; hence, R is also distributive.

Finally, if L^* is the homomorphic image of a lattice L under some homomorphism φ: $L \sim L^*$, and a^*, b^*, c^* are arbitrary elements of L^*, then, by the definition of homomorphism, there may be found n L elements a, b, c such that $\varphi(a) = a^*$, $\varphi(b) = b^*$, $\varphi(c) = c^*$. Con-iequently, if L is distributive, we have

$$a^* \cap (b^* \cup c^*) = \varphi(a) \cap (\varphi(b) \cup \varphi(c)) = \varphi(a) \cap \varphi(b \cup c) =$$
$$= \varphi(a \cap (b \cup c)) = \varphi((a \cap b) \cup (a \cap c)) =$$
$$= \varphi(a \cap b) \cup \varphi(a \cap c) =$$
$$= (\varphi(a) \cap \varphi(b)) \cup (\varphi(a) \cap \varphi(c)) =$$
$$= (a^* \cap b^*) \cup (a^* \cap c^*),$$

and this, by Corollary 1 of Theorem 28, implies L^* to be distributive.

By the first proposition of the theorem, it follows that the dual of every true statement concerning distributive lattices is likewise a true statement concerning distributive lattices. In other words, the duality principle is also valid for the class of distributive lattices.

The same observation was made concerning complete lattices. This is why it is necessary to point out that this is not true for every special class of lattices: for example no such statement would be true concerning the semimodular lattices to be discussed in Chapter VII.

Let us give some examples for distributive lattices.

Example 17. It is easy to see that *every chain is a distributive lattice.*

Example 18. Consider all partitions $\alpha, \beta, \ldots$ of a finite interval which divide it into a finite number of subintervals. Let us mean by the union $\alpha \cup \beta$ of the partitions α and β that partition which includes all points of partition of α and β and by their intersection that partition $\alpha \cap \beta$, the points of which are the common points of partition of α and β. It is easy to see that a distributive lattice is defined in this way.

Example 19. For arbitrary ideals $\mathfrak{x}, \mathfrak{y}$ of a ring R it is said that $\mathfrak{x}$ is a divisor of $\mathfrak{y}$ if $\mathfrak{x} \supseteq \mathfrak{y}$. Accordingly, by the greatest common divisor $(\mathfrak{a}, \mathfrak{b})$ of the ideals $\mathfrak{a}, \mathfrak{b}$ of the ring R, we mean the ideal generated by the set $\mathfrak{a} \cup \mathfrak{b}$ in R, that is, the set of all elements of the form $a + b$ $(a \in \mathfrak{a},\ b \in \mathfrak{b})$; on the other hand, by the least common multiple $(\mathfrak{a}, \mathfrak{b})^*$ of the ideals $\mathfrak{a}$, and $\mathfrak{b}$ we shall mean the set $\mathfrak{a} \cap \mathfrak{b}$ which is itself an ideal of R ([231], I., p. 60). It can be shown by simple considerations that the set of the ideals of R forms a lattice with respect to the operations $\mathfrak{a} \cap \mathfrak{b} = (\mathfrak{a}, \mathfrak{b})^*$, $\mathfrak{a} \cup \mathfrak{b} = (\mathfrak{a}, \mathfrak{b})$; this lattice is called the *ideal lattice* of the ring R.

It is also usual to define the product of ideals, as follows: by the product $\mathfrak{a}\mathfrak{b}$ of the ideals $\mathfrak{a}, \mathfrak{b}$ we mean the ideal generated in R by the elements of the form ab $(a \in \mathfrak{a};\ b \in \mathfrak{b})$ that is, the set of all elements of the form $a_1 b_1 + \ldots + a_r b_r$ $(a_1, \ldots, a_r \in \mathfrak{a};\ b_1, \ldots, b_r \in \mathfrak{b})$ ([231], II, p. 28). It is not difficult to show that if every ideal of R can be represented as a product of prime ideals, and this representation is unique to within the order of the factors, the ideal lattice of R is distributive. (The condition mentioned is satisfied for example in the ring of all integers of any finite algebraic extension of the rational field; see also [231], II, pp. 98—100).

We also remark that the multiplication of ideals is associative and for any ideals $\mathfrak{a}, \mathfrak{b}, \mathfrak{c}$ of R the following equations hold [231], II, p. 28):

$$\mathfrak{a}(\mathfrak{b} \cup \mathfrak{c}) = \mathfrak{a}\mathfrak{b} \cup \mathfrak{a}\mathfrak{c}$$

$$(\mathfrak{b} \cup \mathfrak{c})\mathfrak{a} = \mathfrak{b}\mathfrak{a} \cup \mathfrak{c}\mathfrak{a}$$

More generally, let S be a lattice in which there is defined a multiplication as a third operation. If this multiplication is associative, and if the equations

$$a(b \cup c) = ab \cup ac$$

and

$$(b \cup c)a = ba \cup ca$$

hold for any triplet a, b, c of S, then S is called a *lattice-ordered semigroup*. (Trivial lattice-ordered semigroups are all distributive lattices under the multiplication $ab = a \cap b$.)

The study of the lattice-ordered semigroups is of importance in the ideal theory of rings. We shall not enter upon considerations of this nature here; instead the reader is referred — with no attempt at completeness, however — to works by Fuchs [69], [70], [72], Lesieur [124] and Utumi [203].

Some elementary properties of the lattice-ordered semigroups are enumerated in Exercise 27. As a further example, we shall discuss the "algebra of relations" in Section 45.

For a detailed development of the theory of lattice-ordered semigroups, see, for example [19], Chapter 13.

Example 20. A group G is called a generalized cyclic group if every finite subset of G generates a cyclic subgroup. We shall prove that the subgroup lattice of every group of this type is distributive (Ore [152], Theorem 4).

Let X and Y denote two arbitrary subgroups of G and XY the set of all elements of the form xy ($x \in X$, $y \in Y$). Since G is (evidently) commutative, $X \cup Y = XY$. On the other hand, as established in Example 12., $X \cap Y = X \cap Y$. Hence, by Corollary 2 of Theorem 28, it is sufficient to show that for any subgroups A, B, C of G the inclusion relation

$$A \cap BC \subseteq (A \cap B)(A \cap C) \tag{3}$$

holds.

Suppose $a \in A \cap BC$. Then, by $a \in BC$, there exists a pair of elements b, c ($b \in B$, $c \in C$) such that $a = bc$. By our assumption for G, there can be found an element d and positive integers m, n such that $b = d^m$, $c = d^n$; hence, $a = d^{m+n}$.

Let us denote in general by (k, l) the greatest common divisor and by $(k, l)^*$ the least common multiple of the positive integers k and l. Then, introducing the notations $m' = (m + n, m)^*$, $n' = (m + n, n)^*$, we have clearly $d^{m'} \in A \cap B$ and $d^{n'} \in A \cap C$. Let $h = (m', n')$. It is known that h can be represented in the form $h = m'x + n'y$, where x and y are integers. Hence,

$$d^h = (d^{m'})^x (d^{n'})^y \in (A \cap B)(A \cap C)$$

Since, however, the formation of the least common multiple and greatest common divisor are operations distributive with respect to each other, we have

$$h = (m', n') = \big((m + n, m)^*, \ (m + n, m)^*\big) = \\ = \big(m + n, \ (m, n)\big)^* = m + n$$

Hence

$$a = d^{m+n} = d^h \in (A \cap B)(A \cap C)$$

completing the proof of (3).

Ore has also proved the converse statement, namely that whenever the subgroup lattice of a group G is distributive, G is a generalized cyclic group.

Example 21. A set $\mathcal{M} = \{M_\gamma\}_{\gamma \in \Gamma}$ of sets is usually called a *ring of sets* if for any pair of indices $\gamma', \gamma'' (\in \Gamma)$ $M_{\gamma'} \cap M_{\gamma''}$ as well as $M_{\gamma'} \cup M_{\gamma''}$ are included in $\mathcal{M}$.

It is easy to see that every ring of sets is a lattice with respect to the operations $\cap$, $\cup$. It will further be shown by a simple consideration that this lattice is distributive. Let A, B, C be arbitrary elements of a ring of sets $\mathcal{M}$. If $t \in A \cap (B \cup C)$, then

$$\text{either } t \in A \text{ and } t \in B, \text{ that is, } t \in A \cap B$$
$$\text{or } \quad t \in A \text{ and } t \in C, \text{ that is, } t \in A \cap C$$

(or both), and hence, $t \in (A \cap B) \cup (A \cap C)$. Hence, $A \cap (B \cup C) \subseteq \subseteq (A \cap B) \cap (A \cap C)$ and by Corollary 2 of Theorem 28, this directly implies that $\mathcal{M}$ is distributive.

In particular, the family of all closed (open) sets of a topological space forms a distributive lattice.

We will agree that in rings of sets set union and set intersection will exclusively be regarded as lattice operations.

Example 22. A ring of sets $\mathcal{M} = \{M_\gamma\}_{\gamma \in \Gamma}$ is called a *field of sets* if every difference set $M_{\gamma'} - M_{\gamma''}(\gamma', \gamma'' \in \Gamma)$ is included in $\mathcal{M}$. If $\mathcal{M}$ is a field of sets, then $\mathcal{M} \ni O$ by $O = M_\gamma - M_\gamma$. Furthermore, every field of sets is a relatively complemented lattice, since $A \subseteq R \subseteq B$ $(A, B, R \in \mathcal{M})$ implies $S = B - (R - A) \in \mathcal{M}$ and S is the relative complement of R in $[A, B]$. (In particular, every field of sets bounded above is a Boolean algebra.) Conversely, every complemented ring of sets is a field of sets as well, since if A, $B \in \mathcal{M}$ and B' denotes the complement of B, then $A - B = A \cap B' \in \mathcal{M}$.

In connection with Examples 21—22, we also refer to Theorem 83 (see p. 167).

31. Infinitely Distributive and Completely Distributive Lattices

From the distributive identities L_{10}, L_{11} there follow at once by complete induction on n the identities

$$a \cap \bigcup_{k=1}^{n} b_k = \bigcup_{k=1}^{n} (a \cap b_k) \tag{1}$$

and

$$a \cup \bigcap_{k=1}^{n} b_k = \bigcup_{k=1}^{n} (a \cup b_k) \tag{2}$$

Quite naturally the question arises whether the equations

$$a \cap \bigcup_{\beta \in \mathrm{B}} b_\beta = \bigcup_{\beta \in \mathrm{B}} (a \cap b_\beta) \tag{3}$$

and

$$a \cup \bigcap_{\beta \in \mathrm{B}} b_\beta = \bigcap_{\beta \in \mathrm{B}} (a \cup b_\beta) \tag{4}$$

which can be considered as generalizations of (1) and (2), respectively, are valid for any subset $R = \{b_\beta\}_{\beta \in \mathrm{B}}$ of a distributive complete lattice.

It can be shown by a simple counter-example that the answer to the question is negative in the general case.

Consider for instance the set N_0 of all non-negative integers. It was seen in Example 15 that N_0 ordered by divisibility, forms a complete lattice the least element of which is 1, the greatest 0, and in which the meet of two elements is their greatest common divisor, the join of two elements their least common multiple. By the identities concerning the least common multiple and the greatest common divisor, as affirmed by number theory, the lattice N_0 is distributive as well.

Therefore, N_0 is a distributive complete lattice; nevertheless, (3) fails to hold in it. Consider, for example, the set $\{a_1, a_2, \ldots\}$ $(a_k = 2k - 1)$ of all odd positive integers; then

$$2 \cap \bigcup_{k=1}^{\infty} a_k = 2 \cap 0 = 2$$

but

$$\bigcup_{k=1}^{\infty} (2 \cap a_k) = \bigcup_{k=1}^{\infty} 1 = 1$$

but, by making use of the representation of the greatest common divisor and the least common multiple by their prime factors, it is easy to see that (4) holds in N_0.

Of course, in the dual of the lattice N_0, (3) is satisfied and (4) is not.

From the above example, the first conclusion to be drawn is that (3) and (4) do not hold in any distributive complete lattice; the second, that these equations — contrary to their special cases, the axioms L_{10} and L_{11} — do not mutually imply each other. Accordingly, we introduce the following nomenclature:

A lattice is said to be *infinitely meet-distributive* if it is join--complete and (3) holds for every subset $R = \{b_\beta\}_{\beta \in \mathsf{B}}$ of the lattice. The definition of the *infinitely join-distributive* lattice is dual to the foregoing. Whenever a lattice is infinitely meet- and join-distributive, it is briefly called *infinitely distributive*.

By the definition and by Theorem 28, infinitely meet or join-distributive lattices are, a fortiori, distributive (in the usual sense).

By applying (1) twice, we have for any finite number of elements of a distributive lattice

$$\bigcup_{j=1}^{m} a_{1j} \cap \bigcup_{k=1}^{n} a_{2k} = \bigcup_{j=1}^{m} (a_{1j} \cap \bigcup_{k=1}^{n} a_{2k}) = \bigcup_{j=1}^{m} \bigcup_{k=1}^{n} (a_{1j} \cap a_{2k})$$

and hence, by induction on r,

$$\text{(5)} \qquad \bigcap_{j=1}^{r} \bigcup_{k=1}^{n_j} a_{jk} = \bigcup_{j_1=1}^{n_1} \cdots \bigcup_{j_r=1}^{n_r} (a_{1j_1} \cap \cdots \cap a_{rj_r})$$

The identity (5) can be stated in a form that is more concise, and better suited to generalization. Let us introduce the notation $\mathsf{A} = \{1, \ldots, r\}$, $\mathsf{B}_1 = \{1, \ldots, n_1\}$, $\ldots$, $\mathsf{B}_r = \{1, \ldots, n_r\}$. Furthermore, let γ be some choice function defined on the sets $\mathsf{B}_1, \ldots, \mathsf{B}_r$ (that is, let γ be a function which assigns to each of the sets $\mathsf{B}_1, \ldots, \mathsf{B}_r$

one, and only one, of their respective elements). Let $\gamma(\alpha)$ denote the element selected from B ($\alpha = 1, \ldots, r$). Then

(6) $$a_{1\gamma(1)} \cap \ldots \cap a_{r\gamma(r)}$$

is one of the terms of the right side of (5) and if γ runs through the set Γ of all choice functions definable on the sets $B_1, \ldots, B_r$, expressions of the form (6) give the meet expressions figuring on the right side of (5). Hence, (5) can be rewritten as follows:

(7) $$\bigcap_{\alpha \in A} \bigcup_{\beta \in B_\alpha} a_{\alpha\beta} = \bigcup_{\gamma \in \Gamma} \bigcap_{\alpha \in A} a_{\alpha\gamma(\alpha)}$$

Hence, Formula (7), and its dual formula

(8) $$\bigcup_{\alpha \in A} \bigcap_{\beta \in B_\alpha} a_{\alpha\beta} = \bigcap_{\gamma \in \Gamma} \bigcup_{\alpha \in A} a_{\alpha\gamma(\alpha)}$$

hold for any finite system of elements of a distributive lattice; whereas, for all infinite A or B_α, these formulae are not generally true.

For instance, by choosing $A = \{1, 2\}$, $B_1 = \{1\}$, $B_2 = B$, (7) passes into (3) and (8) passes into (4), which were already shown not to hold in every distributive complete lattice.

A lattice is said to be *completely meet-distributive* if it is complete and satisfies (7) without restrictions. As a dual concept, we can define lattices as *completely join-distributive*. The lattices simultaneously completely meet- and join-distributive are called *completely distributive*. Clearly, a *completely meet- (join-) distributive* lattice is, a fortiori, infinitely meet- (join-)distributive.

An example of completely distributive lattices will be given by the following lemma, which will also prove to be useful later:

LEMMA. *Every complete ring of sets is completely distributive.*

PROOF. Consider arbitrary elements $X_{\alpha\beta}$ ($\alpha \in A$; $\beta \in \bigcup_{\alpha \in A} B_\alpha$) of a complete ring of sets; let Γ denote the set of all choice functions defined on the sets B_α ($\alpha \in A$). The definitions of set union and set intersection directly imply that the following statements 1—6 are equivalent (and the equivalence of the statements succeeding each other is obvious):

1. $x \in \bigcap_{\alpha \in A} \bigcup_{\beta \in B_\alpha} X_{\alpha\beta}$
2. $x \in \bigcup_{\beta \in B_\alpha} X_{\alpha\beta}$ for every α
3. to every α, there is a $\beta (\in B_\alpha)$ such that $x \in X_{\alpha\beta}$
4. there exists a $\gamma (\in \Gamma)$ such that $x \in X_{\alpha\gamma(\alpha)}$ for every α (that is, a choice function which assigns the above β to every α)
5. there exists a γ such that $x \in \bigcap_{\alpha \in A} X_{\alpha\gamma(\alpha)}$
6. $x \in \bigcup_{\gamma \in \Gamma} \bigcap_{\alpha \in A} X_{\alpha\gamma(\alpha)}$

Furthermore, the following statements are likewise equivalent:

1. $x \in \bigcup_{\alpha \in A} \bigcap_{\beta \in B_\alpha} X_{\alpha\beta}$
2. there exists an α such that $x \in \bigcap_{\beta \in B_\alpha} X_{\alpha\beta}$
3. there exists an α such that $x \in X_{\alpha\beta}$ for every index β ($\in B_\alpha$)
4. there exists an α such that for every choice function $\gamma (\in \Gamma)$, $x \in X_{\alpha\gamma(\alpha)}$ (since $\gamma(\alpha) \in B_\alpha$)
5. for every γ, $x \in \bigcup_{\alpha \in A} X_{\alpha\gamma(\alpha)}$
6. $x \in \bigcap_{\gamma \in \Gamma} \bigcup_{\alpha \in A} X_{\alpha\gamma(\alpha)}$

Hence, by substituting everywhere X for a, (7) and (8) are satisfied.

The reader should note that by the above definitions every completely distributive lattice is complete, but not every distributive complete lattice is completely distributive.

Two interesting characterizations of completely distributive lattices were given by Raney [166], [167]. However, these can be fully understood only if the material in this book is known. See also Jakubík [100], Dwinger [55] and Bruns [23]. The paper by Raney [168] also deals with completely distributive lattices.

32. Modular Lattices

It can be shown by simple calculations that in any lattice the equation in L_{10} is true for every triplet of elements a, b, c of the lattice satisfying $a \leqq c$. Numerous important non-distributive lattices in which any triplet of elements a, b, c ($a \leqq c$) also satisfies the equation L_{11} are known. Since in the case $a \leqq c$ the right side of the equation in L_{11} reduces to $(a \cup b) \cap c$, these lattices can be characterized as satisfying the following condition:

L_{12}. *For any triplet of elements a, b, c of a lattice satisfying $a \leqq c$*

$$\textit{the identity } a \cup (b \cap c) = (a \cup b) \cap c \textit{ holds}.$$

The identity figuring in L_{12} is called the *modular identity*, and the lattices having the property L_{12} are called *modular lattices.*

From the above it is clear that *every distributive lattice is modular.*

The definition of modular lattices as well as the above remark is due to Dedekind ([38], pp. 115–116).

The following remark will be found to be useful. For any triplet a, b, c ($a \leqq c$) of elements of any lattice, there holds the *modular inequality*

$$a \cup (b \cap c) \leqq (a \cup b) \cap c$$

Hence, *if for any triplet a, b, c ($a \leqq c$) of elements of a lattice there also holds the reverse inequality, the lattice is modular.*

The following theorem is theoretically important.

THEOREM 30. *A lattice L is modular if, and only if, every triplet a, b, c of L satisfies the equation*

$$a \cup (b \cap (a \cup c)) = (a \cup b) \cap (a \cup c) \tag{1}$$

(Jordan [105]).

PROOF. If L is modular, then by L_{12} and because $a \leqq a \cup c$, (1) holds. Conversely, if (1) is true for any triplet a, b, c of L, then, in particular, L_{12} is true as well, since $a \leqq c$ implies $a \cup c = c$.

The theorem signifies that the class of modular lattices is that class of algebras which can be characterized by the identities $\mathsf{L}_1 - \mathsf{L}_6$ and (1).

The following theorem, corresponding to Theorem 29, holds.

THEOREM 31. *The dual, every sublattice and every homomorphic image of a modular lattice is modular.*

PROOF. By dualizing L_{12} and interchanging a and b in the proposition so obtained, we revert to L_{12} itself. This means that L_{12} is self-dual and hence the first statement of the theorem is true.

The further propositions of the theorem can be proved with the aid of equation (1) in the same manner as the corresponding propositions of Theorem 29 were proved.

Let us now present two examples of modular lattices.

Example 23. Let $\mathscr{N}(G)$ denote the set of all normal subgroups of a group G and let $H, K \in \mathscr{N}(G)$. Then, as confirmed by group theory, $H \cap K$ and HK are also normal subgroups of G. Hence, the prescriptions $H \frown K = H \cap K$ and $H \smile K = HK$ define operations in $\mathscr{N}(G)$, and it is easy to see that $\mathscr{N}(G)$ forms a lattice with respect to these two operations. In the lattice $\mathscr{N}(G)$, $H \leqq K$ if, and only if, $H = H \frown K = H \cap K$, that is, if $H \subseteq K$.

We will show that $\mathscr{N}(G)$ is modular. In group-theoretical symbolism, this means that if $A, B, C \in \mathscr{N}(G)$ and $A \subseteq C$, then $A(B \cap C) = AB \cap C$. By the modular inequality, it is sufficient to prove the inclusion $A(B \cap C) \supseteq AB \cap C$. For this purpose, let ξ be any element of the normal subgroup $AB \cap C$. Then, by $\xi \in AB$, there exists an $\alpha (\alpha \in A)$ and a $\beta (\beta \in B)$ such that $\xi = \alpha\beta$. But then, $\beta = \alpha^{-1}\xi \in AC \subseteq C$, and hence $\beta \in B \cap C$. Consequently, $\xi (= \alpha\beta) \in A(B \cap C)$, meaning that $AB \cap C \subseteq A(B \cap C)$.

It can be verified by analogous considerations that the ideal lattice of any ring is always (at least) modular.

In the same way one can also prove the stronger result that $\mathscr{N}(G)$ is "completely modular" in the following sense due to Kurosch [227]. By a *completely modular* lattice is meant a complete lattice having the property that, if for some system $\{x_\lambda, y_\lambda\}_{\lambda \in \Lambda}$ of elements of the lattice, each x_λ is less than or equal to any $y_{\lambda'}$ with $\lambda' \neq \lambda$ then

$$\bigcup_{\lambda \in \Lambda} x_\lambda \frown \bigcap_{\lambda \in \Lambda} y_\lambda = \bigcup_{\lambda \in \Lambda} (x_\lambda \frown y_\lambda)$$

This type of lattice will not be dealt with here. Let us note only that every lattice of this type is, especially modular (see Exercise 12).

If G is commutative, $\mathscr{N}(G)$ coincides with the subgroup lattice of G; hence, the subgroup lattice of any Abelian group is modular. It is here that the term "modular lattice" has its origin: that is, the Abelian groups written in the additive notation are usually called "modules".

The lattice of all subgroups of a non-commutative lattice in general is not modular. For example, the subgroup lattice of the fourth-degree alternating group $\mathscr{A}_4$ is, if the permutations are written as products of cycles, as follows:

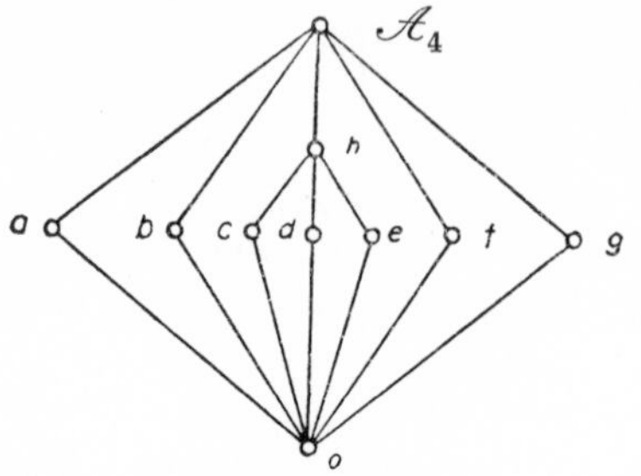

Fig. 16

$$\begin{aligned} a &= \{(1), (123), (132)\}, \\ b &= \{(1), (124), (142)\}, \\ c &= \{(1), (12), (34)\}, \\ d &= \}(1), (13), (24)\}, \\ e &= \{(1), (14), (23)\}, \\ f &= \{(1), (134), (143)\}, \\ g &= \{(1), (234), (243)\}, \\ h &= \{(1), (12)(34), (13)(24), \\ &\quad (14)(23)\}, \\ o &= \{(1)\}. \end{aligned}$$

Here, $c \leqq h$, and nevertheless $c \cup (a \cap h) = c \cup o = c$ and $(c \cup a) \cap h = = \mathscr{A}_4 \cap h = h$.

Let us remark here that the connection between the structure of a group and its subgroup lattice has been treated by numerous mathematicians. In Section 30, we have already characterized the groups having distributive subgroup lattices. All finite groups whose subgroup lattices are modular or semimodular (the latter in the sense to be expounded in Chapter VII) have also been determined.

Clearly, if two groups are isomorphic, their subgroup lattices are likewise isomorphic. On the contrary, groups having isomorphic subgroup lattices are not necessarily isomorphic: for example, the subgroup lattice of every group of prime order is a two-element chain. However, particular classes of groups occur, for example, finitely generated free nilpotent groups (Plotkin [161]) or the groups decomposable into free products (Sadovski [170]), which are uniquely determined to within isomorphism by their subgroup lattices. (Concerning the group theory concepts just mentioned see [227]). Several results in this field are to be found in a paper by Baer [4]. In some cases — for example, that of torsion free Abelian groups — the group is defined by the lattice of its subsemigroups (Petropavlovskaya [158]).

Readers who are interested in a more profound knowledge of this field are referred to Suzuki's book [188].

Example 24. Projective spaces belong to the incidence spaces defined in Example 16. The results of Section 41 will yield, as a special case, the result that the subspace lattice of every projective space is modular.

33. Characterisation of Modular and Distributive Lattices by their Sublattices

For any elements a, b, c of a lattice the following inequality holds:

(1) $\quad (a \cap b) \cup (b \cap c) \cup (c \cap a) \leqq (a \cup b) \cap (b \cup c) \cap (c \cup a)$

If for a triplet of elements a, b, c the symbol "$=$" is valid in (1) instead of the symbol "$\leq$", then this common value of the two sides of (1) is called the *median* of the elements a, b, c and denoted med (a, b, c). Clearly, the permutation of the elements a, b, c does not affect the existence and value of med (a, b, c).

In papers on lattice theory, the following definition of "betweenness" occurs. Given the elements a, x, b of a lattice, x is said to be between a and b whenever $a \cap b \leq x \leq a \cup b$. The term "median" is justified by the fact that in a distributive lattice an element x is between the elements a, b (in the above sense) if, and only if, the median of the three elements equals x (see Exercise 15).

The main purpose of this section is the presentation of two important theorems, one by Dedekind and one by Birkhoff. As a preliminary, we shall prove two lemmas.

LEMMA 1. *A lattice is modular if, and only if, every triplet of elements a, b, c $(a \leq c)$ has a median.*

In fact, if $a \leq c$, then

$$(a \cap b) \cup (b \cap c) \cup (c \cap a) = (a \cap b) \cup (b \cap c) \cup a = a \cup (b \cap c$$

and

$$(a \cup b) \cap (b \cup c) \cap (c \cup a) = (a \cup b) \cap (b \cup c) \cap c = (a \cup b) \cap c$$

From these, by L_{12}, the proposition of the lemma results.

LEMMA 2. *A lattice is distributive if, and only if, every one of its triplets of elements has a median.*

On the one hand, if a, b, c are the elements of a distributive lattice, then

$$\begin{aligned}(a \cup b) \cap (b \cup c) \cap (c \cup a) &= \big((a \cup b) \cap (b \cup c) \cap c\big) \\ \cup \big((a \cup b) \cap (b \cup c) \cap a\big) &= \big((a \cup b) \cap c\big) \cup \big((b \cup c) \cap a\big) = \\ &= \big((a \cap c) \cup (b \cap c)\big) \cup \big((b \cap a) \cup (c \cap a)\big) = \\ &= (a \cap b) \cup (b \cap c) \cup (c \cap a)\end{aligned}$$

whence, every triplet of elements of a distributive lattice has a median.

Conversely, assume that in a lattice L every triplet of elements has a median. Then, even Lemma 1 is sufficient to assert that L is modular. Consider any elements a, b, c of L. Applying first the absorption identity of the meet, then the assumption gives us

$$(2) \qquad \begin{aligned} a \cap (b \cup c) &= a \cap (a \cup b) \cap (a \cup c) \cap (b \cup c) = \\ &= a \cap \big((b \cap c) \cup (c \cap a) \cup (a \cap b)\big)\end{aligned}$$

Since L is modular and $a \geq (c \cap a) \cup (a \cap b)$, the right side of (2) may be re-written

$$(3) \qquad \begin{aligned} a \cap \{(b \cap c) \cup \big((c \cap a) \cup (a \cap b)\big)\} &= \\ = \{a \cap (b \cap c)\} \cup \{(a \cap b) \cup (a \cap c)\} &= (a \cap b) \cup (a \cap c)\end{aligned}$$

where the latter equation is implied by $a \frown b \frown c \leqq (a \frown b) \smile \smile (a \frown c)$. By (2) and (3) L_{10} is satisfied in L; this, however, is sufficient by Theorem 28 for L to be distributive.

In this way, the proof of Lemma 2 is complete. We shall now proceed to prove the above-mentioned theorems.

THEOREM 32 (Dedekind's modularity criterion). *A lattice is modular if, and only if, no sublattice of it is isomorphic with the lattice shown as* Fig. 17a ([39], Theorem IX).

Paraphrased: *A lattice is modular if, and only if, no interval* $[a, b]$ *of the lattice includes an element having two different comparable relative complements in* $[a, b]$.

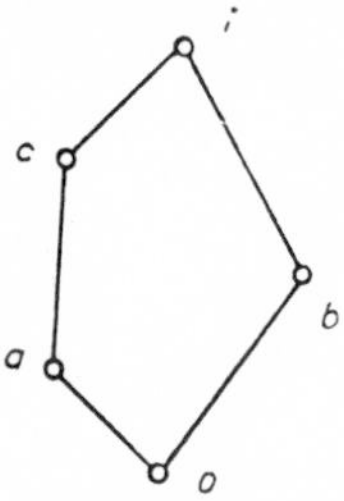

Fig. 17/a

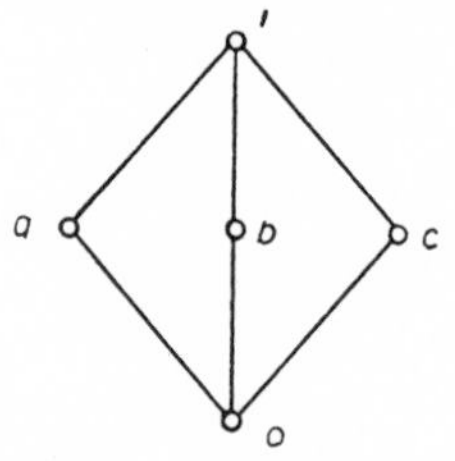

Fig. 17/b

COROLLARY 1. *No element of a bounded modular lattice has two comparable complements.*

COROLLARY 2. *For the elements* x, y, z *of a modular lattice,* $x \frown z = y \frown z$, $x \smile z = y \smile z$ and $x \leqq y$ imply $x = y$.

THEOREM 33 (Birkhoff's distributivity criterion). *A lattice is distributive if, and only if, it has no sublattice isomorphic with either one of the lattices shown as* Figs. 17a *and* 17b ([11], p. 118).

Paraphrased: *A lattice is distributive if and only if no interval* $[a, b]$ *of the lattice includes an element having two different relative complements in* $[a, b]$.

COROLLARY 1. *Every element of a bounded distributive lattice has at most one complement.*

COROLLARY 2. *For the elements* x, y, z *of a distributive lattice* $x \frown z = y \frown z$ *and* $x \smile z = y \smile z$ *imply* $x = y$.

It is quite simple to indirectly verify the statements "only if" of both theorems. The lattice shown in Fig. 17a is non-modular (and hence, a fortiori, non-distributive), since in that lattice, $a \leqq c$, and nevertheless $a \smile (b \frown c) \neq (a \smile b) \frown c$ in fact, $a \smile (b \frown c) = a \smile o = a$ and $(a \smile b) \frown c = i \frown c = c$. The lattice shown as Fig. 17b is non-distributive, since for example $a \smile (b \frown c) \neq (a \smile b) \frown (a \smile c)$: in fact, $a \smile (b \frown c) = a \smile o = a$ and $(a \smile b) \frown (a \smile c) = i \frown i = i$. Hence, by Theorems 29 and 31 no sublattice of a modular lattice can be isomorphic with the lattice of Fig. 17a, and no sublattice of a distributive lattice can be isomorphic with any one of the lattices shown as Figs. 17a and 17b.

The "if" statement of Theorem 32 can be paraphrased as follows. *If a lattice is non-modular, it has a sublattice isomorphic with the lattice of Fig. 17a.* Accordingly, let us consider a non-modular lattice L. By the definition of modular lattices and by the modular inequality, there certainly occurs in L a triplet of elements x, y, z such that

$$(4) \qquad x \leqq z \quad \text{and} \quad x \cup (y \cap z) < (x \cup y) \cap z$$

We shall show that, in L, the subset R consisting of the elements

$$(5) \quad u = y \cap z,\ a = x \cup (y \cap z),\ b = y,\ c = (x \cup y) \cap z,\ v = x \cup y$$

is a sublattice isomorphic to the lattice of Fig. 17a.

By assumption (4),

$$(6) \qquad u \leqq a < c \leqq v, \qquad u \leqq b \leqq v$$

Hence,

$$u \leqq a \cap b \leqq c \cap b = (x \cup y) \cap z \cap y = y \cap z = u$$

$$v \geqq c \cup b \geqq a \cup b = x \cup (y \cap z) \cup y = x \cup y = v$$

that is,

$$(7) \qquad a \cap b = c \cap b = u, \qquad a \cup b = c \cup b = v$$

Since, by (6), u and v are bound elements of the sublattice R, equations (7) immediately imply that R is a sublattice of L. It remains only to prove that the elements defined in (5) are all different. To prove this, by (6), it has to be shown only that $u \neq b$, $v \neq b$, $u \neq a$, $v \neq c$, $a \neq b$, $c \neq b$.

First of all, by (7) and by the property L_9 of lattices,

$$u = b \Longrightarrow a \cap b = b \Longrightarrow a \cup b = a \Longrightarrow v = a$$

which is impossible by (6). Further, likewise by (7) and L_9,

$$v = c \Longrightarrow c \cup b = c \Longrightarrow c \cap b = b \Longrightarrow u = b$$

and

$$a = b \Longrightarrow u = b \cap b = b$$

and it has been shown above that u cannot equal b. Finally, by dualizing the above considerations (interchanging u and v, resp. a and c) we find that neither $v = b$, nor $u = a$, nor $c = b$ is possible.

The statement "if" of Theorem 33 remains to be proved. By Theorem 32, already proved, this is equivalent to the following: *If a modular lattice is non-distributive, it has a sublattice isomorphic with the lattice of Fig. 17b.*

Let therefore L be a modular but non-distributive lattice. Then, by Lemma 2, L has a triplet of elements p, q, r such that

$$(8)\quad (p \cap q) \cup (q \cap r) \cup (r \cap p) < (p \cup q) \cap (q \cup r) \cap (r \cup p)$$

It will be shown that the elements

$$(9)\qquad \begin{aligned} u &= (p \cap q) \cup (q \cap r) \cup (r \cap p) \\ v &= (p \cup q) \cap (q \cup r) \cap (r \cup p) \\ a &= u \cup (p \cap v) = (u \cup p) \cap v^* \\ b &= u \cup (q \cap v) = (u \cup q) \cap v \\ c &= u \cup (r \cap v) = (u \cup r) \cap v \end{aligned}$$

form a sublattice isomorphic with the lattice of Fig. 17b.

It will be shown first of all that for the elements defined in (9)

$$(10)\qquad \begin{cases} a \cap b = b \cap c = c \cap a = u \\ a \cup b = b \cup c = c \cup a = v \end{cases}$$

From these, the fact that the elements figuring here are different will be easy to infer.

We shall start from the first representation of the elements a and b. Let us write out in detail the expressions $p \cap v$ and $q \cap v$, and apply the absorption identity of the meet to them. In this way, the equation

$$a \cup b = u \cup (p \cap v) \cup (q \cap v) =$$
$$= u \cup [(p \cap (q \cup r)) \cup (q \cap (r \cup p))]$$

results. For the expression in the square bracket, $p \cap (q \cup r) \leqq p \leqq \leqq r \cup p$ and thus, transcribing it according to L_{12}, we have

$$a \cup b = u \cup [\{(p \cap (q \cup r)) \cup q\} \cap (r \cup p)]$$

However, by L_{12}, $(p \cap (q \cup r)) \cup q = (p \cup q) \cap (q \cup r)$ and hence, $a \cup b = u \cup v = v$.

Since all the assumptions (namely, (8), (9) and the modular identity) are self-dual**, the dual of the result just obtained, $a \cap b = u$, is also true. The rest of the equations of (10) can be verified in a similar manner.

That the elements defined by (9) are all different remains to be shown. First of all, $u = a$ is impossible, since by (10) and L_9

$$u = a \Longrightarrow \begin{cases} a \cap b = a \Longrightarrow a \cup b = b \Longrightarrow v = b \\ a \cap c = a \Longrightarrow a \cup c = c \Longrightarrow v = c \end{cases}$$

* Since $u \leqq v$ and L is modular, we have indeed $u \cup (p \cap v) = (u \cup p) \cap v$, and similarly for q and r.

** In dualizing (9), u and v are interchanged.

which would further imply $v = v \frown v = b \frown c = u$ in contradiction with assumption (8). Similarly, $u \neq b$ and $u \neq c$. By the dual consideration, $v \neq a, b, c$. Finally, the elements a, b, c are also all different, since — for example — if a and b were equal, $u = a \frown b = a \frown a = a$ would also be satisfied. This completes the proof of Theorem 33.

Other kinds of characterizations of modular and distributive lattices are found in papers by Croisot [33], [34], [50], Ellis [57], Iséki [95]—[98], Kolibiar [119] and Ward [211]. The last discusses lattices satisfying the maximum condition.

34. Distributive Sublattices of Modular Lattices

By Theorem 31, every sublattice of a modular lattice is modular. The interesting problem as to when a sublattice of a modular lattice is distributive arises. The theorem to follow answers this problem.

THEOREM 34. *Let H be a non-void subset of a modular lattice L. For the sublattice $\bar{H}$ of L generated by H to be distributive, it is necessary and sufficient that for every finite subsystem $\{x_1, \ldots, x_m, y_1, \ldots, y_n\}$ of H,*

$$(1) \qquad \bigcup_{j=1}^{m} x_j \frown \bigcap_{k=1}^{n} y_k = \bigcup_{j=1}^{m} \left(x_j \frown \bigcap_{k=1}^{n} y_k \right)$$

(Jónsson [104]).

PROOF. The necessity of the condition is trivial. To prove that it is sufficient, we will first of all show that for any subset X of L, (1) is equivalent to its dual, that is, to the equation

$$(2) \qquad \bigcap_{j=1}^{m} x_j \smile \bigcup_{k=1}^{n} y_k = \bigcap_{j=1}^{m} \left(x_j \smile \bigcup_{k=1}^{n} y_k \right) \quad (x_1, \ldots, x_m, y_1, \ldots, y_n \in X)$$

First of all, (2) holds for $m = 1$. Let us assume that it is also true for $m = r - 1$ and then consider the case $m = r$. By the induction hypothesis we have,

$$(3) \qquad \bigcap_{i=1}^{r} \left(x_j \smile \bigcup_{k=1}^{n} y_k \right) = \bigcap_{j=1}^{r-1} \left(x_j \smile \bigcup_{k=1}^{n} y_k \right) \frown \left(x_r \smile \bigcup_{k=1}^{n} y_k \right) =$$

$$= \left(\bigcap_{j=1}^{r-1} x_j \smile \bigcup_{k=1}^{n} y_k \right) \frown \left(x_r \smile \bigcup_{k=1}^{n} y_k \right)$$

Further, by the modularity,

$$(4) \qquad \left(\bigcup_{k=1}^{n} y_k \smile \bigcap_{j=1}^{r-1} x_j \right) \frown \left(x_r \smile \bigcup_{k=1}^{n} y_k \right) = \bigcup_{k=1}^{n} y_k \smile \left(\bigcap_{j=1}^{r-1} x_j \frown \left(x_r \smile \bigcup_{k=1}^{n} y_k \right) \right)$$

Finally, by (1),

$$(5) \qquad \left(x_r \smile \bigcup_{k=1}^{n} y_k \right) \frown \bigcap_{j=1}^{r-1} x_j = \left(x_r \frown \bigcap_{j=1}^{r-1} x_j \right) \smile \bigcup_{k=1}^{n} \left(y_k \frown \bigcap_{j=1}^{r-1} x_j \right)$$

Since the last join member on the right hand side of (5) is less than or equal to $\bigcup_{k=1}^{n} y_k$ we obtain by (3)—(5) just (2) for the case $m = r$. Hence, (2) is implied by (1). By dualizing the proof we obtain that (1) is implied by (2).*

Now let H be a subset of the modular lattice L satisfying the assumptions of the theorem. Let $\mathcal{M}$ denote the family of all subsets X of L satisfying the following two conditions:

(a) $X \supseteq H$
(b) whenever $x_1, \ldots, x_m, y_1, \ldots, y_m \in X$, (1) and (2) hold.

This $\mathcal{M}$ is, obviously, partly ordered by the set inclusion.

It is easy to see that the set union of any chain of sets belonging to $\mathcal{M}$ also has the properties (a), (b). From this, by applying the Kuratowski—Zorn lemma, we obtain that, among these X, at least one exists which is maximal. That is, L has a subset $\bar{X}$ such that (a) and (b) are satisfied for $X = \bar{X}$, and

(c) if for some subset X of L, (a) and (b) are satisfied and $X \supseteq \bar{X}$, then $X = \bar{X}$.

Let u, v be two arbitrary elements of $\bar{X}$, and let us consider the set $X = \bar{X} \cup \{u \cap v\}$. Clearly, the condition (a) also holds for this X. We will show that (b) holds too. If none of the elements $x_1, \ldots, x_m, y_1, \ldots, y_n$ equals $u \cap v$, then (1) and (2) are true because they were true already in $\bar{X}$. If some y_k equals $u \cap v$, for example, if $y_1 = u \cap v$, then, introducing the notations

$$z_0 = u, z_1 = v, z_k = y_k \quad (k = 2, \ldots, n)$$

we have $z_k \in \bar{X}$ $(k = 0, 1, \ldots, n)$ and by (b), true for $\bar{X}$,

$$\bigcup_{j=1}^{m} x_j \cap \bigcap_{k=1}^{n} y_k = \bigcup_{j=1}^{m} x_j \cap \bigcap_{k=0}^{n} z_k = \bigcup_{j=1}^{m} \left(x_j \cap \bigcap_{k=0}^{n} z_k\right) = \bigcup_{j=1}^{m} \left(x_j \cap \bigcap_{k=1}^{n} y_k\right)$$

and hence (1) is true for X, too; but then, by our preliminary remark, so is (2). Finally, if some x_j equals $u \cap v$, the above line of thought can be repeated with (1) and (2) interchanged. Hence, for the X in question, (a) and (b) are satisfied and $X \supseteq \bar{X}$; but then, by (c), $X = \bar{X}$. This is, however, only possible if $u \cap v \in \bar{X}$. By the dual consideration, $u \cup v \in \bar{X}$, hence, $\bar{X}$ is a sublattice L.

Applying (b) to the case $m = 2$, $n = 1$, we infer that the lattice $\bar{X}$ is distributive. Since by (a), $\langle H \rangle$ is a sublattice of $\bar{X}$ as well, $\langle H \rangle$ itself is distributive. Thus the theorem is proved.

Let us point out that it is sufficient to require (1) for systems of elements $x_1, \ldots, x_m, y_1, \ldots, y_n$ in which all elements are different. For, if there are two equal elements among the x_j or the y_k then,

* The importance of our preliminary result is that, in the following, (2) can also be counted among the assumptions of the theorem, and thereby the set of assumptions becomes a self-dual set of propositions.

by the idempotence of lattice operations, one can be omitted; on the other hand, if $x_j = y_k$ for some pair of indices j, k, both sides of (1) reduce to the meet of all y_k.

Musti and Buttafuoco [142] have proved that in the case of a finite H the condition of Theorem 34 can be weakened: it is sufficient to require (1) for systems of elements of a certain special form. We shall restrict the discussion to the case of three-element subsets:

THEOREM 35. *In a modular lattice, the sublattice generated by the elements x, y, z of the lattice is distributive if, and only if,*

$$x \cap (y \cup z) = (x \cap y) \cup (x \cap z) \tag{6}$$

(Neumann [146], p. 108).

PROOF. The necessity of the condition is evident. To prove its sufficiency, by the foregoing theorem and by the subsequent remark it has only to be shown that in the case of a modular lattice (6) also implies the equations

$$y \cap (z \cup x) = (y \cap z) \cup (y \cap x) \tag{7}$$

$$z \cap (x \cup y) = (z \cap x) \cup (z \cap y) \tag{8}$$

Indeed, if (6) holds, then by absorption and the modular identities,

$$y \cap (z \cup x) = \big(y \cap (z \cup y)\big) \cap (z \cup x) = y \cap \big((z \cup x) \cap (z \cup y)\big) =$$

$$= y \cap \big(z \cup (x \cap (z \cup y))\big) = y \cap \big(z \cup ((x \cap z) \cup (x \cap y)\big) =$$

$$= y \cap \big(z \cup (x \cap y)\big) = (y \cap z) \cup (y \cap x)$$

yielding (7). By interchanging y and z, the same consideration yields (8).

35. The Isomorphism Theorem of Modular Lattices Covering Conditions

Two intervals $[a, b]$, $[c, d]$ of a lattice are called *transposed* if $b \cap c = a$ and $b \cup c = d$. For these, there holds

THEOREM 36 (Isomorphism theorem of modular lattices). *Transposed intervals of a modular lattice are isomorphic* (Dedekind [39], Theorem XI).

SUPPLEMENT. *If $H = [u \cap v, v]$ and $K = [u, u \cup v]$ are two intervals of a modular lattice L, then*

$$\varphi\colon x \to \varphi(x) = u \cup x \quad (x \in H)$$

is an isomorphism of the sublattice H onto the sublattice K, whereas

$$\psi\colon y \to \psi(y) = v \cap y \quad (y \in K)$$

is an isomorphism of the sublattice K onto the sublattice H, and of these two mappings, each is the inverse of the other

COROLLARY. *In a modular lattice bounded below, the elements of finite height form an ideal.*

PROOF. First, let us show that $\varphi(H) \subseteq K$. Indeed, if $x \in H$, then $u \cap v \leqq x \leqq v$, and hence

$$u = u \cup (u \cap v) \leqq u \cup x \leqq u \cup v$$

that is, $\varphi(x) \in K$. Dually, $\psi(K) \subseteq H$.

Consider now the mapping $\psi\varphi$ of H into itself and the mapping $\varphi\psi$ of K into itself. Since $u \cap v \leqq x \leqq v$ $(x \in H)$ and $u \leqq y \leqq u \cup v$ $(y \in K)$ and L is modular, we have

(1) $$\psi\varphi(x) = v \cap (u \cup x) = (v \cap u) \cup x = x \quad (x \in H)$$

(2) $$\varphi\psi(y) = u \cup (v \cap y) = (u \cup y) \cap y = y \quad (y \in K)$$

that is, $\psi\varphi$ and $\varphi\psi$ represent the identical mapping on H and K, respectively. From this, we shall, for the time being, only make use of the circumstance that $\psi\varphi(H) = H$ and $\varphi\psi(K) = K$. By this, together with the facts found in the previous paragraph,

$$H = \psi\varphi(H) = \psi(\varphi(H)) \subseteq \psi(K) \subseteq H$$

and

$$K = \varphi\psi(K) = \varphi(\psi(K)) \subseteq \varphi(H) \subseteq K$$

that is, $\varphi(H) = K$, $\psi(K) = H$.

From (1) and (2), it may also be inferred that φ and ψ are one-to-one. In fact, if $\varphi(x_1) = \varphi(x_2)$ $(x_1, x_2 \in H)$, then by (1), $x_1 = \psi\varphi(x_1) = \psi(\varphi(x_1)) = \psi(\varphi(x_2)) = \psi\varphi(x_2) = x_2$; and by (2), the analogous statement holds for ψ. The equations (1) and (2) also reveal that of φ and ψ, each is the mutually inverse of the other.

It remains to be proved that φ and ψ are isomorphisms. By Theorem 9 it is sufficient to show that φ: $H \overset{o}{\approx} K$, ψ: $K \overset{o}{\approx} H$. The mappings φ and ψ are evidently order homomorphisms. But then, it follows immediately by (1) that if $\varphi(x_1) \leqq \varphi(x_2)$ $(x_1, x_2 \in H)$, then $x_1 = \psi\varphi(x_1) \leqq \psi\varphi(x_2) = x_2$. Hence, φ is an order ismorphism, and by similar considerations, so is ψ.

To prove the corollary, consider an arbitrary pair of elements a, b of a modular lattice bounded below. If a is of finite height, so is, a fortiori, $a \cap b$; further, by the isomorphism $[a \cap b, a] \approx [b, a \cup b]$ the sublattice $[b, a \cup b]$ is of finite length. If consequently, both a and b are of finite height, so is $a \cup b$. This proves the corollary.

The converse of the theorem does not hold in general. In order to show this let us consider the lattice represented on Fig. 18, where both of the broken lines between 0 and 1 stand for chains which are isomorphic to the chain of real numbers between 0 and 1 (more precisely of the numbers x satisfying the condition $0 < x < 1$), ordered according to their natural order. It is to be seen easily that every two transposed intervals in this lattice are isomorphic, nevertheless the lattice is not a modular one. (Example by Ward; see [212].)

In the case of a lattice, however, which satisfies the maximum or the minimum condition, the converse of the theorem is true (Ward [212]), and this holds even in the more general case of a compactly generated lattice, too (Crawley [28]).

Let us apply the isomorphism theorem to the particular case $u \frown v \prec v$. Then the interval $[u \frown v, v]$ is a two-element chain. But then so is $[u, u \smile v]$, whence $u \prec u \smile v$.

We have thus obtained the result that for any pair of elements u, v of a modular lattice

Fig. 18

(3) $$u \frown v \prec v \Longrightarrow u \prec u \smile v$$

and, as can also be proved by the above consideration,

(4) $$u \prec u \smile v \Longrightarrow u \frown v \prec v$$

In brief, for any pair of elements u, v of a modular lattice

(5) $$u \frown v \prec v \Longleftrightarrow u \prec u \smile v$$

Let L denote an arbitrary (that is, not necessarily modular) lattice. If for any pair of elements u, v of L, $\begin{Bmatrix}(3)\\(4)\end{Bmatrix}$ holds, L is said to satisfy the $\begin{Bmatrix}\textit{lower}\\ \textit{upper}\end{Bmatrix}$ *covering condition*. Furthermore, if for any pair of elements u, v, (5) that is, both (3) and (4) holds, L is said to satisfy the *double covering condition*.

By the above, there holds

THEOREM 37. *Every modular lattice satisfies the double covering condition* (Dedekind [39], Theorem XII).

Let $\mathscr{S}(E)$ denote the subspace lattice of the Euclidean plane E (that is, a plane having no point at infinity). By investigating all possible cases it is easily verified that $\mathscr{S}(E)$ satisfies the lower covering condition. On the other hand, it fails to satisfy the upper covering condition: for example, if g and h are two parallel lines of E, then $g \smile h = E$ and $g \frown h = O$, whence $g \smile h \succ g$ holds, while $g \frown h \prec h$ does not.

The lattice shown as Fig. 17a (p. 90) satisfies none of the covering conditions. That is, in that lattice, (3) fails for the pair of elements a, b, while (4) fails for the pair c, b.

The examples quoted show that the lower and upper covering conditions are mutually independent and likewise independent of the lattice axioms.

36. Meet Representations in Modular and Distributive Lattices

By Theorem 16, if a lattice satisfies the maximum condition, then each of its elements can be represented as a meet of a finite number of meet-irreducible elements. This representation is, however, by no means unique, not even in finite lattices. For example, in the lattice shown as Fig. 17b (p. 90) $o = a \frown b = b \frown c = c \frown a$, in spite of the elements a, b, c being all meet-irreducible.

In this section we shall deal with the problem as to what positive results can be stated concerning the different representations of a given element as the meet of meet-irreducible elements in the case of modular and distributive lattices.

A representation of the form

(1) $$a = a_1 \cap \ldots \cap a_r \quad (r \text{ finite})$$

of an element a is said to be a *meet-representation* of a, while the elements $a_1, \ldots, a_r$ are called the *components of the meet-representation* (1). If the elements $a_1, \ldots, a_r$ are all meet-irreducible, (1) is said to be an *irreducible meet-representation* of a. Furthermore, if among the components of (1) there is one which can be deleted so that the join of the elements left still equals a, (1) is said to be *redundant*; in the opposite case, the representation is said to be *irredundant*. Naturally, the latter type of representation is of greater interest.

THEOREM 38 (Kurosh—Ore Theorem). *All irredundant irreducible meet-representations (provided any exist) of any element of a modular lattice have the same number of components* (Kurosh [123], Ore [150], II, p. 270).

In [44] and [46], Dilworth has studied the generalization and the conversion, in a certain sense, of this theorem.

As a preliminary, we shall prove

LEMMA 1. *Let*

(2) $$u = x_1 \cap \ldots \cap x_r$$

and

(3) $$u = y_1 \cap \ldots \cap y_s$$

be any two irredundant irreducible meet-representations of some element u *of a modular lattice. Any component* x_j *of* (2) *can be exchanged for a suitable* y_k *in the sense that*

$$x_1 \cap \ldots \cap x_{j-1} \cap y_k \cap x_{j+1} \cap \ldots \cap x_r = u$$

PROOF. Let us introduce the notations

$$u_j = x_1 \cap \ldots \cap x_{j-1} \cap x_{j+1} \cap \ldots \cap x_r$$

and

$$v_{jk} = u_j \cap y_k \quad (k = 1, \ldots, s)$$

For the elements thus defined, we have by (2) and (3)

(4) $$u_j \cap x_j = u$$

(5) $$v_{j1} \cap \ldots \cap v_{js} = u$$

(6) $$u \leqq v_{jk} \leqq u_j \quad (k = 1, \ldots, s)$$

Now by Theorem 36, (4) implies $[u, u_j] \approx [x_j, u_j \cup x_j]$. However, x_j is meet-irreducible in $[x_j, u_j \cup x_j]$ — being meet-irreducible in the entire lattice — and hence, so is u in $[u, u_j]$. On the other hand, (5) is — considering (6) — a meet-representation of u in $[u, u_j]$. Hence, some v_{jk} must equal u, as postulated by Lemma 1.

PROOF OF THEOREM 38. Let (2) and (3) be two irredundant irreducible meet-representations of some element u of a modular lattice, and let (2) be one such that the number of its components is the least possible. Applying Lemma 1, exchange x_1 for a suitable y_{k_1}. The meet-representation $u = y_{k_1} \cap x_2 \cap \ldots \cap x_r$ is likewise irredundant (since, by the assumption, every irreducible meet-representation of u consists of at least r elements); hence, again by Lemma 1, it is legitimate to exchange x_2 for some y_{k_2} and so forth. Finally, every x_j $(j = 1, \ldots, r)$ is substituted by one y_k. On the other hand, since the representation (3) was likewise irredundant, the representation just obtained must include every y_k. By the two last remarks, $s \leqq r$. However, by the assumption, r is minimal; hence, also, $s \geqq r$, completing the proof.

For distributive lattices, the following, stronger proposition also holds:

THEOREM 39. *Every element of a distributive lattice has at most one irredundant irreducible meet-representation (if the order of the components is disregarded)* (Birkhoff [15], p. 452).

It is first necessary to prove

LEMMA 2. *If an element x of a distributive lattice is meet-irreducible and $x \geqq \bigcap_{j=1}^{r} x_j$, then $x \geqq x_j$ for some j.**

PROOF. By the assumptions of Lemma 2,

$$x = x \cup (x_1 \cap \ldots \cap x_r) = (x \cup x_1) \cap \ldots \cap (x \cup x_r)$$

Since x is meet-irreducible, this is only possible if $x = x \cup x_j$, that is, $x \geqq x_j$ for some j.

Now, to begin with the proof of the theorem, assume that some element u of a distributive lattice can be represented in the forms (2) and (3), both representations being irredundant and irreducible. Then, $x_j \geqq y_1 \cap \ldots \cap y_s$ $(j = 1, \ldots, r)$ and hence, by Lemma 2, there exists a y_k (k being one of $1, \ldots, s$) such that $x_j \geqq y_k$. Similarly, there can be found an x_l such that $y_k \geqq x_l$, and hence, $x_j \geqq y_k \geqq x_l$. However, this is compatible with the irredundancy of (2) only if $j = l$. That implies, however, $x_j = y_k$. Considering also the irredundancy of the representation (3), we reach the conclusion that to every j, there exists exactly one such k and conversely;

* For generalizations of Lemma 2, see Exercise 25 and the paper [49] by Dilworth and Crawley. In the latter the statement of Lemma 2 is generalized for a certain class of the compactly generated lattices.

hence, the two representations are identical to within the order of the components.

It has already been mentioned in Section 32 that the ideal lattice of every ring is modular. Therefore, one gets as a simple corollary of Theorem 14 and of the Kurosh—Ore Theorem the well known theorem ([231], II, p. 36) that every ideal of a ring satisfying the maximum condition can be represented as the meet ofa finite number of irreducible ideals, and that the number of ideals in every irredundant representation of this kind of an ideal is the same. Furthermore, if the ideal lattice of the ring is distrubutive, the irredundant representation of the ideals as the meet of irreducible ideals is unique by Theorem 39.

There are also non-distributive lattices for which Theorem 39 is true (see for example Fig. 11 on p. 43). We present a necessary condition in Theorem 40.

THEOREM 40. *If every element of a lattice has a unique irredundant, irreducible meet-representation, then the lattice satisfies the lower covering condition.*

PROOF. We give an indirect proof. Let L be a lattice in which there exists an irreducible meet-representation for every element. Let us suppose that L has a triplet of elements a, b, c, for which

$$a \cap b \prec b \text{ and } a < c < a \cup b \tag{7}$$

Owing to the latter there exist meet-irreducible elements q_1 and q_2 such that

$$q_1 \geqq a, \quad q_1 \not\geqq c \quad \text{and} \quad q_2 \geqq c, q_2 \quad \not\geqq a \cup b \tag{8}$$

Obviously

$$b \cap a \leqq b \cap q_1 \leqq b \quad \text{and} \quad b \cap a \leqq b \cap q_2 \leqq b \tag{9}$$

Since we have, by (8)

$$b \cap q_1 = b \Longrightarrow q_1 \geqq a \cup b > c$$

and

$$b \cap q_2 = b \Longrightarrow q_2 \geqq b \cup c \geqq b \cup a$$

it also follows from (8) that neither $b \cap q_1 = b$, nor $b \cap q_2 = b$ can hold. Consequently, by (7) and (9) we have

$$b \cap a = b \cap q_1 = b \cap q_2 (\neq b)$$

Let $b = b_1 \cap \ldots \cap b_r$ be an irredundant, irreducible meet-representation of b. Since neither $b \cap q_1$ nor $b \cap q_2$ equal b, every b_j ($j = 1, \ldots, r$) is different from q_1 as well as from q_2; that means the element $b \cap a$ has two different irredundant, irreducible meet-representations

$$b \cap a = b_1 \cap \ldots \cap b_r \cap q_1 \text{ and } b \cap a = b_1 \cap \ldots \cap b_r \cap q_2$$

Thus we arrive at the following result: If every element of the lattice L has an irredundant, irreducible meet-representation, while the lattice itself does not satisfy the lower covering condition, then L has an element possessing two different representations of this kind, this being equivalent to the statement of the theorem.

In [42], Dilworth has given a necessary and sufficient condition for the existence of a unique irredundant irreducible meet-representation of every element of a lattice satisfying the maximum condition.

Exercises to Chapter IV

1. Show that by adding an element $\bar{o}$ and an element $\bar{i}$ to a distributive (modular) lattice so that $\bar{o} < x < \bar{i}$ for any element x of the lattice, the resulting new lattice is likewise distributive (modular).
2. Show that a lattice is distributive if, and only if, for any triplet a, b, c of its elements $(a \cup b) \cap c \leqq a \cup (b \cap c)$.
3. Show that for a lattice to be distributive, it is necessary and sufficient that for any triplet a, b, c of its elements, $c \cap a \leqq c \cap b$ and $c \cup a \leqq c \cup b$ be true simultaneously only if $a \leqq b$.
4. Show that for any elements a, b, c of a modular lattice $(a \cup b) \cap \cap c = b \cap c$ implies $(c \cup b) \cap a = b \cap a$.
5. Show that the modular identity is equivalent to the following proposition: if $x < z$, then $x \cup (y \cap z)$ is not less than $(x \cup y) \cap z$.
6. Show that a lattice L is modular if, and only if, $x \leqq z$ and $t \leqq \leqq y$ $(x, y, z, t \in L)$ imply $x \cup (y \cap (z \cup t)) = ((x \cup y) \cap z) \cup t$.
7. Show that a lattice L is modular if, and only if, for any elements a, b, c of L, the inequalities $a \leqq c \leqq a \cup b$ imply $a \cup (b \cap c) = c$.
8. Show that a lattice is modular if, and only if, from any quartet a, b, c, d of its elements

$$\left.\begin{array}{l} a \leqq b \leqq c \cup d \\ a \cap c = b \cap c \\ (a \cup c) \cap d = (b \cup c) \cap d \end{array}\right\} \Longrightarrow a = b\,*$$

9. Prove Corollary 2 of Theorem 32 direct calculation.
10. Prove Corollary 2 of Theorems 33 by direct calculation.
11. Prove by considering the lattice of Fig. 19 (on the next page) that a distributive lattice can have even non-modular meet-homomorphic and nonmodular join-homomorphic images.
12. Prove that every completely modular lattice is modular.

* From the statement of the exercise, it is easy to infer the following interesting result: Whenever for a pair of elements a, b of a modular lattice L, bounded above, $a \cup b = i$ holds and both $(a]$ and $(b]$ satisfy the minimum or the maximum condition, L itself also satisfies this same condition (Pickert [159]).

13. Prove that every infinitely meet-distributive lattice is completely modular.

14. Prove that in every lattice med $(a, b, a) = a$; in bounded lattices, moreover, med $(o, a, i) = a$, med $(a, i, b) = a \cup b$ and med $(a, o, b) = a \cap b$.

15. Prove that in a distributive lattice med (a, x, b) equals x if, and only if, $a \cap b \leq x \leq a \cup b$.

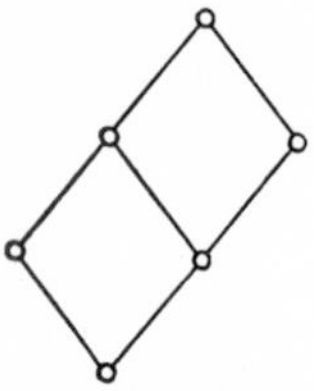

Fig. 19

16. Prove that for the elements $x_1, \ldots, x_n$ and a of a modular lattice bounded below, $(x_1 \cup \ldots \cup x_n) \cap a = o$ implies $(x_1 \cap \ldots \cap x_n) \cup a = (x_1 \cup a) \cap \ldots \cap (x_n \cup a)$.

17. Prove that in a distributive lattice any sublattice generated by a finite set is finite.

18. Show that with respect to the elements x, y, z of a modular lattice, the equations (6)—(8) of Section 34. and their duals are all equivalent.

19. Let u and v be arbitrary elements of a modular lattice L, and φ and ψ mappings as defined in Theorem 36. Show that φ and (ψ) maps every sub-interval T of the interval $[u \cap v, v]$ (and $[u, u \cup v]$ respectively) into an interval transposed to T.

20. Let L be a lattice in which every two transposed intervals are isomorphic and p, q be a pair of elements of L for which $p \succ q$. It is to be shown that for an arbitrary element r of L is $r \cap p \succ r \cap q$.

21. Show that for any lattice L, the following two statements are equivalent:

(A) L satisfies the lower covering condition;
(B) for every triplet a, b, x of elements of L

$$a \succ b \Longrightarrow a \cup x \succeq b \cup x$$

22. For an arbitrary element a of a lattice L let u_a denote (like that of Exercise 2 of Chapter III) the join of all the elements of L such that $x \succ a$. Show that

$$a = q_1 \cap \ldots \cap q_n \quad (q_1, \ldots, q_n \in L)$$

is an irredundant meet-representation of a in L if, and only if,

$$a = (u_a \cap q_1) \cap \ldots \cap (u_a \cap q_n)$$

is a representation of a of the same property in the sublattice $[a, u_a]$.

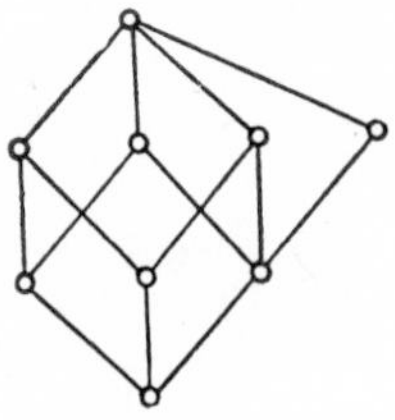

Fig. 20

23. Verify by utilizing the lattice of Fig. 20 that the Kurosh—Ore theorem is not true ingeneral for a non-modular lattice.

24. Show that a join-representation by join-irreducible elements $x_1, \ldots, x_r$ of an element u of a distributive lattice is redundant if and only if there exists a pair x_j, x_k such that $x_j \leq x_k$.

25. An element a of a complete lattice L is called *completely join-irreducible*, if every representation of the form $a = \bigcup_{\lambda \in \Lambda} a_\gamma$ $(a_\gamma \in L)$ implies $a_\lambda = a$ for at least one λ. Show that if for a completely join-irreducible element x of a completely distributive lattice $x \leqq \bigcup_{\mu \in M} x_\mu$, then $x \leqq x_\mu$ for some μ.

26. Prove that an element of a distributive lattice is irreducible (in respect of some operation) if, and only if, it is prime (in respect of the same operation).

27. Show that every lattice-ordered semigroup possesses properties as follows:

(A) $a \leqq b$ implies $xa \leqq xb$ and $ax \leqq bx$ for every x;

(B) $(a \cap b)(a \cup b) \leqq ba \cup ab$ for every pair a, b;

(C) if the semigroup has a unit element e (i.e. an element e, for which $ex = xe = x$ for every x) then $a \cup b = e$ implies $a \cap b = ba \cup ab$.

CHAPTER V

SPECIAL SUBCLASSES OF THE CLASS OF MODULAR LATTICES

37. Preliminary Theorems

In this section two theorems of rather general validity will be discussed.

THEOREM 41. *Whenever any interval* $[a, b]$ *of a lattice, considered as a sublattice, satisfies one of the covering conditions, the Jordan—Dedekind chain condition is also satisfied in* $[a, b]$ (Szász [189]).

COROLLARY. *Whenever a lattice of locally finite length* satisfies one of the covering conditions, it also satisfies the Jordan—Dedekind chain condition and has a dimension function as well.*

PROOF. According to the lattice-theoretical duality principle, it is sufficient to deal with the case when $[a, b]$ satisfies the lower covering condition. For this case, the theorem can be paraphrased as follows: *If* $[a, b]$ *satisfies the lower covering condition, and there exists between* a *and* b *a maximal chain*

$$(1) \qquad a = a_0 \prec a_1 \prec \ldots \prec a_n = b$$

then the length of every chain between a and b is at most n. This paraphrased proposition will be proved by induction.

In the case $n = 1$ the proposition is obvious. In what follows we shall consider the case $n \geqq 2$ and assume the proposition to be true for every interval including a maximal chain of the length of at most $n - 1$.

Let

$$(2) \qquad a = x_0 < x_1 < \ldots < x_m = b$$

be any subchain connecting a with b, and let us form the chain

$$(3) \qquad a_1 = a_1 \cup x_0 \leqq a_1 \cup x_1 \leqq a_1 \cup x_2 \leqq \ldots \leqq a_1 \cup x_m = b$$

Since by (1) a maximal chain of the length $n - 1$ exists between a_1 and b, by the induction hypothesis, the length of the chain (3) cannot exceed $n - 1$ either.

* By a lattice of locally finite length we mean, in agreement with the definition given in Section 9, a lattice, every subinterval of which is of finite length.

Let us denote by t the least (obviously, positive) integer for which $x_t \geqq a_1$. If $j \geqq t$, then $a_1 \cup x_j = x_j$ and $a_1 \cup x_{j+1} = x_{j+1}$; thus, by (2)

$$a_1 \cup x_j < a_1 \cup x_{j+1} \quad \text{if} \quad j \geqq t \tag{4}$$

For the case $j = t - 1$ we shall be satisfied with the inequality

$$a_1 \cup x_{t-1} \leqq a_1 \cup x_t (= x_t)$$

furnished by (3). Finally, consider the j's for which $0 \leqq j \leqq t - 2$. For these, by the meaning of t, $a \leqq a_1 \cap x_j < a_1$ and $a \leqq a_1 \cap x_{j+1} < < a_1$. On the other hand, $a \prec a_1$ and hence, in the present case,

$$a = a_1 \cap x_j \prec a_1 \text{ and } a = a_1 \cap x_{j+1} \prec a_1$$

From these two coverings we have by the lower covering condition and by (2)

$$x_j \prec a_1 \cup x_j \leqq a_1 \cup x_{j+1} \text{ and } x_j < x_{j+1} \prec a_1 \cup x_{j+1}$$

and by these two sequences of inequalities, $a_1 \cup x_j \neq a_1 \cup x_{j+1}$. However, again by (3),

$$a_1 \cup x_j < a_1 \cup x_{j+1} \quad \text{if} \quad 0 \leqq j \leqq t - 2 \tag{5}$$

By (4) and (5), the length of the chain (3) is at least $m - 1$, and hence, by the last sentence of the previous paragraph, $m - 1 \leqq \leqq n - 1$, that is, $m \leqq n$, completing the proof.

The first proposition of the corollary is a special case of the proposition of the theorem; the second proposition is implied by the fact that the way of constructing a dimension function described in Section 9 can be applied to the present case.

Independently from Szász and almost simultaneously, the theorem was also found by Croisot ([50], p. 88). For modular lattices, the theorem was already known to Dedekind ([39], Theorem XVI).

There arises the problem as to what more precise statements can be made concerning the maximal chains of $[a, b]$, if there is not even one finite maximal chain between a and b. In this field, only few results are known at present, and even these are of a rather negative nature. Thus it is known that in this case even distributivity is insufficient to guarantee that the maximal chains between a and b will be of the same power. (The postulation of this identity of powers would be one of the possible and natural strengthenings of the Jordan—Dedekind condition.) This statement will be illustrated by a very simple example (the example is due to Grätzer and Schmidt [78]; for the first example of this kind, see [191]).

Let V denote the chain of all real numbers, R the chain of all rational numbers with their natural ordering. Let us form the product set $V \times R$ and let us introduce in that set a meet and a join operation by the formulae (3), (4) of Section 19. It is not difficult to see that $V \times R$ is a distributive lattice with respect to these operations. Further, in $V \times R$, $(v_1, r_1) \leqq (v_2, r_2)$ $(v_1, v_2 \in V;\ r_1, r_2 \in R)$ if, and only if, $v_1 \leqq v_2$ in V and $r_1 \leqq r_2$ in R. Accordingly, the elements of the form

$$(x, x) \quad (0 \leqq x \leqq 1, x \in R) \tag{6}$$

form a maximal chain between the elements (0, 0) and (1, 1). In fact, if $y \neq z$, then there can be found an $x (\in R)$ such that either $y < x < z$ or $y < x < z$, (depending on whether $y < z$ or $y > z$) and in both cases $(y, z) \parallel (x, x)$. On the other hand, another maximal chain between (0, 0) and (1, 1) is formed by all elements of the form

$$(7) \qquad (0, x) \quad (0 \leqq x \leqq 1, x \in R) \text{ and } (y, 1) \quad (0 \leqq y \leqq 1, y \in V)$$

The chain (6) is countable, while (7) has the power of the continuum.

The lattice $V \times R$ is not complete. It is also possible to define a distributive complete lattice whose maximal chains do not have the same powers (Jakubík [99]; however, the discussion of this example would require more set-theoretical knowledge than is assumed in the present book). See also Jakubík [102].

A result of a positive nature is the following theorem of Grätzer and Schmidt [78]: If every maximal chain of the interval $[a, b]$ of a distributive lattice L is carried over by any homomorphism φ of L into some maximal chain of $(\varphi(a), \varphi(b))$, then the maximal chains between a and b have the same number of Dedekind cuts. (See also Vilhelm [208], Theorems 2 and 3).

By the Corollary of Theorem 41, a lattice of locally finite length satisfying one of the covering conditions has a dimension function. Concerning the dimension functions definable in lattices of this kind, we have

THEOREM 42. *Let L be a lattice of locally finite length. If L satisfies the lower covering condition, then for every dimension function definable in L there holds the inequality*

$$(8) \qquad d(a) + d(b) \geqq d(a \frown b) + d(a \smile b) \quad (a, b \in L)$$

On the other hand, if L satisfies the upper covering condition, then for every dimension function definable in L there holds the inequality

$$(9) \qquad d(a) + d(b) \leqq d(a \frown b) + d(a \smile b) \quad (a, b \in L)$$

COROLLARY. *If a lattice L of locally finite length satisfies the double covering condition, then for every dimension function definable in L there holds the equation*

$$(10) \qquad d(a) + d(b) = d(a \frown b) + d(a \smile b) \quad (a, b \in L)$$

Equation (10) will be called the *dimension equation.*

It will be seen in the next Section that all lattices conforming to the above corollary are modular.

The above statements are essentially due to Dedekind ([39], p. 399); in their present form they occur first in Birkhoff's paper [10] (as Theorem 9.2).

PROOF. Let L be a lattice of locally finite length satisfying the lower covering condition, and a, b any pair of elements of L. If a and b are comparable, the truth of (8) is obvious; it is therefore sufficient to investigate the case when $a \parallel b$. In this case, let us consider some maximal chain

$$(11) \qquad a \frown b = t_0 \prec t_1 \prec \dots \prec t_j \prec t_{j+1} \prec \dots \prec t_r = b$$

connecting the element $a \frown b$ with b (see Fig. 21). We shall show that

$$a \smile t_j \preceq a \smile t_{j+1} \quad (j = 0, 1, \ldots, r-1) \tag{12}$$

For this purpose, let us compare the elements $a \smile t_j$ and t_{j+1} for every index j. For these, $a \smile t_j \leqq t_{j+1}$ is impossible, since this would imply $a \leqq t_{j+1} \leqq b$; hence, either $a \smile t_j > t_{j+1}$ or $a \smile t_j \parallel t_{j+1}$. In the former case

$$a \smile t_j = (a \smile t_j) \smile t_{j+1} = \\ = a \smile (t_j \smile t_{j+1}) = a \smile t_{j+1}$$

In the latter case, however, $t_j \leqq (a \smile t_j) \frown t_{j+1} < t_{j+1}$; whence, by (11)

$$t_j = (a \smile t_j) \frown t_{j+1} \prec t_{j+1}$$

but then, by the lower covering condition,

$$a \smile t_j \prec (a \smile t_j) \smile t_{j+1} = a \smile t_{j+1}$$

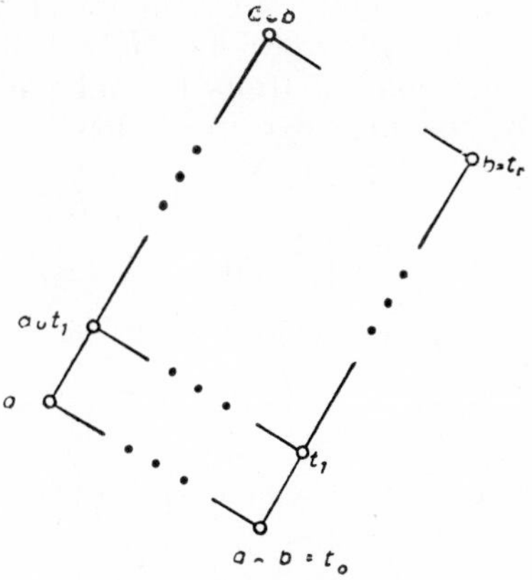

Fig. 21

Summing up the two cases, we obtain (12).

Hence, for every dimension function d of L

$$d(a \smile t_{j+1}) - d(a \smile t_j) \leqq 1 \quad (j = 0, 1, \ldots, r-1)$$

Then, by (11),

$$d(a \smile b) - d(a) = d(a \smile t_r) - d(a \smile t_0) = \\ = \sum_{j=0}^{r-1} \bigl(d(a \smile t_{j+1}) - d(a \smile t_j)\bigr) \leqq r = d(b) - d(a \frown b)$$

which yields by simple rearrangement the inequality (8).

If L satisfies the upper covering condition, the dualization of the above line of thought yields inequality (9).

In this way, the statement of the theorem is proved; the corollary is, however, a trivial consequence of the theorem.

38. Modular Lattices of Locally Finite Length

The results obtained in the previous chapter will now be applied to the case of modular lattices.

THEOREM 43. *For a lattice L of locally finite length the following four conditions are equivalent* (Birkhoff [10], Theorem 10.2):

(A) *L is modular;*

(B) *L satisfies the double covering condition;*

(C) *L satisfies the Jordan—Dedekind chain condition and, it is possible to define on it a dimension function d for which the dimension equation holds;*

(D) *Every sublattice of L satisfies the Jordan—Dedekind chain condition.*

PROOF. (A) *implies* (B) by Theorem 37.

(B) *implies* (C) by the Corollaries to Theorems 41 and 42.

(C) *implies* (A). Let d be a dimension function of L satisfying the dimension equation. Consider elements x, y, z of L for which $x \leqq z$. By the modular inequality,

$$(x \cup y) \cap z \geqq x \cup (y \cap z)$$

On the other hand,

$$d\big((x \cup y) \cap z\big) = d(x \cup y) + d(z) - d(x \cup y \cup z) =$$
$$= d(x) + d(y) - d(x \cap y) + d(z) - d(y \cup z)$$

and

$$d\big(x \cup (y \cap z)\big) = d(x) + d(y \cap z) - d(x \cap y \cap z) =$$
$$= d(x) + d(y) + d(z) - d(y \cup z) - d(x \cap y)$$

that is,

$$d\big((x \cup y) \cap z\big) = d\big(x \cup (y \cap z)\big)$$

Hence, $(x \cup y) \cap z$ cannot be greater than $x \cup (y \cap z)$. Consequently $(x \cup y) \cap z = x \cup (y \cap z)$, implying that L is modular.

By the above considerations, (A), (B) and (C) are equivalent.

(A) *is equivalent* to (D). If L is of locally finite length and modular, then, by definition, and by Theorem 31, every sublattice of it has the same properties. Thus by Theorem 37 and by the Corollary of Theorem 41 the Jordan—Dedekind chain condition holds in every sublattice of L. Conversely, if the lattice L is non-modular, it has, by Theorem 32, a sublattice isomorphic with the lattice shown as Fig. 17a (p. 90), in which the Jordan—Dedekind chain condition fails.

We call attention here to the result of Dilworth [48] as follows: In a modular lattice consisting of a finite number of elements the elements covering exactly k elements (k is any positive integer) are of the same number as the elements covered by exactly k elements.

39. The Valuation of a Lattice. Metric and Quasimetric Lattices

Let v be a function defined on a lattice L which assigns to each element of L either a real number or, eventually, one of the symbols $\pm\infty$. Such a v is called a *valuation* of L if for any pair of elements a, b of L

$$v(a) + v(b) = v(a \cap b) + v(a \cup b) \tag{1}$$

The valuation v is called *order preserving* if $a \leqq b$ implies $v(a) \leqq v(b)$, and *positive* if $a < b$ implies $v(a) < a(b)$.

Particularly, any dimension function of a modular lattice of locally finite length is a positive valuation of the lattice. Furthermore, every real-valued function of a chain is a valuation.

For relatively complemented lattices bounded below we have

THEOREM 44. *Let v be a real-valued function defined on a section complemented lattice bounded below. Whenever v satisfies the condition*

$$(2) \qquad a \frown b = o \Longrightarrow v(a \smile b) = v(a) + v(b) \quad (a, b \in L)$$

then v is a valuation of L and $v(o) = 0$.

PROOF. By taking $b = o$ in (2) we obtain $v(o) = 0$. We will show that if (2) is satisfied, then (1) holds for every pair of elements of L. Consider an arbitrary pair of elements a, b of L and let t be a relative complement of $a \frown b$ in $[o, b]$. Then, by definition,

$$(a \frown b) \frown t = o \text{ and } (a \frown b) \smile t = b$$

and thus, by (2),

$$(3) \qquad v(b) = v(a \frown b) + v(t)$$

Furthermore, since $t \leqq b$,

$$a \frown t = a \frown (b \frown t) = (a \frown b) \frown t = o$$

and by the definition of t,

$$a \smile t = \big(a \smile (a \frown b)\big) \smile t = a \smile \big((a \frown b) \smile t\big) = a \smile b$$

From these two equations, again by (2),

$$(4) \qquad v(a \smile b) = v(a) + v(t)$$

Subtracting (3) from (4) and rearranging we obtain (1).

A lattice L, on which a positive valuation is defined, is called a *metric lattice* (with respect to that valuation). More generally, L is said to be *quasimetric* if an order preserving valuation is defined on L. We shall deal with these classes of lattice in greater detail.

THEOREM 45. *Every metric lattice is modular.*

PROOF. The part of the proof of Theorem 43 dealing with the statement (C) implies (A) utilizes from the properties of d only the property that d is a positive valuation on the lattice considered. Hence, the line of thought followed there can be repeated word for word for any positive valuation v.

The following theorem deals with the criteria for distributivity of metric lattices.

THEOREM 46. *If L is a metric lattice with respect to the valuation v, then the following identities are equivalent in L:*

(5) $$a \cup (b \cap c) = (a \cup b) \cap (a \cup c) \qquad (a, b, c \in L)$$

(6) $$v(a \cup (b \cap c)) = v((a \cup b) \cap (a \cup c)) \qquad (a, b, c \in L)$$

(7) $$v(a \cup b \cup c) - v(a \cap b \cap c) = v(a \cup b) + v(b \cup c) + v(c \cup a) - v(a) - v(b) - v(c) \qquad (a, b, c \in L)$$

(8) $$v(a \cup b \cup c) - v(a \cap b \cap c) = v(a) + v(b) + v(c) - v(a \cap b) - v(b \cap c) - v(c \cap a) \qquad (a, b, c \in L)$$

(9) $$2v(a \cup b \cup c) - 2v(a \cap b \cap c) = v(a \cup b) + v(b \cup c) + v(c \cup a) - v(a \cap b) - v(b \cap c) - v(c \cap a) \qquad (a, b, c \in L)$$

Hence, L is distributive if, and only if, one of (7)—(9) *is satisfied by* v.

Accordingly, valuations satisfying the conditions (7)—(9) are usually called *distributive valuations.*

PROOF. We shall show that

$$(5) \Longrightarrow (9) \Longrightarrow (8) \Longrightarrow (7) \Longrightarrow (6) \Longrightarrow (5)$$

(5) *implies* (9). If (5) is satisfied, then (by Theorem 28) L is distributive. Hence, applying (1) repeatedly, we obtain

$$\begin{aligned} v(a \cup (b \cup c)) - v(a \cap (b \cap c)) &= v(a) + v(b \cup c) - \\ - v(a \cap (b \cup c)) - v(a) - v(b \cap c) + v(a \cup (b \cap c)) &= \\ = v(b \cup c) - v((a \cap b) \cup (a \cap c)) - v(b \cap c) &+ \\ + v((a \cup b) \cap (a \cup c)) = v(b \cup c) - v(a \cap b) - v(a \cap c) &+ \\ + v(a \cap b \cap c) - v(b \cap c) + v(a \cup b) + v(a \cup c) - v(a \cup b \cup c) \end{aligned}$$

yielding (9) on rearrangement.

(9) *implies* (8). On the right side of (9), by performing the substitution $v(a \cup b) = v(a) + v(b) - v(a \cap b)$ justified by (1) as well as similar substitutions concerning the pairs b, c and a, c and then dividing by 2, we obtain (8).

(8) *implies* (7). By performing on the right side of (8) the substitution $- v(a \cap b) = v(a \cup b) - v(a) - v(b)$ justified by (1) and the similar substitutions concerning the pairs b, c and a, c, we obtain (7).

(7) *implies* (6), since by applying (1) repeatedly and (7) once (in the third step)

$$\begin{aligned} v(a \cup (b \cap c)) &= v(a) + v(b \cap c) - v(a \cap b \cap c) = \\ &= v(a) + v(b) + v(c) - v(b \cup c) - v(a \cap b \cap c) = \\ &= v(a) + v(b) + v(c) - v(b \cup c) + v(a \cup b) + v(b \cup c) + \\ &+ v(c \cup a) - v(a) - v(b) - v(c) - v(a \cup b \cup c) = \\ &= v(a \cup b) + v(a \cup c) - v((a \cup b) \cup (a \cup c)) = \\ &= v((a \cup b) \cap (a \cup c)) \end{aligned}$$

(6) *implies* (5). By the distributive inequalities, $a \cup (b \cap c) \leqq \leqq (a \cup b) \cap (a \cup c)$ is necessarily true, but if (6) is satisfied, then $a \cup (b \cap c) < (a \cup b) \cap (a \cup c)$ is impossible, v being a positive valuation.

We have thus proved the equivalence of the identities (5)—(9). The statement of the final sentence of the theorem now becomes trivial.

Trevisan [202] and Hashimoto [88] have shown independently from one another that a lattice L is distributive if, and only if, for any pair of elements x, y $(x < y)$ of L one can construct a distributive valuation v for which $v(x) < < v(y)$. See further Vaida [205].

On a set S let a real-valued function f of two variables be defined. We say that S is a *quasimetric space* with respect to the function f if the three conditions below hold:

Q_1. *$f(x, x) = 0$ for every $x \in S$*
Q_2. *$f(x, y) = f(y, x)$ for every $x, y \in S$*
Q_3. *$f(x, y) + f(y, x) \geqq f(x, z)$ for every $x, y, z \in S$*
S is called a *metric space* with respect to f if besides $Q_1 - Q_3$ also the condition
Q_4. *$f(x, y) = 0$ implies $x = y$ for every $x, y \in S$*
is satisfied.

THEOREM 47. *Every (quasi)metric lattice is a (quasi)metric space with respect to the function*

$$\delta(x, y) = v(x \cup y) - v(x \cap y)$$

where v denotes the valuation of the lattice as it has been taken into consideration.

PROOF. Q_1 and Q_2 hold trivially for $f = \delta$. We will prove that for an isotonic v, Q_3 also holds.

Let us introduce for sake of brevity the notation

$$s(x, y, z) = \frac{1}{2}\big(\delta(x, y) + \delta(y, z) - \delta(x, z)\big)$$

In case of an arbitrary v, applying first the definition of δ, then the equality $v(x \cup y) = v(x) + v(y) - v(x \cap y)$ as well as the similar equalities with respect to the pairs y, z and x, z, respectively, we get the following:

$$s(x, y, z) = \big(v(y) + v(x \cap z)\big) - \big(v(x \cap y) + v(z \cap y)\big)$$

Hence, owing to (1)

$$\begin{aligned} s(x, y, z) &= \big(v(y) \cup (x \cap z)\big) + v\big(x \cap y \cap z)\big) - \\ &\quad - v\big((x \cap y) \cup (z \cap y)\big) + v(x \cap y \cap z)\big) = \\ &= v\big(y \cup (x \cap z)\big) - v\big((x \cap y) \cup (z \cap y)\big) \end{aligned}$$

Since $y \cup (x \cap z) \geqq y \geqq (x \cap y) \cup (z \cap y)$, we have for an isotonic v

$$v(y \cup (x \cap z)) \geqq v((x \cap y) \cup (z \cap y))$$

i.e. $s(x, y, z) \geqq 0$.

Finally, if the valuation v is positive, then (with regard to the Corollary of Theorem 5) we have

$$x \neq y \Longrightarrow x \cup y > x \cap y \Longrightarrow v(x \cup y) > v(x \cap y) \Longrightarrow \delta(x, y) > 0$$

i.e. in this case Q_4 also holds.

40. Complemented Modular Lattices

THEOREM 48. *Every complemented lattice is relatively complemented* (Neumann [147], p. 5).

SUPPLEMENT. *More generally, if a, b, r are elements of a bounded modular lattice such that $a \leqq r \leqq b$, and if t is complement of r, then the element*

$$s = (a \cup t) \cap b = a \cup (t \cap b) \tag{1}$$

is a relative complement of r in $[a, b]$.

PROOF. Clearly, it is sufficient to prove the supplement to the theorem. This is done by direct calculation. Provided the mentioned assumptions are satisfied,

$$r \cap s = (a \cup t) \cap b \cap r = (a \cup t) \cap r = a \cup (t \cap r) = a \cup o = a$$

$$r \cup s = r \cup a \cup (t \cap b) = r \cup (t \cap b) = (r \cup t) \cap b = i \cap b = b$$

A proposition which can be regarded as the converse of the supplement is

THEOREM 49. *If a, b, r are elements of a bounded relatively complemented lattice such that $a \leqq r \leqq b$, then it is possible to find for any relative complement s of r in $[a, b]$ a complement t of r satisfying equation* (1) (Szász [192]).

PROOF. Let y be some relative complement of a in $[o, s]$, z a relative complement of b in $[s, i]$ and t a relative complement of s in $[y, z]$ (see Fig. 22). Then, by the definition of the relative complement, we have the following:

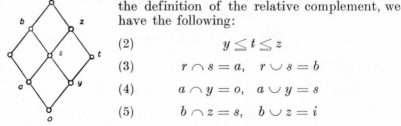

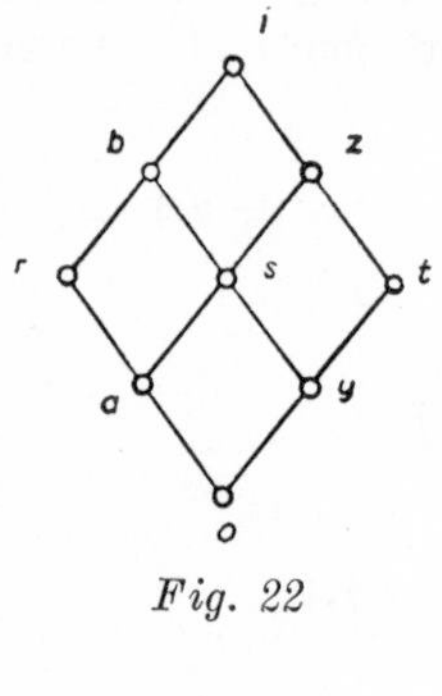

Fig. 22

$$y \leqq t \leqq z \tag{2}$$

$$r \cap s = a, \quad r \cup s = b \tag{3}$$

$$a \cap y = o, \quad a \cup y = s \tag{4}$$

$$b \cap z = s, \quad b \cup z = i \tag{5}$$

$$s \cap t = y, \quad s \cup t = z \tag{6}$$

Utilizing these, we will first show that t is a complement of r. Indeed, since by the assumption $r = r \cap b$, we obtain by applying (2), (5), (3), (6) and (4) one by one

$$r \cap t = (r \cap b) \cap (z \cap t) = r \cap (b \cap z) \cap t =$$
$$= r \cap s \cap t = (r \cap s) \cap (s \cap t) = a \cap y = o$$

and, by dualizing the calculation, $r \cup t = i$.

Furthermore, t also satisfies equation (1). That is, by applying (2), (4), (6) and (5) one by one,

$$(a \cup t) \cap b = (a \cup (y \cup t)) \cap b =$$
$$= \big((a \cup y) \cup t\big) \cap b = (s \cup t) \cap b = z \cap b = s$$

and similarly, $a \cup (t \cap b) = s$, which completes the proof.

THEOREM 50. *If a modular lattice is section complemented, then it is also relatively complemented.*

PROOF. Let L be a section complemented modular lattice and $r \in [a, b] \subseteq L$. Then L has a least element o and the interval $[o, b]$ is, by our assumption, a complemented modular sublattice of L. Then, by Theorem 48, $[o, b]$ is also relatively complemented. Consequently, as $[a, b] \subseteq [o, b]$, the element r has a relative complement in $[a, b]$ as asserted.

A further interesting consequence of Theorem 49 is

THEOREM 51. *Every uniquely complemented modular lattice is distributive.*

PROOF. Let a, r, b be arbitrary elements of a complemented modular lattice L such that $a \leq r \leq b$. By Theorem 48, the statement of Theorem 49 may be applied to any complemented modular lattice. Hence, every relative complement of the element r in $[a, b]$ can be represented in the form $s = (a \cup t) \cap b$, where t denotes some complement of r. Consequently if L is moreover uniquely complemented, every one of its elements r has in any interval containing it at most one relative complement, and hence, by Theorem 33, L is distributive.

This simple proof of the theorem is due to Szász [194]. For an earlier proof see [19], p. 171, Exercise 2.

41. Complemented Modular Lattices and Projective Spaces

In this section we shall make use of the concepts, notations and results obtained in Example 16.

An incidence space is called a *projective space*, if the following axioms, $\mathsf{P}_1 - \mathsf{P}_3$, hold in it:

P_1. *On every line there are at least two points.*

P_2. *Two different points are situated on one, and only one, common line.*

P_3. *If, of the points α, β, γ, α', β', the triplet α, β', γ is collinear on the one hand and the triplet α', β, γ on the other then there exists a point γ' such that α, β, γ' on the one hand and α', β', γ' on on the other are likewise collinear.* (This axiom is illustrated in Fig. 23.)

If a linear space satisfies the axioms P_2 and P_3 only, it is called a *generalized projective space.*

Let P be a generalized projective space and α, β different points of P; then, by Axiom P_2, it is legitimate to speak of "the line defined by the pair of points α, β". This line will be denoted $\alpha\beta$. Clearly, $\alpha, \beta \in [\alpha\beta]$. By Axiom P_1, any line $\mathfrak{g}$ of a projective space P can be given in the form $\mathfrak{g} = \mu\nu$ ($\mu, \nu \in P$; $\mu \neq \nu$).

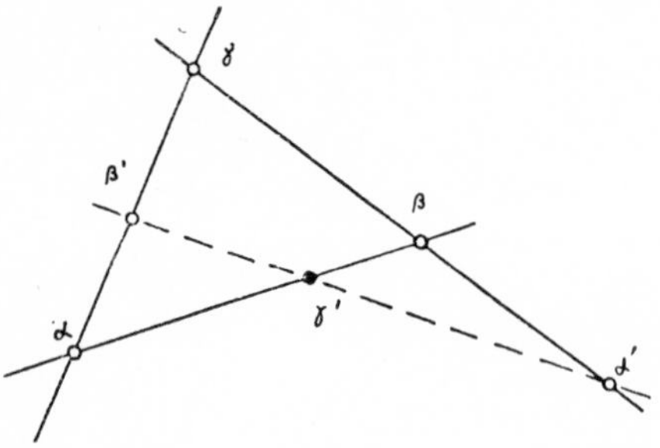

Fig. 23

In the first part of this section, let us discuss the set of all linear subspaces of generalized projective spaces.

LEMMA. *The set $\mathscr{L}(P)$ of all linear subspaces of a generalized projective space P is partly ordered by set-inclusion. With respect to this ordering $\mathscr{L}(P)$ is an atomic complete lattice, in which the meet of the elements coincides with its set intersection. The join in $\mathscr{L}(P)$ can be described as follows: Disregarding the trivial cases when the right side of equation* (1) *below makes no sense, there holds in the lattice $\mathscr{L}(P)$*

$$a \cup b = \bigcup_{\substack{\alpha\in a;\ \beta\in b\\ \alpha\neq\beta}} [\alpha\beta] \tag{1}$$

(Frink [68], Theorem 3).

Formula (1) can be verbally expressed as follows: $a \cup b$ consists of the points $\xi (\in P)$ to which there can be found points α, β ($\alpha \neq \beta$) such that $\alpha \in a$, $\beta \in b$ and $\xi \in [\alpha\beta]$.

The exceptional cases are the following: 1. $a = 0$; 2. $b = 0$; 3. $a = b = \{\pi\}$, where π is some point of P. The meaning of $a \cup b$ is clear in all three cases.

Let us now prove the lemma. The propositions contained in the first and second sentence of the lemma were proved for every linear space in the discussion of Example 16. Accordingly, only Formula (1) remains to be proved.

Let us denote for brevity the right side of (1) by u. We have to prove that

(A) u is a linear subspace,
(B) $a, b \subseteq u$;
(C) if c is a linear subspace and $c \supseteq a, b$, then $c \supseteq u$.

To begin with the simpler statements (B) and (C) will be discussed.

PROOF OF (B). It is sufficient to show that $a \subseteq u$ (since the statement $b \subseteq u$ can be proved along the same lines). Disregarding the case $a \supset b = \{\pi\}$ $(\pi \in P)$ there can be found to every point α of a a $\beta\,(\in b)$ such that $\alpha \neq \beta$. But then, by Axiom P_2, α and β define a line $\alpha\beta$ and $\alpha \in [\alpha\beta] \subseteq u$. Hence, $a \subseteq u$.

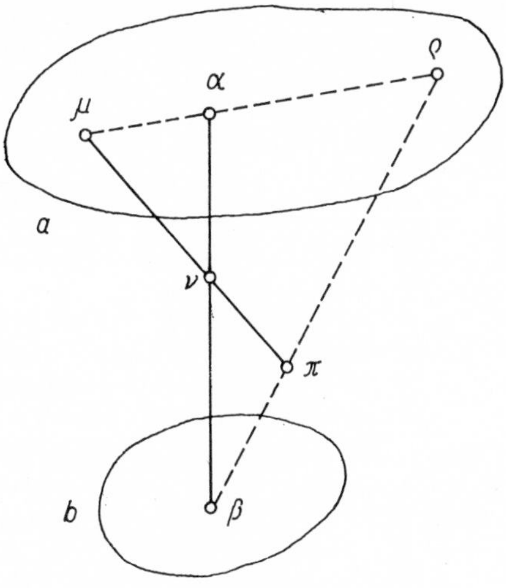

Fig. 24/a

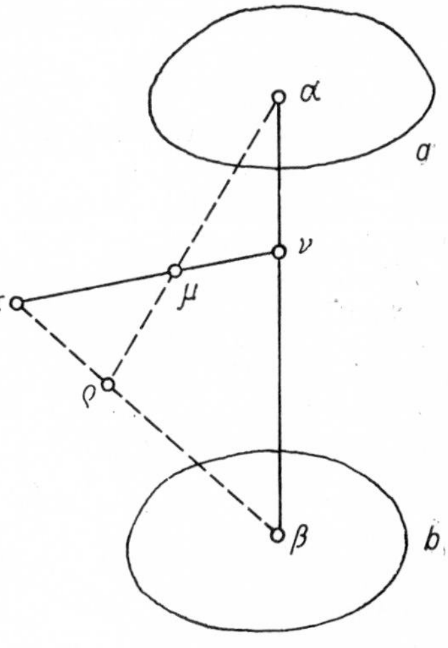

Fig. 24/b

In the exceptional case mentioned, the above consideration only yields $a - \{\pi\} \subseteq u$. However, now a certainly includes an α' differing from π and $\pi \in [\alpha' \pi]$ $(\alpha' \in a; \pi \in b)$; hence, $\pi \in u$.

PROOF OF (C). If c is a linear subspace, and $c \supseteq a, b$, then c includes all sets of points of the form $[\alpha\beta]$ $(\alpha \in a,\ \beta \in b;\ \alpha \neq \beta)$ and hence it includes u as well.

PROOF OF (A). It has to be shown that $\mu, \nu \in u$, $\mu \neq \nu$ and $\pi \in [\mu\nu]$ imply $\pi \in u$. Depending on the relative position of μ and ν, several cases can be distinguished.

Case 1. $\mu, \nu \in a$ or $\mu, \nu \in b$. Then, by the statement (B) just proved, $\pi \in u$.

Case 2. $\mu \in a$, $\nu \in b$ or $\mu \in b$, $\nu \in a$. Then, $\pi \in u$ by the definition of u.

Case 3. $\mu \in a \cup b$, $\nu \notin a \cup b$; by the symmetrical role of a and b it can be assumed without loss of generality that, exactly, $\mu \in a$. Since $\nu \in u$, there exists a pair of points α, β $(\alpha \neq \beta)$ such that $\alpha \in a$, $\beta \in b$ and $\nu \in [\alpha\beta]$ (see Fig. 24a). Thus, in the present case,

μ, π, ν and β, α, ν are collinear triplets of points. Hence, by Axiom P_3, a point ϱ exists such that the triplets of points β, π, ϱ and μ, α, ϱ are also collinear; by the latter, $\varrho \in a$. But $\varrho \neq \beta$ (since otherwise we should have $\nu \in a$, in contradiction to the assumption $\nu \notin a \cup b$) Thus ϱ and β define a line $\varrho\beta$, and $\pi \in [\varrho\beta]$, $\varrho \in a$, $\beta \in b$. Hence, in this case, too, $\pi \in u$.

Case 4. $\mu \notin a \cup b$, $\nu \in a \cup b$. This case can be discussed just as in Case 3.

Case 5. μ, $\nu \notin a \cup b$. Just as in Case 3 there can be found points α, β, ϱ ($\alpha \neq \beta$) such that $\nu \in [\alpha\beta]$ ($\alpha \in a, \beta \in b$), and the points μ, α, ϱ and β, π, ϱ are respectively collinear (see Fig. 24b). For the former triplet, Case 3 prevails, that is, $\varrho \in u$. If now $\beta \neq \varrho$, then for the latter triplet of points Case 4 prevails, and hence $\pi \in u$; if, on the other hand, $\beta = \varrho$, then μ, $\nu \in [\alpha\beta]$ and thus, by Axiom P_2, $\pi \in [\mu\nu] = [\alpha\beta] \subseteq u$, completing the proof of the lemma.

We now give the proof of the following theorem:

THEOREM 52. *All linear subspaces of a generalized projective space form a complete lattice with respect to the set inclusion. This lattice is atomic, complemented and modular, and if $\{y_\delta\}$ is an up-directed subset of this lattice, then for every element x of the lattice there holds*

(2)
$$x \frown \bigcup_{\delta} y_\delta = \bigcup_{\delta} (x \frown y_\delta)$$

(Frink [68], Theorems 2 and 5).

PROOF. Part of the statement of the theorem is already contained by the foregoing lemma. Let P be, for the moment an arbitrary incidence space and $\{y_\delta\}_{\delta \in \Delta}$ be an up-directed subset of the subspace lattice $\mathscr{L}(P)$ of P. We will show that

(3)
$$\bigcup_{\delta \in \Delta} y_\delta = \bigcup_{\delta \in \Delta} y_\delta$$

To do this, it is sufficient to show that the right side of (3) — denoted for short by y in the following — is included in $\mathscr{L}(P)$.

Consider an arbitrary pair of elements μ, ν ($\mu \neq \nu$) of y. By the definition of y, there exists a y_{δ_1} and a y_{δ_2} (δ_1, $\delta_2 \in \Delta$) such that $\mu \in y_{\delta_1}$, $\nu \in y_{\delta_2}$. Since $\{y_\delta\}_{\delta \in \Delta}$ is an up-directed set, there exists a y_{δ_0} ($\delta_0 \in \Delta$) such that y_{δ_1}, $y_{\delta_2} \subseteq y_{\delta_0}$. However, then μ, $\nu \in y_{\delta_0}$. Consequently, if, $\pi \in [\mu, \nu]$, then $\pi \in y_{\delta_0} \subseteq y$ and hence y is a linear subspace.

Since together with $\{y_\delta\}$, $\{x \frown y_\delta\}$ is also up-directed, (3) retains its validity on replacing y_δ by $x \frown y_\delta$. Hence, (2) is equivalent to the equation

(4)
$$x \cap (\bigcup_{\delta} y_\delta) = \bigcup_{\delta} (x \cap y_\delta)$$

However, x and the y_δ can be considered as elements of the subset lattice of P and hence, by the lemma proved in Section 31, (4) holds.

In the rest of this proof we suppose P to be a generalized projective space. We shall prove that the subspace lattice $\mathscr{L}(P)$ is modular. Let a, b, c be linear subspaces of P satisfying $a \leq c$. If $a = O$, or $b = O$, or $a = b$, then the equality $(a \cup b) \cap c = a \cup (b \cap c)$ is obviously true. Consider the remaining cases. Take an arbitrary point γ of the linear subspace $(a \cup b) \cap c$. By the lemma, there exists a pair of points α, β such that $\alpha \in a(\subseteq c)$ and $\beta \in b$, $\alpha \neq \beta$ with α, β, γ collinear. If now $\gamma = \alpha$ then, trivially, $\gamma \in a \subseteq a \cup (b \cap c)$. If on the other hand $\gamma \neq \alpha$, then the line $\alpha\gamma$ is uniquely determined and $\beta \in [\alpha\gamma] \subseteq c$. Hence, $\beta \in b \cap c$ and thus, by $\gamma \in [\alpha\beta]$, again $\gamma \in a \cup (b \cap c)$. Hence, $(a \cup b) \cap c \subseteq a \cup (b \cap c)$ and by the modular inequality the reverse inclusion also holds.

We shall finally show that $\mathscr{L}(P)$ is complemented. Let a be an arbitrary inner element of $\mathscr{L}(P)$ and X the set of the proper semicomplements of a. The set X is non-void, since in P there exists (at least) one point π not incuded in a and for this π, $a \cap \{\pi\} = a \cap \{\pi\} = O$. Furthermore, if $C = \{c_\gamma\}$ is an arbitrary subchain of X, then $\bigcup_j c_\gamma$ is an upper bound of C and $\bigcup c_\gamma \in X$, since by (2), $a \cap \bigcup_\gamma c_\gamma = \bigcup_\gamma (a \cap c_\gamma) = \bigcup_\gamma O = O$. Consequently, by the Kuratowski—Zorn lemma, X has at least one maximal element. In other words every inner element of $\mathscr{L}$(P) has a maximal proper semicomplement. Hence, by Corollary 1 of Theorem 79 (to be proved later) $\mathscr{L}(P)$ is complemented. Thus Theorem 52 is proved.

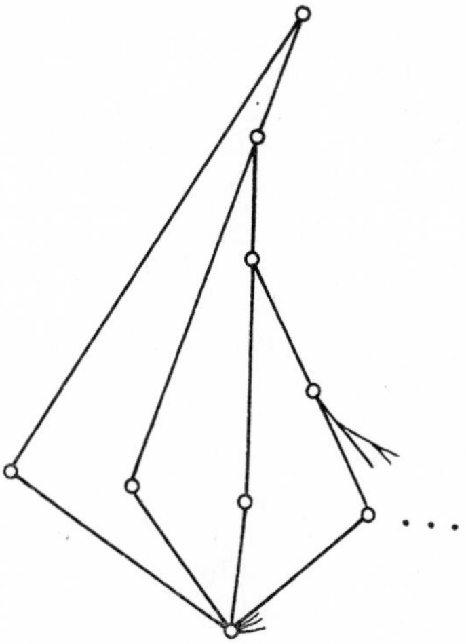

Fig. 25

Because of this Theorem we introduce the following definition: A projective space P is called of *finite* or *infinite dimensions* according as the subspace lattice of P is of finite or infinite length.

To formulate the converse of the problem just discussed, let us now start from a lattice L bounded below and let us form from it a linear space in the following way: Let the atoms (that is, the elements of height 1) of L be the points, and the elements of height 2 the lines of the space; finally, let the ordering relation of the lattice L serve as the relation of incidence. (Accordingly there is at least one point on every line, but there may exist points which are not incident on any line.) Let us denote the incidence space thus obtained by $\mathscr{T}(L)$.

Of course, it can happen that $\mathscr{T}(L)$ contains no point; this is the case for every lattice having no atoms.

Furthermore, consider the lattice illustrated by the generalized diagram of Fig. 25. Starting from it and forming the corresponding incidence space, we get one having points but no line.

THEOREM 53. *If a lattice L bounded below is modular, then the linear space $\mathcal{T}(L)$ formed from it is a generalized projective space; and if, moreover, L is also complemented, then $\mathcal{T}(L)$ is a projective space.*

This Theorem is equivalent to Theorem 13 of Frink [68].

PROOF. Let L be a modular lattice bounded below. If $\mathcal{T}(L)$ contains one point only, P_2 makes no sense and P_3 is satisfied trivially. Accordingly, in the following we will assume that $\mathcal{T}(L)$ contains at least two points (that is, L has at least two atoms).

Just as in Section 9, let us denote the height of an arbitrary element x of L by $h(x)$. If p and q are atoms of L and $p \neq q$, then $p \cap q = o \prec p, q$ and thus, by the lower covering condition, $p, q \succ p \cup q$. Hence, $h(p \cup q) = 2$ (since in a modular lattice, the Jordan—Dedekind chain condition holds), and thus, by definition, $p \cup q$ is a line of the space $\mathcal{T}(L)$. Since $p, q \leq p \cup q$, we have found that for any two distinct points of $\mathcal{T}(L)$ there can be found a line including both of them. However, there is only one such line, since if e is a line of $\mathcal{T}(L)$ such that $e \geq p, q$, then $e \geq p \cup q$ and $h(e) = 2 = h(p \cup q)$, that is, $e = p \cup q$. Hence, Axiom P_2 holds on $\mathcal{T}(L)$.

It is also evident that

P_4. *Every point is incident on at least, one line,* Since by our assumption to any point p of $\mathcal{T}(L)$ there exists a point q such that $q \neq p$.

Consider now the points $p, q, r, \bar{p}, \bar{q}$ of $\mathcal{T}(L)$ to which there can be found lines f, g such that $\bar{p}, \bar{q}$ and r are on f, while p, q and r are on g. We shall show that $\mathcal{T}(L)$ has a point $\bar{r}$ such that both $p, q, \bar{r}$ and $\bar{p}, \bar{q}, \bar{r}$ are collinear.

If $p = q$, then the choice $\bar{r} = \bar{q}$ is satisfactory, since then, in the triplets $p, q, \bar{r}$ and $\bar{p}, \bar{q}, \bar{r}$, two of the points or all three are coincident, and in the first case P_2, in the second, P_4 can be applied. With $\bar{p} = \bar{q}$, the case is similar. Hence, only the case $p \neq q$, $\bar{p} \neq \bar{q}$ is left. We will show that in this case $h\big((p \cup q) \cap (\bar{p} \cup \bar{q})\big) \geq 1$, that is, that the lines $p \cup q$ and $\bar{p} \cup \bar{q}$ have at least one point in common, which can be taken as $\bar{r}$.

Since all three of the points $\bar{p}$, q and r are incident on the line f, so $h(\bar{p} \cup q \cup r) \leq h(f) = 2$. Similarly, $h(p \cup \bar{q} \cup r) \leq 2$. Hence, by the Corollary to Theorem 42,* we obtain

$$\begin{aligned} h\big((p \cup q) \cap (\bar{p} \cup \bar{q})\big) &= h(p \cup q) + h(\bar{p} \cup \bar{q}) - h(p \cup q \cup \bar{p} \cup \bar{q}) \geq \\ &\geq 2 + 2 - h\big((\bar{p} \cup q \cup r) \cup (p \cup \bar{q} \cup r)\big) = \\ &= 4 - h(\bar{p} \cup q \cup r) - h(p \cup \bar{q} \cup r) + \\ &+ h\big((\bar{p} \cup q \cup r) \cap (p \cup \bar{q} \cup r)\big) \geq 4 - 2 - 2 + h(r) = 1 \end{aligned}$$

completing the proof of the validity of P_3.

* We may apply this Corollary because the elements of finite height in L form, by the Corollary to Theorem 36, a sublattice of finite length.

In the remaining part of the proof, let us assume that L is also complemented. From the way of constructing $\mathcal{T}(L)$ it follows (as already pointed out above) that to every line there is at least one point p incident on e. However, by Theorem 48, L is also relatively complemented, and hence P has at least one relative complement q in $[o, e]$. Clearly $q \neq p$. Furthermore, $h(p \cup q) = h(e) = 2$, and hence, by the Corollary to Theorem 42,

$$h(q) = h(p \cup q) + h(p \cap q) - h(p) =$$

$$= h(e) + h(o) - h(p) = 2 + 0 - 1 = 1$$

Consequently, q is a point of $\mathcal{T}(L)$. Since $q < e$, now Axiom P_1 also holds.

It is apparent even by the foregoing that complemented modular lattices and projective spaces are related. We wish to emphasize that this relation is a very close one. To a lattice L, let us construct first the incidence space $\mathcal{T}(L)$, then the subspace lattice $\mathcal{L}(\mathcal{T}(L))$ of the linear space $\mathcal{T}(L)$. It can be shown that if L is an atomic, complemented, modular complete lattice, and (2) holds for every up-directed subset of L, then $\mathcal{L}(\mathcal{T}(L)) \approx L$.

Conversely, let us start with an incidence space P — the set of whose lines is denoted by $\mathfrak{G}$ — and let us first form the subspace lattice $\mathcal{L}(P)$ of P, then the corresponding incidence space $\mathcal{T}(\mathcal{L}(P))$. It can be shown that if P is a projective space, then so is $\mathcal{T}(\mathcal{L}(P))$ and both spaces are isomorphic in the following sense: there exists a one-to-one mapping φ which maps the points and the lines of P onto the points and the lines respectively of $\mathcal{T}(\mathcal{L}(P))$, and $\pi \in [\mathfrak{g}]$ $(\pi \in P;\ \mathfrak{g} \in \mathfrak{G}) \Longleftrightarrow \varphi(\pi) \in [\varphi(\mathfrak{g})]$.

The proof of these results is rather tedious, so we merely refer to § 15 of Hermes's book [91].

The lattice-theoretical study of projective spaces was begun by Birkhoff [14] and Menger [139]. The clarification of the connection between modular lattices and projective spaces is connected with the names of Prenowitz [162], Frink [68] and Mousinho [141]. Jónsson [103] discussed an interesting special problem.

For investigations of a similar nature on more general incidence spaces (among others, the affine spaces), we call attention to papers by Menger [139], Prenowitz [163], [164], Sasaki [171], [173] and Maeda [130].

One of the most important classes of projective spaces of infinite dimension is that of the *continuous geometries*. This concept was introduced by the Hungarian-born mathematician, János von Neumann, who also developed its theory. Unfortunately, lack of space prevents us from describing even so much as the foundation of the theory which has considerably developed since. The interested reader is refered, in addition to Neumann's own works [145]—[147], to Maeda's book [133] and to the descriptive paper by Halperin [85] and his paper in [165]. These last two also contain extensive bibliographies.

Exercises to Chapter V

1. Show that if d_1 and d_2 are both dimension functions of the same lattice L of locally finite length, then an integer c exists such that $d_1(x) = d_2(x) + c$ for any element x of L. Show further that on substituting L by a partly ordered set P (of locally finite length), the statement will not be true in general.

2. Prove that if a, b, c are elements of a modular lattice of locally finite length such that $a \leq b$, then the length of the interval $[a, b]$

is at least as great as that of the interval $[a \cap c, b \cap c]$ or of $[a \cup c, b \cup c]$.

3. Prove that some valuation v of a relatively complemented lattice bounded below is order preserving if, and only if, for every x, $v(x) \geqq v(o)$.

4. Prove that a lattice of locally finite length is modular if, and only if, it is metric.

5. Let L be a lattice bounded below, in which there exists to each pair p_j, p_k $(j \neq k)$ of atoms a further atom p_l such that $p_l \prec p_j \cup p_k$. Show that if v is any valuation of L, then the value of $v(p)$ is, for all atoms p the same.*

6. Show that if to every pair of elements x, y of a lattice satisfying the condition $x < y$, there exists a valuation v such that $v(x) < v(y)$, then the lattice is modular.

7. Let L be a metric lattice and let δ denote the function defined in Section 39 (in Theorem 47). Show that for any elements a, b, c of L, the equation $\delta(a, b) + \delta(b, c) = \delta(a, c)$ implies $b \in [a \cap c, a \cup c]$.

8. Prove that in a complemented modular lattice the join-irreducible elements are the atoms of the lattice and the least element o.

9. Show that for any triplet a, b, c of the elements of a complemented modular lattice the equations $a \cup c = i$ and $b \cap c = o$ can hold simultaneously only if either $b \parallel a$ or $b \leqq a$; show moreover, that in distributive lattices only the latter case is possible.

10. Let x, y, z, t be elements of a complemented modular lattice. Prove that if t is a complement of the element $x \cup y$, and z is either
(a) a relative complement of x in $[o, x \cup y]$, or
(b) a relative complement of $x \cap y$ in $[o, y]$,
then z is a complement of $x \cup t$.

11. Let a and b be elements of a complemented modular lattice such that $a \leqq b$. Show that some element c of the lattice is the relative complement of a in $[o, b]$ if, and only if, a has a complement a' such that $c = a' \cap b$.

12. Prove the following proposition: If to the elements r_1, and r_2 of a bounded relatively complemented lattice there can be found elements a, b such that $r_1, r_2 \in [a, b]$ and the elements r_1, r_2 have a common relative complement in $[a, b]$, then they have a common complement as well.

13. Show that if to some pair of elements a, b of a bounded relatively complemented lattice an element c exists such that $a \cap c = b \cap c$ and $a \cup c = b \cup c$, then a and b have a common complement.

14. Let L be a relatively complemented lattice and u, v elements of L such that $u < v$. Show that to any pair p, q $(p \neq q)$ of elements $[u, v]$ an element exists which is a relative complement of p and is not a relative complement of q in $[u, v]$.

* This statement and that of Exercise 12 of Chapter VII are special cases of very important theorems in the dimension theory of continuous geometries. For an elementary proof, see Szász [196].

15. Prove that a bounded relatively complemented lattice is modular if, and only if, it has no sublattice containing the bound elements of the lattice and would be isomorphic with the lattice shown in Fig. 17a (p. 90).*

16. Let a, b, c be arbitrary elements of a generalized projective space. Without making use of the modular inequality, show that $a \cup (b \cap c) \subseteq (a \cup b) \cap c$.

* See Szász [194]. Let us note that if the phrase "relatively complemented" is exchanged for "atomic", the statement of this exercise remains true. The latter theorem is due to McLaughlin and is a strengthening of an earlier theorem by Dilworth (see [138] and [41]).

CHAPTER VI

BOOLEAN ALGEBRAS

42. Boolean Algebras. De Morgan Formulae

It was stated in Section 30 that complemented distributive lattices are also called Boolean algebras. By Corollary 1 of Theorem 33 and by Theorem 48, *every Boolean algebra is a uniquely complemented and relatively complemented lattice.*

The conjecture that every uniquely complemented lattice is a Boolean algebra was considered to be true for quite a long time. This is indeed the case if some further conditions are imposed: for example, if the lattice is complete (Ogasawara—Sasaki [149]), or if the De Morgan formulae to be discussed below hold for it (see Birkhoff [19], p. 171, and also exercise 7), or if the lattice is modular (Theorem 51). In the general case, however, the conjecture has proved to be false. Dilworth succeeded in finding a procedure by which it is possible to construct for every lattice a uniquely complemented lattice including the given lattice as a sublattice (Dilworth [45]) and this result, by Theorem 29, refutes the conjecture.

Let us agree upon the following symbolism: If every element of a bounded lattice L has at most one complement, then the complement of x ($\in L$) — provided it exists — will be denoted by x'.

Owing to the fact (quoted above) that every Boolean algebra is a uniquely complemented lattice, the formation of the complements in Boolean algebra may be regarded as a (unitary) operation, consequently, Boolean algebras can be considered as three-operation algebras.

In accordance with this fact, it is usual to distinguish, in the case of Boolean algebras, between "sublattices" and "Boolean subalgebras"; that is, by a Boolean subalgebra of a Boolean algebra B, is usually meant a sublattice of B which is closed also with respect to complementation, that is, which includes together with every element its complement. In particular every Boolean subalgebra of a Boolean algebra B includes the bound elements of B.

Similarly, a homomorphism φ of a Boolean algebra is called a *Boolean homomorphism* if

$$(\varphi(a))' = \varphi(a')$$

for each a.

A good explanation of the theory of Boolean algebras and of their many-sided applications is given by Sikorski [179].

The following very useful theorem deals with the complemented elements of bounded distributive lattices.

THEOREM 54. *If the elements a and b of a bounded distributive lattice have complements, then so have the elements $a \frown b$, and $a \smile b$:*

$$(1) \qquad (a \frown b)' = a' \smile b', \ (a \smile b)' = a' \frown b'$$

COROLLARY 1. *The complemented elements of a bounded distributive lattice form a sublattice.*

COROLLARY 2. *If the elements a and b of a bounded distributive lattice are complemented and $a \leqq b$, then $a' \geqq b'$.*

The formulae (1) are called the *De Morgan formulae.*

These formulae were known long ago; in [156], Peirce refers to the work "On the syllogism" by De Morgan, published in 1858.

PROOF. The theorem is proved by direct calculation:

$$(a \frown b) \frown (a' \smile b') = \big((a \frown b) \frown a'\big) \smile \big((a \frown b) \frown b'\big) =$$
$$= (a \frown a' \frown b) \smile (a \frown b \frown b') = o \smile o = o$$
$$(a' \smile b') \smile (a \frown b) = \big((a' \smile b') \smile a\big) \frown \big((a' \smile b') \smile b\big) =$$
$$= (a' \smile a \smile b') \frown (a' \smile b' \smile b) = i \frown i = i$$

and dually for $a \smile b$.

Corollary 1 is trivial. Corollary 2 is obtained as follows: If the elements a and b of a distributive lattice are complemented, and $a \leqq b$, then by (1), $a' = (a \frown b)' = a' \smile b'$.

It is known from the supplement to Theorem 9 that any one of the two operations of a lattice uniquely determines the other one. In the case of a Boolean algebra the connection between the two operations can also be formulated with the aid of the complements. Namely, by the De Morgan formulae, for any elements a, b of a Boolean algebra,

$$(2) \qquad a \frown b = (a' \smile b')', \quad a \smile b = (a' \frown b')'$$

The formulae (2) suggest the intrinsic possibility of defining Boolean algebras by axioms concerning the meet or join and complementation alone. This idea has been developed in papers by Huntington [94] and Byrne [24].

Incidentally, a great number of axiomatizations of Boolean algebras, independent of lattice theory, are known. Concerning literature on this point prior to 1933 see the list of references of [94]; of the literature since that date, let us refer without any attempt at comprehensiveness to Stone [185], Frink [66], Grau [77], Sholander [176], [177] and Byrne [25]. Diamond and McKinsey [40] have obtained the significant result that every system of axioms of Boolean algebras must include an axiom containing a proposition on triplets of elements.

The following result by Takeuchi [198] is of interest: every proper sublattice of a Boolean algebra can be extended into a maximal proper sublattice of the lattice by the adjoining of certain elements. Hashimoto ([89], Theorem 9.4) has shown this statement to hold for relatively complemented distributive lattices as well. For any distributive lattice, however, as revealed by Takeuchi's counterexample, no similar statement holds in general.

43. Complete Boolean Algebras

It was seen in Section 31 that there are distributive complete lattices which fail to be infinitely distributive. However, in complete Boolean algebras, there holds

THEOREM 55. *Every complete Boolean algebra is infinitely distributive* (Neumann [147], III, p. 7, Theorem A. 2).

PROOF. Let $R = \{y_\gamma\}_{\gamma \in \Gamma}$ be some subset of the complete Boolean algebra B, and y_a an arbitrary fixed element of R. Then, for every element x of B,

$$x \cap y_a \leqq \bigcup_{\gamma \in \Gamma} (x \cap y_\gamma)$$

and, by distributivity,

$$y_a \leqq i \cap (x' \cup y_a) = (x' \cup x) \cap (x' \cup y_a) = x' \cup (x \cap y_a)$$

These two inequalities imply

$$y_a \leqq x' \cup \bigcup_{\gamma \in \Gamma} (x \cap y_\gamma)$$

Now let a also run through Γ; by the completeness of B, $\bigcup_{a \in \Gamma} y_a$ exists and clearly

$$\bigcup_{a \in \Gamma} y_a \leqq x' \cup \bigcup_{\gamma \in \Gamma} (x \cap y_\gamma)$$

Forming the meet with x on both sides of the inequality, and substituting the index γ for a on the left side, we have by distributivity

$$x \cap \bigcup_{\gamma \in \Gamma} y_\gamma \leqq x \cap \big(x' \cup \bigcup_{\gamma \in \Gamma} (x \cap y_\gamma)\big) = (x \cap x') \cup \big(x \cap \bigcup_{\gamma \in \Gamma} (x \cap y_\gamma)\big)$$

and hence

$$x \cap \bigcup_{\gamma \in \Gamma} y_\gamma \leqq \bigcup_{\gamma \in \Gamma} (x \cap y_\gamma) \tag{1}$$

Conversely, by (1) of Section 22, in every complete lattice

$$\bigcup_{\gamma \in \Gamma} (x \cap y_\gamma) \leqq \bigcup_{\gamma \in \Gamma} y_\gamma$$

and

$$\bigcup_{\gamma \in \Gamma} (x \cap y_\gamma) \leqq x$$

and hence

$$\bigcup_{\gamma \in \Gamma} (x \cap y_\gamma) \leqq x \cap \bigcup_{\gamma \in \Gamma} y_\gamma \tag{2}$$

(1) and (2) imply that B is infinitely meet-distributive. By dualizing the proof, B is found to be infinitely join-distributive too.

Applying the above reasoning to the sublattice $\langle x, y_\gamma \rangle_{\gamma \in \Gamma}$ we obtain that *every relatively complemented distributive lattice is infinitely distributive.*

Further it follows from the theorem that a lattice can be completely isomorphic to a sublattice of a Boolean algebra only if it is infinitely distributive. Funayama's [75] result indicates that this necessary condition is sufficient as well.

Now let us consider the problem as to when a complete Boolean algebra is completely distributive.

THEOREM 56. *For a complete Boolean algebra B, the following conditions are equivalent:*

(A) *B is completely meet-distributive,*
(B) *B is completely join-distributive,*
(C) *B is atomic,*
(D) *B is dually atomic,*
(E) *B is isomorphic with the subset lattice of a set.*

The theorem is due to Lindenbaum and Tarski (see Tarski [200], Theorem 5); Interesting generalizations can be found in a paper by Smith—Tarski [181] and by Sikorski [178].

PROOF. It is sufficient to show that (A) $\Longrightarrow$ (C) $\Longrightarrow$ (E) $\Longrightarrow$ (A), since dualization then yields (B) $\Longrightarrow$ (D) $\Longrightarrow$ (E) $\Longrightarrow$ (B).

(A) *implies* (C). Assume that the Boolean algebra $B = \{x_\lambda\}_{\lambda \in \Lambda}$ is completely meet-distributive. Introduce the notation

$$z_{\lambda 0} = x_\lambda, \qquad z_{\lambda 1} = x'_\lambda \qquad (\lambda \in \Lambda)$$

Let Γ denote the set of all functions γ assigning to every λ one of the values 0 or 1. By our assumption,

$$i = \bigcap_{\lambda \in \Lambda} (x_\lambda \cup x'_\lambda) = \bigcap_{\gamma \in \Gamma} \bigcup_{\mu \in \{0,1\}} z_{\lambda\mu} = \bigcup_{\gamma \in \Gamma} \bigcap_{\lambda \in \Lambda} z_{\lambda\gamma(\lambda)} \tag{3}$$

Introduce the symbol $u_\lambda = \bigcap_{\lambda \in \Lambda} z_{\lambda\gamma(\lambda)}$. It is proposed that

$$u_\gamma \succeq o \quad (\gamma \in \Gamma) \tag{4}$$

Indeed, if $x_{\lambda_0} < u_\gamma$ for some $\lambda_0 (\in \Lambda)$ then $z_{\lambda_0\gamma(\lambda_0)} = x'_{\lambda_0}$ (since otherwise, the definition of u_γ would imply $x_{\lambda_0} = z_{\lambda_0\gamma(\lambda_0)} \geqq u_\gamma$); but then $x_{\lambda_0} = x_{\lambda_0} \cap u_\gamma = x_{\lambda_0} \cap x'_{\lambda_0} \cap \bigcap_{\lambda \neq \lambda_0} z_{\lambda\gamma(\lambda)} = o$

Consider now an arbitrary element x_{λ_1} of B $(\lambda_1 \in \Lambda)$, $x_{\lambda_1} \neq o$. Since by our assumption B is completely meet-distributive and thus, a fortiori, infinitely meet-distributive, by (3) and by the meaning of u_γ

$$x_{\lambda_1} = x_{\lambda_1} \cap i = x_{\lambda_1} \cap \bigcup_{\gamma \in \Gamma} u_\gamma = \bigcup_{\gamma \in \Gamma} (x_{\lambda_1} \cap u_\gamma)$$

Hence, $x_{\lambda_1} \cap u_\gamma \neq O$ for some γ. It follows from (4) that $x_{\lambda_1} \cap u_\gamma$ is an atom of B, for which $x_{\lambda_1} \cap u_\gamma \leq x_{\lambda_1}$.

(C) *implies* (E). Assume B to be atomic. Denote the set of its atoms by M. Furthermore, let M_x $(x \in B)$ denote the sets of all atoms of B in $(x]$. Clearly,

$$\varphi : x \to M_x \quad (x \in B; \quad M_x \in \mathscr{P}(M))$$

(where $\mathscr{P}(M)$ is the subset lattice of M) is a one-to-one order preserving mapping of B into $\mathscr{P}(M)$. We will show that $\varphi : B \approx \mathscr{P}(M)$.

We first prove that φ maps B onto $\mathscr{P}(M)$. Among the image elements there occurs the void set O, since $\varphi(o) = O$. Let $\{p_\delta\}$ be any non-void subset of M. If $p \in M$ and $p \leq \bigcup p_\delta$, then

$$p = p \frown \bigcup_\delta p_\delta = \bigcup_\delta (p \frown p_\delta) \tag{5}$$

since by Theorem 55, B is infinitely distributive. However, (5) can be true only if some p_δ is identical with p. Hence, $\varphi(\bigcup_\delta p_\delta) = \{p_\delta\}$.

Now let us prove that

$$x = \bigcup M_x \quad (x \in B) \tag{6}$$

Introduce the notation $\bigcup M_x = u$. Clearly, $x \geq u$. It is now sufficient to prove that

$$x \frown u' = o \tag{7}$$

since then the distributivity implies

$$u = (x \frown u') \smile u = (x \smile u) \frown (u' \smile u) = x \smile u$$

that is, also $x \leq u$. Should (7) not be true, then by the assumed atomicity there would exist an atom p such that $p \leq x \frown u'$. But then, p would belong, by $p \leq x$, to the set M_x and thus it would satisfy (by the definition of u) the inequality $p \leq u$ and also the inequality $p \leq u'$ would be true, hence we should have $p \leq u \frown u' = o$. The latter cannot, however, be true. Hence, (7) and consequently also (6) are true.

(6) implies that the inverse of the mapping φ is also single-valued and order preserving. Hence, $\varphi : B \overset{o}{\approx} \mathscr{P}(M)$ and thus, by Theorem 9, $\varphi : B \approx \mathscr{P}(M)$.

(E) *implies* (A). Assume that there exists a set K such that $B \approx \mathscr{P}(K)$. By the Lemma in Section 31, $\mathscr{P}(K)$ is completely distributive. Consequently, by the assumed isomorphism B is also completely distributive. The theorem is, therefore, proved.

There are also non-atomic complete Boolean algebras (one is discussed by Hermes in § 24 of his book [91]). By the two theorems of the present section, this implies that the class of completely distributive lattices is indeed narrower than that of infinitely distributive lattices.

44. Boolean Algebras and Boolean Rings

A ring whose elements are all idempotent under multiplication (that is, in which $x^2 = x$ for every x) is called a *Boolean ring*. We show that every Boolean ring is commutative and of characteristic two. If x and y are arbitrary elements of the Boolean ring R, then

$$x + y = (x + y)(x + y) = x^2 + xy + yx + y^2 = x + xy + yx + y$$

and hence

$$xy + yx = 0 \tag{1}$$

Applying (1) to $y = x$, we obtain $0 = x^2 + x^2 = x + x = 2x$, and that means that R is of characteristic two. But then, adding xy to both sides of (1), we get

$$xy = xy + xy + yx = yx$$

There is a very close relation between the class of Boolean algebras and that of Boolean rings with unit:

THEOREM 57. *On defining on the elements of a Boolean algebra B an addition and a multiplication by the formulae**

$$\left.\begin{aligned} x + y &= (x \cap y') \cup (x' \cap y) \quad (2) \\ xy &= x \cap y \quad (3) \end{aligned}\right\} (x, y \in B)$$

a Boolean ring with unit $\mathfrak{R}(B)$ is obtained, the zero element of which is the least element of B, and the unit of which is the greatest element of B.

Conversely, on defining on a Boolean ring R with unit 1 *a join and a meet operation by the formulae*

$$\left.\begin{aligned} x \cup y &= x + y - xy \quad (4) \\ x \cap y &= xy \quad (5) \end{aligned}\right\} (x, y \in R)$$

a Boolean algebra $\mathfrak{B}(R)$ is obtained, the least element of which is the zero element of R and the greatest element of which is the unit of R and the complement of the element x is the element

$$x' = 1 - x \tag{6}$$

Furthermore, $\mathfrak{B}(\mathfrak{R}(B)) = B$ for every Boolean algebra B and $\mathfrak{R}(\mathfrak{B}(R)) = R$ for every Boolean ring (Stone [184] and [185], Theorem 3).

PROOF. It is obvious that the addition defined by (2) is commutative, the multiplication defined by (3) is associative and commutative, and that every element is idempotent with respect to this multiplication. Furthermore, the least element o of B is the zero element of $\mathfrak{R}(B)$, and the greatest element i of B is the unit of $\mathfrak{R}(B)$ since by (2) and (3), for every element x of B

$$x + o = (x \cap o') \cup (x' \cap o) = (x \cap i) \cup o = x$$

and

$$xi = x \cap i = x$$

* If B is a bounded field of sets, the right side of (2) equals the symmetric difference of x and y.

Again by (2) the additive inverse of every element x exists: that is, it is the element x itself, because

$$x + x = (x \cap x') \cup (x' \cap x) = o$$

Concerning $\Re(B)$, it remains to show that the addition defined by (2) is associative and the multiplication defined by (3) is distributive with respect to this addition.

Let us first perform a preparatory calculation. By the De Morgan formulae, in every distributive lattice

$$\big((x \cap y') \cup (x' \cap y)\big)' = (x \cap y) \cup (x' \cap y') \tag{7}$$

Indeed,

$$\big((x \cap y') \cup (x' \cap y)\big)' = (x \cap y')' \cap (x' \cap y)' = (x' \cup y) \cap (x \cup y') =$$
$$= (x' \cap x) \cup (y \cap x) \cup (x' \cap y') \cup (y \cap y') = (x \cap y) \cup (x' \cap y')$$

By (7) and utilizing the distributivity of B we have in $\Re(B)$

$$(x + y) + z = \big((x \cap y') \cup (x' \cap y)\big) + z =$$
$$= \{\big((x \cap y') \cup (x' \cap y)\big) \cap z'\} \cup \{((x \cap y') \cup (x' \cap y))' \cap z\} =$$
$$= \{\big((x \cap y') \cup (x' \cap y)\big) \cap z'\} \cup \{\big((x \cap y) \cup (x' \cap y')\big) \cap z\} =$$
$$= (x \cap y' \cap z') \cup (x' \cap y \cap z') \cup (x \cap y \cap z) \cup (x' \cap y' \cap z\}$$

that is

$$x + y + z = (x \cap y \cap z) \cup (x' \cap y' \cap z) \cup (x' \cap y \cap z') \cup (x \cap y' \cap z'). \tag{8}$$

But by the commutativity of the addition defined by (2),

$$x + (y + z) = (z + y) + x,$$

and thus, after having interchanged x and z in (8) we obtain

$$x + (y + z) = (z + y) + x =$$
$$= (z \cap y \cap x) \cup (z' \cap y' \cap x) \cup (z' \cap y \cap x') \cup$$
$$\cup (z \cap y' \cap x') = x + (y + z)$$

Finally, for any triplet of elements x, y, z of B

$$xy + xz = (x \cap y) + (x \cap z) =$$
$$= \big((x \cap y) \cap (x \cap z)'\big) \cup \big((x \cap y)' \cap (x \cap z)\big) =$$
$$= \big((x \cap y) \cap (x' \cup z')\big) \cup \big((x' \cup y') \cap (x \cap z)\big) =$$

$$= (x \cap y \cap x') \cup (x \cap y \cap z') \cup (x' \cap x \cap z) \cup$$
$$\cup (y' \cap x \cap z) = o \cup \big(x \cap (y \cap z')\big) \cup o \cup \big(x \cap (y' \cap z)\big) =$$
$$= x \cap \big((y \cap z') \cup (y' \cap z)\big) = x(y + z)$$

completing the proof of the first statement of the theorem.

Consider now, a Boolean ring R with unit 1. By the commutativity and associativity of the operations in R, the join defined by (4) is commutative, and the meet defined by (5) is commutative and associative. Moreover, the join is also associative, since

$$(x \cup y) \cup z = (x + y - xy) \cup z =$$
$$= x + y - xy + z - (x + y - xy)z =$$
$$= x + (y + z - yz) - x(y + z - yz) =$$
$$= x \cup (y + z - yz) = x \cup (y \cup z)$$

The absorption identities also hold. By (4) and (5)

$$x \cap (x \cup y) = x(x + y - xy) = x^2 + xy - x^2y = x$$

and

$$x \cup (x \cap y) = x + xy - x^2y = x$$

because, by our assumption, $x^2 = x$.

By the above, $\mathfrak{B}(R)$ is a lattice; we shall now show that it is distributive. To do so, it is sufficient, by Theorem 28, to verify L_{10}. Now

$$(x \cap y) \cup (x \cap z) = xy + xz - xyxz = xy + xz - xyz =$$
$$= x(y + z - yz) = x \cap (y \cup z)$$

The lattice $\mathfrak{B}(R)$ is bounded: its least (greatest) element is the zero element 0 (unit element 1) of the ring R, since for every x in $\mathfrak{B}(R)$, $0 \cap x = 0x = 0$ and $1 \cap x = 1x = x$. Moreover

$$x(1 - x) = x - x^2 = 0 \quad \text{and} \quad x + (1 - x) - x(1 - x) = 1$$

thus $1 - x$ is the complement of x in $\mathfrak{B}(R)$.

Now only the proof of the last proposition of the theorem is left. Let B be any Boolean algebra and construct from it by (2) and (3) the Boolean ring $\mathfrak{R}(B)$. Subsequently, form from $\mathfrak{R}(B)$ by the formulae

$$x \boldsymbol{\cup} y = x + y - xy$$

$$x \boldsymbol{\cap} y = xy$$

corresponding to (4) and (5) respectively, the Boolean algebra $\mathfrak{B} = \mathfrak{B}(\mathfrak{R}(B))$. By the latter and by (3), $x \boldsymbol{\cap} y = xy = x \cap y$, that is $\mathfrak{B}^{\cap} = B^{\cap}$. But then, by Theorem 9, $\mathfrak{B} = B$.

Similarly, let R be a Boolean ring with unit, and form from it by (4) — (6) the Boolean algebra $\mathfrak{B}(R)$. Subsequently, define the Boolean ring $\mathfrak{R}(\mathfrak{B}(R))$ by the formulae

$$x \dotplus y = (x \frown y') \smile (x' \frown y) \tag{9}$$

$$x \bullet y = x \frown y \tag{10}$$

corresponding to (2) and (3) respectively.

By (10) and (5), $x \bullet y = x \frown y = xy$. Furthermore, by (9), (6), (5) and (4)

$$\begin{aligned} x \dotplus y &= (x \frown y') \smile (x' \frown y) = (x(1-y)) \smile ((1-x)y) = \\ &= x(1-y) + (1-x)y - xy(1-x)(1-y) = \\ &= x + y - 2xy = x + y \end{aligned}$$

because $xy(1-x) = 0$ and R is of characteristic two.

It is readily observed that in proving the second statement of the theorem the unit of R was only utilized in verifying that $\mathfrak{B}(R)$ is complemented. Hence, it is possible by means of formulae (4) and (5) to form lattices also from Boolean rings without unit, the resulting lattices being by the above considerations bounded below and distributive. It is none too difficult to prove that they will also be relatively complemented. Relatively complemented distributive lattices bounded below are also called *generalized Boolean algebras*.

Conversely, let B be a generalized Boolean algebra and let us define in B an addition and a multiplication as follows: let $x + y$ $(x, y \in B)$ denote the relative complement of $x \frown y$ in the interval $[o, x \smile y]$,* and let xy equal, as above, $x \frown y$. It can be proved that in this way a Boolean ring is obtained.

The results described in the two preceding paragraphs are likewise due to Stone (see [186], Theorem 4).

Grätzer and Schmidt have shown ([79], Theorem 16 and [180], Theorem 8) that starting from the lattice operations in a distributive lattice L it is possible to define ring operations with the aid of a finite number of parameters and equations if, and only if, L is relatively complemented; for this latter case, they have given all operations of this kind definable on L.

45. The Algebra of Relations

Consider the set $\mathcal{R}(M)$ of all relations definable on a set M. In Example 6, we have introduced among the elements of $\mathcal{R}(M)$ an ordering relation in the following way: Let

$$\left\{ \begin{array}{l} \Phi \leqq \Psi \ (\Phi, \Psi \in \mathcal{R}(M)) \text{ if, and only if,} \\ \text{for any pair of elements } x, y \text{ of } M, \\ x\Phi y \text{ implies } x\Psi y. \end{array} \right. \tag{1}$$

* By Theorem 49 or by the supplement of Theorem 48, it can be immediately proved that this definition includes Formula (2) as a special case.

With respect to this ordering, $\mathcal{R}(M)$ is bounded: its greatest element is the relation I defined by $x \mathrm{I} y$ for every pair of elements x, y of M, whereas its least element is the relation Ω for which $x\Omega y$ is true for no pair of elements x, y of M.

Concerning the partly ordered set $\mathcal{R}(M)$ we shall prove the following

THEOREM 58. *The set $\mathcal{R}(M)$ of all relations definable on a set M forms a complete Boolean algebra with respect to the ordering by* (1).

SUPPLEMENT. Let $\{\Phi_\gamma\}_{\gamma\in\Gamma}$ *be any subset of the set* $\mathcal{R}(M)$. *With respect to the ordering by* (1), *the infimum (supremum) of the set is the relation Π (Σ), determined by the definition*

$$\left.\begin{aligned} x\Pi y &\longleftrightarrow x\Phi_\gamma y \quad \text{for every } \gamma, \\ x\Sigma y &\longleftrightarrow x\Phi_\gamma y \quad \text{for at least one } \gamma \end{aligned}\right\} \quad (\gamma \in \Gamma)$$

The Boolean algebra $\mathcal{R}(M)$ is called the *algebra of the relations* on M.

PROOF. Clearly, $\Pi \leq \Phi_\gamma \leq \Sigma$ for every γ, ["$\leq$" is to be meant of course as defined by (1)]. Let Ψ be any lower bound of $\{\Phi_\gamma\}$. If $x\Psi y$ for some pair of elements x, y of M, then by (1) $x\Phi_\gamma y$ holds for every γ, that is $x\Pi y$. This implies $\Psi \leq \Pi$; hence, $\Pi = \inf\{\Phi_\gamma\}$.

Now let Ψ be any upper bound of $\{\Phi_\gamma\}$. If for any pair of elements x, y of M we have $x\Sigma y$, then by the definition of Σ there exists a $\gamma(\in \Gamma)$ such that $x\Phi_\gamma y$; but then, by our assumption, also $x\Psi y$. Hence, $\Psi \geq \Sigma$, that is, $\Sigma = \sup\{\Phi_\gamma\}$.

The above considerations prove the supplement to the theorem, revealing at the same time that $\mathcal{R}(M)$ forms a lattice with respect to the ordering (1).

Now let Θ, Φ and Ψ be three arbitrary elements of the lattice $\mathcal{R}(M)$. By the above, for any pair of elements x, y of M the following statements 1—4 are equivalent:

1. $x(\Theta \cap (\Phi \cup \Psi))y$
2. $x\Theta y$, and either $x\Phi y$ or $x\Psi y$
3. either $x(\Theta \cap \Phi)y$ or $x(\Theta \cap \Psi)y$
4. $x((\Theta \cap \Phi) \cup (\Theta \cap \Phi))y$

Hence, $\Theta \cap (\Phi \cup \Psi) = (\Theta \cap \Phi) \cup (\Theta \cap \Psi)$ implying $\mathcal{R}(M)$ to be distributive.

Finally, the lattice $\mathcal{R}(M)$ is complemented: the complement of the relation Φ is the relation Φ'. The proof of Theorem 58 is thus completed.

It is usual to introduce a multiplication in the set $\mathcal{R}(M)$ besides the lattice operations, The product $\Theta\Phi$ of the relations Θ and Φ is defined so that for any pair of elements x, y of M, $x\Theta\Phi y$ is true if, and only if, there exists an element t ($\in M$) such that $x\Theta t$ and $t\Phi y$. It is easily shown that in general $\Theta\Phi \neq \Phi\Theta$; if $\Theta\Phi = \Phi\Theta$ should nevertheless be true for a pair of relations Θ, Φ, then Θ and Φ are said to be *permutable relations*.

THEOREM 59. *The algebra of relations $\mathcal{R}(M)$ of any set M forms a lattice-ordered semigroup with respect to the operations defined in the supplement of the foregoing theorem and to the multiplication of relations.*

PROOF. With regard to the previous theorem we have only to show that the multiplication of relations is associative and — with respect to the join operation — it is distributive, too.

For the arbitrary elements Θ, Φ, Ψ of $\mathcal{R}(M)$ there holds $a(\Theta\Phi)\Psi b$ $(a, b \in M)$ by definition if, and only if, there exists a $y \in M$ such that

$$a\Theta\Phi y \quad \text{and} \quad y\Psi b \tag{2}$$

This holds however if, and only if, there exists an $x \in M$ such that

$$a\Theta x \quad \text{and} \quad x\Phi y \tag{3}$$

But from (2) and (3) it follows that

$$a\Theta x \quad \text{and} \quad x(\Phi\Psi)b$$

i.e. $a\Theta(\Phi\Psi)b$; therefore

$$a(\Theta\Phi)\Psi b \Longrightarrow a\Theta(\Phi\Psi)b$$

In the same way we can show that

$$a\Theta(\Phi\Psi)b \Longrightarrow a(\Theta\Phi)\Psi b$$

and as a consequence of these we get $(\Theta\Phi)\Psi = \Theta(\Phi\Psi)$.

Further we have by the corresponding definitions

$$a(\Theta \cup \Phi)\Psi b \qquad (a, b \in M) \tag{4}$$

if, and only if, for an element x of M

$$a\Theta x \quad \text{or} \quad a\Phi x \tag{5}$$

and

$$x\Psi b \tag{6}$$

But (5) and (6) together are equivalent to the statement that either $a\Theta\Psi b$ or $a\Phi\Psi b$, i.e.

$$a(\Theta\Psi \cup \Phi\Psi)b \tag{7}$$

Summing up we see that (4) and (7) are equivalent. The proof is thus completed.

46. The Lattice of Propositions

The propositional calculus of mathematical logic deals with propositions in the logical sense. The *logical value* of a proposition is either "true" or "false"; in classical logic, both cannot exist simultaneously.

In this section, propositions will be denoted by Gothic letters and the logical value of a proposition $\mathfrak{x}$ will be denoted $w(\mathfrak{x})$. To express the logical values "true" and "false", the logical symbols $\uparrow$ and $\downarrow$ will be employed, as in Section 2. That is, if a proposition $\mathfrak{a}$ is true, this fact is expressed as $w(\mathfrak{a}) = \uparrow$, and if it is false, we write $w(\mathfrak{a}) = \downarrow$.

The calculus of propositions utilises several "logical operations". By a logical operation, we mean a procedure by which it is possible to form in a well-defined manner, more complex propositions from given ones. The given propositions will be called the components of the new proposition. Here, only three such operations will be dealt with, namely: 1. *Conjuction*: the connection of two propositions by the word "and"; 2. *Disjunction :* the connection of two propositions by the word "or" (in the sense which permits both cases), and 3. *Negation :* the denial of a given proposition. The conjunction of two propositions, $\mathfrak{a}$ and $\mathfrak{b}$, is symbolized by $\mathfrak{a} \wedge \mathfrak{b}$, their disjunction by $\mathfrak{a} \vee \mathfrak{b}$ and the negation of a proposition $\mathfrak{x}$ by $\overline{\mathfrak{x}}$. The logical values of the propositions, so composed, are defined by the following operation tables:

$\wedge$	$\uparrow$	$\downarrow$
$\uparrow$	$\uparrow$	$\downarrow$
$\downarrow$	$\downarrow$	$\downarrow$

$\vee$	$\uparrow$	$\downarrow$
$\uparrow$	$\uparrow$	$\uparrow$
$\downarrow$	$\uparrow$	$\downarrow$

negation		
if $\mathfrak{a} =$	$\uparrow$	$\downarrow$
then $\overline{\mathfrak{a}} =$	$\downarrow$	$\uparrow$

The proposition

$$(\mathfrak{a} \wedge \mathfrak{b}) \vee (\overline{\mathfrak{a}} \wedge \overline{\mathfrak{b}}) \tag{1}$$

is of special importance. It can be verified by means of the above three tables that the proposition (1) is true if $w(\mathfrak{a}) = w(\mathfrak{b})$ and false if $w(\mathfrak{a}) \neq w(\mathfrak{b})$. Hence, this proposition is essentially the formalization of the "if and only if" type of conclusion, frequently used in mathematical proofs.

The logical value of a composite proposition formed by logical operations can, in the general case, be determined only in the knowledge of the logical values of the component propositions. There are, however, some composite propositions the logical values of which are independent of those of the component propositions. Thus

$$w\{((\mathfrak{x} \wedge (\mathfrak{y} \vee \mathfrak{x}) \vee \mathfrak{x}) \vee (\overline{\mathfrak{x} \wedge (\mathfrak{y} \vee \mathfrak{x})} \wedge \overline{\mathfrak{x}})\} = \uparrow \tag{2}$$

whether the propositions $\mathfrak{x}$, $\mathfrak{y}$ are true or not. Propositions which are $\begin{Bmatrix}\text{true}\\ \text{false}\end{Bmatrix}$ independently of the logical value of their simple components (that is, components which cannot be decomposed into still simpler propositions by the above three logical operations) are called *formally* $\begin{Bmatrix}\textit{true}\\ \textit{false}\end{Bmatrix}$. If in a proposition of this sort every simple component is exchanged for another simple proposition, taking care to substitute everywhere the same proposition for a proposition occurring several times, then, of course, the proposition arrived at will likewise be true or false respectively.

If $\mathfrak{a}$ and $\mathfrak{b}$ are simple propositions, then the composite proposition (1) is neither formally true nor formally false. If, however, $\mathfrak{a}$ and $\mathfrak{b}$ are composite propositions, it is possible that (1) if formally true: for example, by (2), this is the case if $\mathfrak{a} = \mathfrak{x} \wedge (\mathfrak{y} \vee \mathfrak{x})$, $\mathfrak{b} = \mathfrak{x}$. If for the propositions $\mathfrak{a}$ and $\mathfrak{b}$, (1) is formally true, $\mathfrak{a}$ and $\mathfrak{b}$ are called *equivalent* propositions and denoted $\mathfrak{a} \equiv \mathfrak{b}$.

We will prove that the relation "$\equiv$" thus defined is indeed a relation of equivalence. Its reflexivity is trivial. Let furthermore $\mathfrak{x}^*$ denote an arbitrary proposition obtained from $\mathfrak{x}$ by replacing the simple components of $\mathfrak{x}$ by other propositions (observing the above restrictions.†) Now if $\mathfrak{a} \equiv \mathfrak{b}$, then for every pair of propositions $\mathfrak{a}^*$, $\mathfrak{b}^*$ there holds the equality $w(\mathfrak{a}^*) = w(\mathfrak{b}^*)$; but then, for every $\mathfrak{a}^*$ and $\mathfrak{b}^*$, $w((\mathfrak{b}^* \wedge \mathfrak{a}^*) \vee (\overline{\mathfrak{b}^*} \wedge \overline{\mathfrak{a}^*})) = \uparrow$. Hence, $(\mathfrak{b} \wedge \mathfrak{a}) \vee (\overline{\mathfrak{b}} \wedge \overline{\mathfrak{a}})$ is formally true, that is, $\mathfrak{b} \equiv \mathfrak{a}$. This means that the relation $\equiv$ is symmetrical. Finally, if $\mathfrak{a} \equiv \mathfrak{b}$ and $\mathfrak{b} \equiv \mathfrak{c}$, then for every propositions $\mathfrak{a}^*$, $\mathfrak{b}^*$, $\mathfrak{c}^*$ $w(\mathfrak{a}^*) = w(\mathfrak{b}^*)$, and $w(\mathfrak{b}^*) = w(\mathfrak{c}^*)$, that is, $w(\mathfrak{a}^*) = w(\mathfrak{c}^*)$, consequently $\mathfrak{a} \equiv \mathfrak{c}$ and the relation $\equiv$ is also transitive.

Further important properties of the relation are the following:††

(3) $$\mathfrak{a} \equiv \mathfrak{b} \text{ implies } \overline{\mathfrak{a}} \equiv \overline{\mathfrak{b}};$$

(4) $$\mathfrak{a} \equiv \mathfrak{c} \text{ and } \mathfrak{b} \equiv \mathfrak{d} \text{ imply } \mathfrak{a} \wedge \mathfrak{b} \equiv \mathfrak{c} \wedge \mathfrak{d};$$

(5) $$\mathfrak{a} \equiv \mathfrak{c} \text{ and } \mathfrak{b} \equiv \mathfrak{d} \text{ imply } \mathfrak{a} \vee \mathfrak{b} \equiv \mathfrak{c} \vee \mathfrak{d}.$$

All three properties are easily verified by the method applied in the previous paragraph.

Now let us classify propositions by grouping equivalent propositions in classes. The class containing the proposition $\mathfrak{x}$ will be denoted $[\mathfrak{x}]$ and called the *class of propositions* represented by $\mathfrak{x}$.

Concerning the classes of propositions, we have

THEOREM 60. *With respect to a meet and join operation defined on the set* $\mathfrak{L}$ *of all classes of propositions by the formulae*

(6) $$[\mathfrak{a}] \cap [\mathfrak{b}] = [\mathfrak{a} \wedge \mathfrak{b}]$$

(7) $$[\mathfrak{a}] \cup [\mathfrak{b}] = [\mathfrak{a} \vee \mathfrak{b}]$$

$\mathfrak{L}$ *forms a Boolean algebra, in which the complement of* $[\mathfrak{x}]$ *is the class* $[\overline{\mathfrak{x}}]$.

PROOF. We first show that the classes of propositions $[\mathfrak{a} \wedge \mathfrak{b}]$ and $[\mathfrak{a} \vee \mathfrak{b}]$ are uniquely determined by $[\mathfrak{a}]$ and $[\mathfrak{b}]$. For this purpose choose, arbitrarily, a proposition $\mathfrak{a}_1$ from $[\mathfrak{a}]$ and a proposition $\mathfrak{b}_1$ from $[\mathfrak{b}]$. Then, by (4) and (5), $\mathfrak{a} \wedge \mathfrak{b}_1 \equiv \mathfrak{a} \wedge \mathfrak{b}$ and $\mathfrak{a}_1 \vee \mathfrak{b}_1 \equiv \mathfrak{a} \vee \mathfrak{b}$, that is, $[\mathfrak{a}_1 \wedge \mathfrak{b}_1] = [\mathfrak{a} \wedge \mathfrak{b}]$, and $[\mathfrak{a}_1 \vee \mathfrak{b}_1] = [\mathfrak{a} \vee \mathfrak{b}]$. Similarly, by (3), $[\overline{\mathfrak{x}}]$ is also determined uniquely by $\mathfrak{x}$. Hence, the operations defined

† Particularly $\mathfrak{x}^*$ can also coincide with $\mathfrak{x}$.

†† By (3)—(5) the equivalence relation $\equiv$ is, as a matter of fact, a congruence relation by a term to be introduced in Chapter IX.

in the theorem are indeed operations among classes of propositions. We shall prove that, with respect to these operations, $\mathfrak{L}$ is a distributive lattice. Let $\mathfrak{a}$, $\mathfrak{b}$, $\mathfrak{c}$ be any triplet of elements of $\mathfrak{L}$, and let $\mathfrak{a}^*$, $\mathfrak{b}^*$, $\mathfrak{c}^*$ denote arbitrary propositions, each of which is obtained by a substitution described above. Further — for the sake of brevity — introduce the notation $\mathfrak{l} = (\mathfrak{a} \wedge \mathfrak{b}) \wedge \mathfrak{c}$ and $\mathfrak{r} = \mathfrak{a} \wedge (\mathfrak{b} \wedge \mathfrak{c})$ and the symbols $\mathfrak{l}^*$, $\mathfrak{r}^*$ analogously. By the definition of conjunction,

$$w(\mathfrak{l}^*) = \uparrow \Longleftrightarrow w(\mathfrak{a}^* \wedge \mathfrak{b}^*) = w(\mathfrak{c}^*) = \uparrow \Longleftrightarrow w(\mathfrak{a}^*) = w(\mathfrak{b}^*) = w(\mathfrak{c}^*) = \uparrow$$

$$w(\mathfrak{r}^*) = \uparrow \Longleftrightarrow w(\mathfrak{a}^*) = w(\mathfrak{b}^* \wedge \mathfrak{c}^*) = \uparrow \Longleftrightarrow w(\mathfrak{a}^*) = w(\mathfrak{b}^*) = w(\mathfrak{c}^*) = \uparrow$$

that is, $w(\mathfrak{l}^*) = w(\mathfrak{r}^*)$. Hence, the proposition $(\mathfrak{l} \wedge \mathfrak{r}) \vee (\bar{\mathfrak{l}} \wedge \bar{\mathfrak{r}})$ is formally true, that is, $\mathfrak{l} \equiv \mathfrak{r}$. But then, by (6),

$$([a] \frown [b]) \frown [c] = [(a \wedge b) \wedge c] = [a \wedge (b \wedge c)] = [a] \frown ([b] \frown [c])$$

The rest of the lattice axioms and the distributive identities can be proved by similar considerations.†

Let us now determine the bound elements of $\mathfrak{L}$. For every $\mathfrak{x}$, $w(\mathfrak{x} \wedge \bar{\mathfrak{x}}) = \downarrow$ and $w(\mathfrak{x} \vee \bar{\mathfrak{x}}) = \uparrow$; hence, for any pair of propositions $\mathfrak{a}$, $\mathfrak{b}$, $\mathfrak{a} \wedge \bar{\mathfrak{a}} \equiv \mathfrak{b} \wedge \bar{\mathfrak{b}}$, and $\mathfrak{a} \vee \bar{\mathfrak{a}} \equiv \mathfrak{b} \wedge \bar{\mathfrak{b}}$ hold. The class $[\mathfrak{a} \wedge \bar{\mathfrak{a}}]$ is the least element of $\mathfrak{L}$, since by (6) $[\mathfrak{a} \wedge \mathfrak{a}] \frown [\mathfrak{y}] = [\mathfrak{a} \wedge \bar{\mathfrak{a}} \wedge \mathfrak{y}] = [\mathfrak{a} \wedge \bar{\mathfrak{a}}]$ for each $[\mathfrak{y}]$ in $\mathfrak{L}$. Similarly, by (7), $[\mathfrak{a} \vee \bar{\mathfrak{a}}]$ is the greatest element of $\mathfrak{L}$. This implies already, also by (6) and (7), that $[\bar{\mathfrak{x}}]$ is the complement of $[\mathfrak{x}]$.

47. Valuations of Boolean Algebras

A valuation v of a lattice L is said to be *additive* if for any finite subset $\{x_1, \ldots, x_n\}$ of mutually disjoint elements of L

$$v\left(\bigcup_{j=1}^{n} x_j\right) = \sum_{j=1}^{n} v(x_j)$$

Particularly, if L is a σ-lattice and for every countable subset $\{x_1, x_2, \ldots\}$ of L consisting of mutually disjoint elements

$$v\left(\bigcup_{j} x_j\right) = \sum_{j} v(x_j)$$

v is said to be a *completely additive valuation* of L.

In the modern foundation of probability theory, probability is, in fact a completely additive valuation defined on Boolean σ-algebra (on the set of events), assuming values between 0 and 1, with $v(o) = 0$ and $v(i) = 1$.

Boolean algebras with completely additive valuations are called *measure algebras* and are used mainly in measure theory.

† However, in verifying the axioms concerning the operation $\smile$, it is more expedient to consider the cases in which the logical value of the two sides is "false".

THEOREM 61. *A valuation v of a Boolean algebra is additive if, and only if,* $v(o) = 0$.

PROOF. If $x_1, \ldots, x_n$ are mutually disjoint elements of the Boolean algebra considered, then

$$(x_1 \cup \ldots \cup x_{n-1}) \cap x_n = (x_1 \cap x_n) \cup \ldots \cup (x_{n-1} \cap x_n) = o$$

Hence, if $v(o) = 0$, then

$$v(x_1 \cup \ldots \cup x_n) = v(x_1 \cup \ldots \cup x_{n-1}) + v(x_n)$$

The statement "if" is then verified by induction.

Conversely, if the valuation v is additive, then

$$v(o) = v(o \cup o) = v(o) + v(o)$$

implying $v(o) = 0$. Thus, the statement "only if" is also proved.

Let S be any (but henceforward fixed) Boolean subalgebra of a Boolean σ-algebra A and v an order preserving valuation on S such that $v(o) = 0$; v will also be permitted to assume the value $+\infty$. (By the condition $v(o) = 0$, v is additive.) By an *S-covering* of some element a of A we mean any countable system of elements $\{x_1, x_2, \ldots\}$ of S satisfying the condition $\bigcup_j x_j \geqq a$. Further, the *outer measure* of the element a with respect to S is defined as the greatest lower bound of all $v(\bigcup_j x_j)$ with $\bigcup_j x_j \geqq a$ and denoted by $m(a)$.

This definition and the foundation of the measure theory resting upon it is due to Carathéodory [220]. Incidentally, the Carathéodory outer measure is a direct generalization of the Borel—Lebesgue outer measure well-known from real analysis. Consider the case when A consists of all subsets of a line, and S of those subsets of the line which are composed of a finite number of open, half-open or closed intervals. If we mean by $v(x)$ the sum of lengths of all intervals constituting a pair-like disjoint decomposition of x, we obtain precisely the Borel—Lebesgue outer measure.

The definition directly implies the following simple properties of the outer measure:

(1) $$m(o) = 0$$

(2) $$a \leqq b \Longrightarrow m(a) \leqq m(b)$$

(3) $$m(\bigcup_j a_j) \leqq \sum_j m(a_j)$$

An element a of A is called *measurable* (with respect to S and v) if for any element x of A

(4) $$m(x) = m(x \cap a) + m(x \cap a')$$

For the set M of all measurable elements of A there holds

THEOREM 62. *The set M of all measurable elements of A is a Boolean subalgebra of A including S.* (Carathéodory [220], Theorems 1, 2 and 5).

PROOF. If $a \in M$, then by (4) also $a' \in M$. Furthermore, if $a, b \in M$, then by (3) and by the De Morgan formulae,

$$m(x) = m(x \cap a) + m(x \cap a') =$$

$$= m(x \cap a \cap b) + m(x \cap a \cap b') + m(x \cap a' \cap b) +$$

$$+ m(x \cap a' \cap b') \geqq m(x \cap (a \cap b)) + m\left((x \cap a \cap b') \cup\right.$$

$$\left.\cup (x \cap a' \cap b) \cup (x \cap a' \cap b')\right) = m(x \cap (a \cap b)) +$$

$$+ m\{x \cap ((a \cap b') \cup (a' \cap b) \cup (a' \cap b'))\} =$$

$$= m(x \cap (a \cap b)) + m(x \cap (a' \cup b')) =$$

$$= m(x \cap (a \cap b)) + m(x \cap (a \cap b)')$$

that is,

$$m(x) \geqq m(x \cap (a \cap b)) + m(x \cap (a \cap b)') \tag{5}$$

On the other hand,

$$x = x \cap ((a \cap b) \cup (a \cap b)') = (x \cap (a \cap b)) \cup (x \cap (a \cap b)'),$$

and hence, by (3),

$$m(x) \leqq m(x \cap (a \cap b)) + m(x \cap (a \cap b)') \tag{6}$$

By inequalities (5) and (6) $a \cap b \in M$. But then, by the De Morgan formulae (more precisely, by formula (2) of Section 42), $a \cup b \in M$ also holds.

Now let a be any element of S. If $\{x_1, x_2, \ldots\}$ is any S-covering of x ($\in A$), then $\{x_1 \cap a, x_2 \cap a, \ldots\}$ is an S-covering of $x \cap a$ and $\{x_1 \cap a', x_2 \cap a_1', \ldots\}$ one of $x \cap a'$. Since $(x_j \cap a)$ and $(x_j \cap a')$ are disjoint,

$$\sum_j v(x_j) = \sum_j v((x_j \cap a) \cup (x_j \cap a')) =$$

$$= \sum_j v(x_j \cap a) + \sum_j v(x \cap a') \geqq m(x \cap a) + m(x \cap a')$$

and hence, by the definition of the outer measure,

$$m(x) \geqq m(x \cap a) + m(x \cap a')$$

On the other hand, by (3),

$$m(x) = m((x \cap a) \cup (x \cap a')) \leqq m(x \cap a) + m(x \cap a')$$

and hence a is measurable.

Exercises to Chapter VI

1. Find a bounded modular lattice in which the complemented elements do not form a sublattice.

2. Show that the dual, every homomorphic image and every interval of a Boolean algebra is likewise a Boolean algebra whereas not every sublattice of a Boolean algebra is a Boolean algebra.

3. Show that a homomorphism $\varphi : B_1 \sim B_2$ of a Boolean algebra B_1 into the Boolean algebra B_2 is a Boolean homomorphism if, and only if, $\varphi(o_1) = o_2$ and $\varphi(i_1) = i_2$.

4. Verify that in every Boolean algebra

a) $\operatorname{med}(a', b', c') = \big(\operatorname{med}(a, b, c)\big)'$;

b) $(x \cap y') \cup (x' \cap y) = \big((x \cap y) \cap (x \cup y)'\big) \cup$
$\cup \big((x \cap y)' \cap (x \cup y)\big)$;

c) $x \leqq y \Leftrightarrow x \cap y' = o \Leftrightarrow x' \cup y = i$.

5. Introduce in a Boolean algebra a "subtraction" by the following definition: let $x - y$ be the relative complement of y in $[o, x \cup y]$. Verify the following identities:

a) $x - y = x \cap y'$;

b) $x - x = o$;

c) $x - (x - y) = x \cap y$;

d) $x - (y - z) = (x - y) \cup (x \cap z)$;

e) $x - (y \cap z) = (x - y) \cup (x - z)$;

f) $x - (y \cup z) = (x - y) \cap (x - z)$.

6. Show that if a lattice L is uniquely complemented and the De Morgan formulae hold in it, then L is a Boolean algebra. As a preliminary, prove the following:

a) If $u, v \in L$ and $u \leqq v$, then $\big((v \cap u') \cup u\big)'$ is a complement of v, and $\big((u \cup v') \cap v\big)'$ a complement of u;

b) If $a \leqq x \leqq b$ and y is a relative complement of x in $[a, b]$, then y is a complement of the element $b' \cup (x \cap a')$.

7. Generalize the De Morgan formulae to complete Boolean algebras.

8. A bounded lattice L is called *orthocomplemented* if it admits a dual automorphism $a \rightarrow a^{\perp}$ satisfying $(a^{\perp})^{\perp} = a$ and $a \leqq a^{\perp} \Rightarrow a = o$. Show that for each element a of an orthocomplemented lattice, $a^{\perp}$ is a complement of a.

9. Show that every complete lattice is the meet-homomorphic image of a suitably chosen Boolean algebra.

10. Show that a subset R of a Boolean algebra B is a Boolean subalgebra in B if, and only if, R is a subring with unit of the Boolean ring $\mathfrak{R}(B)$ formed from B (see Section 44). Show, also, that a Boolean algebra B may have a sublattice S such that the subset S is not a subring of $\mathfrak{R}(B)$.

11. Show that some subset of a Boolean algebra B is an ideal of B if, and only if, this same subset is an ideal (in ring theoretical sense) in $\mathfrak{R}(B)$.

12. Let B be a generalized Boolean algebra. Introduce in B an addition and a multiplication by the definition given in Section 44 on p. 130. Prove that in this way a Boolean ring is obtained.

13. Let R be any Boolean ring, and define in R a meet and a join operation by the formulae (4), (5) of Section 44. Prove that in this way a generalized Boolean algebra is obtained.

14. Show that with respect to the operations defined in Section 45, $\mathcal{R}(M)$ is a lattice-ordered semigroup. Prove further that

a) for every element Θ, Φ, Ψ of $\mathcal{R}(M)$, there holds the inequality $\Theta(\Phi \frown \Psi) \leqq \Theta\Phi \frown \Theta\Psi$;

b) $\Phi \leqq \Psi$ implies $\Theta\Phi \leqq \Theta\Psi$;

c) $\Phi \neq \Omega$ implies $\mathsf{I}\,\Phi\,\mathsf{I} = \mathsf{I}$;

d) $\Theta\Phi \leqq \mathsf{E}'$ (where E is the relation of equality) implies $\Phi\Theta \leqq \mathsf{E}'$;*

e) if $\Phi(\in \mathcal{R}(M))$ is transitive, then $\Phi^2 \leqq \Phi$.

15. Prove that in the lattice $\mathfrak{L}$ of propositions, $[\mathfrak{x}] \geqq [\mathfrak{y}]$ if, and only if, $\mathfrak{x} \vee \mathfrak{y}'$ is formally true.

16. Let v be a valuation of a Boolean algebra B whose domain of value consists exactly of the integers 0 and 1. Show:

a) $v(o) = 0$, $v(i) = 1$;

b) $v(x') = 1 - v(x)$ for every $x \in B$

c) $v(x \frown y) = v(x)\, v(y)$ for each pair $x, y \in B$.

17. Let A be an arbitrary Boolean σ-algebra. Show that the bound elements of A are measurable and that for every element a of A there hold the following:

a) If $m(a) = 0$, then a is measurable;

b) If a is measurable, then $m(a) + m(a') = m(i)$.

* By the definitions of E and of the ordering in $\mathcal{R}(M)$, $\Pi \leqq \mathsf{E}'$ means that there is no x for which $x\Pi x$ would hold.

CHAPTER VII

SEMIMODULAR LATTICES

48. Birkhoff Lattices

In Section 35. we have, after having formulated the covering conditions, illus trated by an example that, even among lattices of finite length, there are som which satisfy one covering condition but fail to satisfy the other. This fact gives rise to the following definition.

Lattices of finite length satisfying the lower covering condition are called *Birkhoff lattices*.† By Theorem 37, *every modular lattice of finite length is a Birkhoff lattice ;* on the other hand, it follows from Theorem 43 that *a Birkhoff lattice is modular if, and only if, its dual is also a Birkhoff lattice.*

The first to treat these lattices was Birkhoff (for the definition see [10], p. 445); the term is due to Klein-Barmen [116].

Example 25. Classical examples of Birkhoff lattices are the subspace lattices of the affine spaces of finite dimensions. Let P be a projective space of finite dimension, on every line of which there are incident at least three points. Consider some dual atom m of the subspace lattice $\mathscr{L}(P)$ and delete from P all points and lines included in m. In this way, another linear space P^* is obtained. Linear spaces of this kind are called *affine spaces* (of finite dimensions).

In accordance with the formation of P^*, delete from $\mathscr{L}(P)$ all elements of $(m]$ differing from O. In this way, we obtain the set $\mathscr{L}(P^*)$ of all linear subspaces of P^*. The set $\mathscr{L}(P^*)$ is bounded below with respect to the ordering relation in $\mathscr{L}(P)$ and closed with respect to the join in $\mathscr{L}(P)$; hence, $\mathscr{L}(P^*)$ is, by the dual of Theorem 17, a complete lattice with respect to the ordering relation of $\mathscr{L}(P)$. It can be shown that $\mathscr{L}(P^*)$ is a Birkhoff lattice which, however, is not modular in the general case (see Exercise 11).

MacLane [127] discussed two further important examples, the understanding of which requires rather profound algebraic knowledge.

The theorem below essentially gives two further definitions of Birkhoff lattices, equivalent to the above:

THEOREM 63. *For a lattice L of finite length, the following conditions are equivalent* (Birkhoff [10], p. 448):

† In some works especially in earlier ones, only Birkhoff lattices are called semimodular lattices.

(A) *The lattice* L *satisfies the lower covering condition.*

(B) *If* a, u, v *are elements of the lattice* L *such that* $u \neq v$ *and* $u, v \succ a$, *then* $u \cup v \succ u, v$;

(C) *In the lattice* L *there can be defined at least one dimension function and for every dimension function* d *of* L *there holds the inequality*

$$d(a) + d(b) \geqq d(a \cap b) + d(a \cup b) \qquad (a, b \in L) .$$

PROOF.

(A) *implies* (C) by the Corollary to Theorems 41 and by Theorem 42.

(C) *implies* (B). Let a, u, v be elements of L such that $u, v \succ a$. Then $u, v \geqq u \cap v \geqq a$, too. Hence, either $u \cap v = u = v$, or $u \cap v = a$. Consequently, for $u \neq v$, only the second case is possible. Thus, if (C) is satisfied in L, then for any dimension function of L

$$d(u \cup v) - d(u) \leqq d(v) - d(u \cap v) = d(v) - d(a) = 1$$

since by assumption $v \succ a$. However, $d(u \cup v) - d(u) = 0$ is impossible, since it would imply $u \cup v = u$. that is $u \geqq v$, in contradiction to the assumptions made for the elements u,v. Hence, $d(u \cup v) - d(u) = 1$, that is, $u \cup v \succ u$. Similarly, $u \cup v \succ v$.

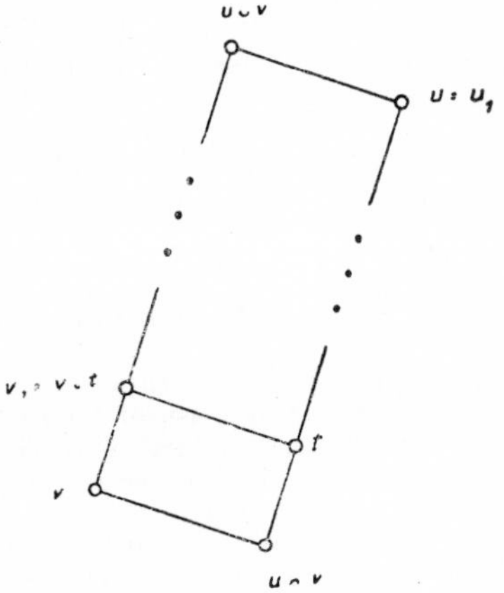

Fig. 26

(B) *implies* (A). Let u, v be elements of the lattice L of finite length satisfying (B) and let u, v be elements of L such that

$$(1) \qquad u \cap v \prec v$$

We shall show that then $u \prec u \cup v$ also holds.

First of all, $u \geqq v$ is impossible by (1). Hence, either $u < v$ or $u \parallel v$.

If $u < v$, then, again by (1), $u = u \cap v \prec v = u \cup v$, verifying the proposition in this simple manner.

There remains the case $u \parallel v$. Denote the length of the sublattice $[u \cap v, u]$ by l and apply complete induction on l. If $l = 1$, then by (B) we have at once $u \prec u \cup v$. In the rest of the proof let $l > 1$, and suppose that the proposition holds for every pair of elements u_1, v_1 for which the length of $[u_1 \cap v_1, u_1]$ is less than l. Since $l > 1$, there can be found in L an element t such that

$$(2) \qquad u \cap v \prec t < u$$

By the assumption $u \parallel v$, the element t differs from v. Hence, by (B), we obtain from (1) and (2)

$$(3) \qquad t \prec v \cup t$$

At the same time, by (2),

(4) $$t \leqq (v \cup t) \cap u \leqq v \cup t$$

But, again by the assumption $u \parallel v$, $(v \cup t) \cap u \neq v \cup t$ and hence by (4) and (3)

(5) $$(v \cup t) \cap u = t \prec v \cup t$$

Hence, the length of the interval $[(v \cup t) \cap u, u]$ is less than l. We shall show that $v \cup t \parallel u$. We have seen previously that $v \cup t \leqq u$ is impossible; so is, by (2) and (3), $v \cup t > u$. Consequently, the induction hypothesis can be applied to the pair of elements $u_1 = u$, $v_1 = v \cup t$; accordingly by (5), $(v \cup t) \cup u \succ u$. But by (2) $(v \cup t) \cup u = v \cup (t \cup u) = v \cup u$. Hence, $u \cup v \succ u$, completing the proof of the theorem.

Several other definitions of Birkhoff lattices are to be found in papers by Wilcox [215], [216], and Croisot [32], [36].

49. Semimodular Lattices

In the preceding paragraph we have pointed out, after having defined Birkhoff lattices, that this class of lattices can be regarded as a generalization of the concept of modular lattices of finite length. In the course of the evolution of lattice theory, there arose quite naturally the necessity to generalize Birkhoff lattices, in such a way that the class of lattices resulting from generalization should include all modular lattices, and that the lattices of finite length included in that class should be just the Birkhoff lattices.* From this point of view, Croisot has investigated numerous properties of Birkhoff lattices (see [36]) and adopted an axiom due to MacLane [127] as the defining property of semimodular lattices.

A narrower generalization of the concept of Birkhoff lattices has been given by Dilworth [43]. See also Maeda [132] and Sasaki [172].

A lattice L is called *semimodular* if to any triplet of elements a, b, x of L satisfying the conditions

(1) $$a \parallel b \quad \text{and} \quad a \cap b < x < a$$

there can be found a t such that

(2) $$a \cap b < t \leqq b$$

and

(3) $$(x \cup t) \cap a = x$$

This rather involved condition is illustrated by Fig. 27, in which the two elements connected by a brace can eventually coincide.

* It is not expedient to take any one of the conditions (A) — (C) figuring in Theorem 63, as a basis of such a generalization, since every one of them contains essential restrictions concerning certain pairs of covering elements of the lattice, and covering relations fail in many cases to reveal anything essential concerning the structure of a lattice of infinite length.

It is obvious that *every modular lattice is semi-modular*. In fact, if a triplet of elements a, b, x of a modular lattice satisfies the conditions (1), then $(x \cup b) \cap a = x \cup (b \cap a) = x$, so that taking $t = b$ (2) and (3) are satisfied.

We shall show below (see the Corollary to Theorem 65) that the class of the semimodular lattices of finite length and that of Birkhoff lattices coincide. As a preliminary we have the following theorem, which is also interesting and important in itself:

THEOREM 64. *Every semimodular lattice satisfies the lower covering condition.*

The theorem is essentially due to MacLane ([127], Theorem 15); see further Croisot [36].

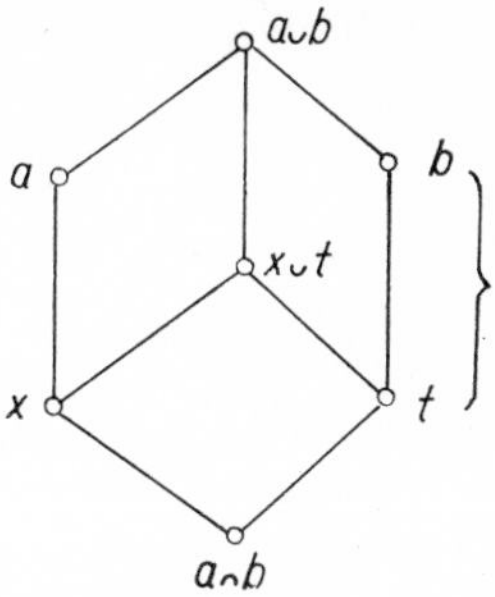

Fig. 27

PROOF. Let u, v be a pair of elements of a semimodular lattice such that $u \cap v \prec v$. If the elements u, v are comparable, then $u = u \cap v \prec v = u \cup v$. Hence, it is sufficient to treat the case $u \parallel v$. Suppose that — contrary to the proposition — there is an element q such that $u < q < u \cup v$. This q is incomparable with v, since $q \leqq v$ would imply $u < q \leqq v$, and $q \geqq v$ would imply $q \geqq u \cup v$, both in contradiction to our assumptions. Furthermore,

$$u \cap v \leqq q \cap v \leqq (u \cup v) \cap v = v$$

so that, by the assumption $u \cap v \prec v$, and by the result $q \parallel v$ just obtained, $q \cap v = u \cap v$. Hence, by substituting q for a, u for x and v for b (1) is satisfied. On the other hand, the inequalities $q \cap v < t \leqq v$ (corresponding to (2)) hold — considering that $q \cap v (= u \cap v) \prec v$ — only for $t = v$, but $(u \cup v) \cap q \neq u$. Hence, if in a lattice the lower covering condition fails, the lattice cannot be semimodular, and thus the theorem is proved.

Let us call a lattice L *relatively atomic** if each interval of L is an atomic sublattice in L, that is if to every pair of elements a, b $(a < b)$ of L there can be found an x $(\in L)$ covering a and less than or equal to b. For lattices of this kind, we have

THEOREM 65. *A relatively atomic lattice is semimodular if, and only if, it satisfies the lower covering condition.*

This result is again due essentially to MacLane, being a corollary of Theorems 14 and 8 of [127].

COROLLARY. *A lattice of finite length is semimodular if, and only if, it is a Birkhoff lattice.*

* Note that the term "relatively atomic" is employed in a different sense by Maeda [133].

Proof. Every lattice of finite length is relatively atomic, and hence the corollary is a particular case of the theorem. Further, by the preceding theorem, every semimodular lattice satisfies the lower covering condition. Hence, it only has to be proved that if a relatively atomic lattice satisfies the lower covering condition, it is semimodular.

We give an indirect proof. Let L be a relatively atomic lattice which is not semimodular. Then, there exists in L a triplet of elements a, b, x for which (1) is satisfied and for every t satisfying (2) there holds (instead of (3)) the inequality

(4) $$(x \cup t) \cap a > x$$

Since L is relatively atomic, there exists among these t one which covers $a \cap b$; in the following, we shall consider an element t having this property.

From the sequence of inequalities (1) and (2) we obtain by the meet operation $a \cap b \leqq x \cap t \leqq a \cap b$, hence, $a \cap b = x \cap t$. Thus (by the foregoing agreement concerning t),

(5) $$x \cap t \prec t$$

On the other hand, by (4), $x < (x \cup t) \cap a \leqq x \cup t$. But $(x \cup t) \cap a = x \cup t$ is impossible, since from that would follow $t \leqq x \cup t \leqq a$ which, together with (2), would imply $t \leqq a \cap b$. Consequently,

(6) $$x < (x \cup t) \cap a < x \cup t$$

However, inequalities (5) and (6) together imply precisely that the lower covering condition fails in L, completing the proof of the theorem.

It follows from our results that the class of semimodular lattices is broader than that of modular lattices. Every non-modular Birkhoff lattice is an example of a semimodular but non-modular lattice of finite length. An important class of semimodular lattices of infinite length will be cited in the following section.

The dual of a semimodular lattice is, contrary to that of a distributive or a modular lattice, not necessarily semimodular: for example, the lattice of Fig. 11 (p. 43) is semimodular, but in the dual of this lattice, $c \cap e \prec c$ is true while $e \prec c \cup e$ is not. Consequently the duals of true statements concerning semimodular lattices do not all hold for semimodular lattices.

It would be a likely conjecture that a semimodular lattice whose dual is semimodular is modular as well. This is, however, not necessarily true even in the lattice satisfies the maximal or minimal chain conditions ([50], p. 95).

The lattice of Fig. 11 also shows that the sublattices of a semimodular lattice are not all semimodular.* In fact, the set $\{o, b, e, i, c\}$ of that lattice forms a sublattice which is not semimodular.

* This implies, by a deep theorem in the theory of algebra, that the class of semimodular lattices cannot be characterised by identities alone.

On the other hand, we have

THEOREM 66. *Every convex sublattice of a semimodular lattice is semimodular.*

PROOF. Let R be a convex sublattice of the semimodular lattice L, and let a, b, x be elements of R satisfying (1). Then, there exists in L a t satisfying (2) and (3). We shall show that $t \in R$. Since R is a sublattice of L and $a, b \in R$, we have $a \frown b \in R$. Hence, by the convexity of R and by (2), t is indeed included in R.

Finally, we note that a semimodular lattice may have homomorphic images which are not semimodular (see, for example, [50], p. 101, Exercise 5). However if a lattice satisfies the maximum condition, then its homomorphic images are themselves semimodular ([50], p. 95, Theorem 2).

50. Equivalence Lattices

Let M be any lattice and let $\mathscr{E}(M)$ denote the set of all equivalence relations definable on the set M.

It is known* that by a *partition* of the set M we mean a decomposition of M into mutually disjoint subsets, that is, its representation in the form

$$M = \bigcup_{\gamma} M_\gamma \qquad (M_{\gamma'} \cap M_{\gamma''} = O, \text{ if } \gamma' \neq \gamma'')$$

The subsets M_γ are called the *classes of the partition* considered. In the following, the classes will be denoted by gothic letters while the set of all partitions of M will be denoted $\mathfrak{Z}(M)$.

It is also known that, starting from any equivalence relation Φ of M, we can form a partition $\mathfrak{c}(\Phi)$ of M as follows: the elements x and y of M shall belong to the same class of $\mathfrak{c}(\Phi)$ if, and only if, $x \equiv y(\Phi)$.

Conversely, every partition $\mathfrak{a}$ of a set M gives rise to an equivalence $\Theta(\mathfrak{a})$ in M. For some elements x, y of M, let $x \equiv y(\Theta(\mathfrak{a}))$ hold if, and only if, x and y are in the same class of $\mathfrak{a}$.

Further, having formed the partition $\mathfrak{c}(\Phi)$ started from the equivalence relation Φ as described above, and the equivalence relation $\Theta(\mathfrak{c}(\Phi))$ from $\mathfrak{c}(\Phi)$ as just defined, we get back to Φ; this can be expressed symbolically $\Theta\big(\mathfrak{c}(\Phi)\big) = \Phi$. Similarly, $\mathfrak{c}\big(\Theta(\mathfrak{a})\big) = \mathfrak{a}$. Hence, the correspondence

$$(1) \qquad \Phi \longrightarrow \mathfrak{c}(\Phi) \quad \big(\Phi \in \mathscr{E}(M);\ \mathfrak{c}(\Phi) \in \mathfrak{Z}(M)\big)$$

is a one-to-one mapping of $\mathscr{E}(M)$ onto $\mathfrak{Z}(M)$. Accordingly, it is usual to say that $\mathfrak{c}(\Phi)$ is the *partition belonging to the equivalence relation* Φ. Clearly, any equivalence relation and the partition belonging to it

* Concerning the definitions to follow, and the facts to be cited below without proof, see for example [228], pp. 18—20.

mutually determine each other. The classes of $\mathfrak{c}(\Phi)$ are frequently termed the *classes of the equivalence relation* Φ, or, for short, Φ*-classes*.

The determination of the equivalence relations of a given finite set M is most readily accomplished with the aid of their partitions. That is, the partitions of a finite set M of this kind can be described by subsuming the elements of M belonging to one class under one and the same pair of parentheses. In this notation, all partitions of the four-element set $M = \{1, 2, 3, 4\}$ can be enumerated as follows:

(1) (2) (3) (4);	(1, 2) (3) (4);	(1, 3) (2) (4);
(1, 4) (2) (3);	(1) (2, 3) (4);	(1) (2, 4) (3);
(1) (2) (3, 4);	(1, 2) (3, 4);	(1, 3) (2, 4);
(1, 4) (2, 3);	(1, 2, 3) (4);	(1, 2, 4) (3);
(1, 3, 4) (2);	(1) (2, 3, 4);	(1, 2, 3, 4).

Note that — as is readily seen — the set $\mathfrak{Z}(M)$ is finite if, and only if, M is finite.

In Section 45 we have discussed the set $\mathcal{R}(M)$ of all relations definable on a set M. The set $\mathscr{E}(M)$, as a subset of $\mathcal{R}(M)$, is of course itself partly ordered with respect to the ordering relation introduced on $\mathcal{R}(M)$ by (1) of Section 45. In the following, this ordering of $\mathscr{E}(M)$ will be considered throughout.

The greatest element I of $\mathcal{R}(M)$ and the equality relation E are equivalence relations; the former is the greatest, the latter the least element of $\mathscr{E}(M)$. Under the partition belonging to I, every element belongs to a single class, whereas under the partition belonging to E, each element of M forms a separate class.

It follows from the definition of the ordering relation introduced in $\mathscr{E}(M)$ that $\Theta \leq \Phi$ $(\Theta, \Phi \in \mathscr{E}(M))$ if, and only if, every Φ-class is the set union of certain Θ-classes. Particularly, $\Theta \prec \Phi$ if, and only if, one Φ-class is the set-union of exactly two Θ-classes while the rest of the classes of Φ coincide with the rest of the classes of Θ.

Now we shall proceed to prove

THEOREM 67. *The set* $\mathscr{E}(M)$ *of all equivalence relations of a set* M *is a relatively complemented semimodular complete lattice with respect to the ordering relation defined by* (1), *in Section* 45.

Accordingly, $\mathscr{E}(M)$ is called the *equivalence lattice* of the set M.

SUPPLEMENT. *Let* $\{\Theta_\gamma\}_{\gamma\in\Gamma}$ *be any subset of* $\mathscr{E}(M)$. *The* $\begin{Bmatrix} \textit{infinum} \\ \textit{supremum} \end{Bmatrix}$ *of the set* $\{\Theta_\gamma\}_{\gamma\in\Gamma}$ *in* $\mathscr{E}(M)$ *is the relation* $\begin{Bmatrix} \Pi \\ \Sigma \end{Bmatrix}$ *defined as follows: For a pair of elements* x, y *of* M,

$x \equiv y(\Pi)$ *if, and only if,* $x \equiv y(\Theta_\gamma)$ *for every* γ;

$x \equiv y(\Sigma)$ *if, and only if, in the set* M *a finite sequence of elements* $x = t_0, t_1, \ldots, t_r = y$ *exists such that to every one of the indices* $j = 1, \ldots, r$ *there can be found a* Θ_{γ_j} $(\gamma_j \in \Gamma)$ *such that* $t_{j-1} \equiv t_j(\Theta_{\gamma_j})$.

The statement of the Theorem was recognised for finite M by Birkhoff ([12], Theorems 18 and 19) and for arbitrary M by Ore ([153], Theorems 5 and 17 in Chapter 1 and Theorem 3 in Chapter 2).

The theorem will be proved together with its supplement. Let us, however, make some preliminary remarks.

Remark 1. By the one-to-one correspondence established by (1), the theorem is also valid — with suitable paraphrasing — for the set $\mathfrak{Z}(M)$. Accordingly, $\mathfrak{Z}(M)$ will be termed the *partition lattice* of M.

Moreover, in order to prove that $\mathscr{E}(M)$ is relatively complemented and semimodular, we shall utilize throughout partitions belonging to some equivalence relations, that is, the appropriate properties will be essentially proved for $\mathfrak{Z}(M)$.

Remark 2. It is to be seen from the supplement that $\mathscr{E}(M)$ is not a sublattice of $\mathscr{R}(M)$, since in the two lattices only the rule of meet is the same. The rule of the join in $\mathscr{E}(M)$ deviates from that in $\mathscr{R}(M)$, since the join of equivalence relations in $\mathscr{R}(M)$ is non-transitive in the general case; that is, it is not an equivalence relation.

For example let $M = \{x, y, z\}$, $\mathfrak{a} = (x, y)\,(z)$, $\mathfrak{b} = (x)\,(y, z)$; let the join in $\mathscr{R}(M)$ be denoted by $\cup$ and that in $\mathscr{E}(M)$ by $\smile$. Then we have $x \equiv y(\Theta(\mathfrak{a}) \cup \Theta(\mathfrak{b}))$, $y \equiv z(\Theta(\mathfrak{a}) \cup \Theta(\mathfrak{b}))$, but $x \not\equiv Z\,(\Theta\,(\mathfrak{a}) \cup \Theta\,(\mathfrak{b}))$. Nevertheless $x \equiv z(\Theta(\mathfrak{a}) \smile \Theta(\mathfrak{b}))$ holds.

PROOF. It follows immediately from the definition of Π and Σ that they are both equivalence relations on M and in particular, that the rule of infimum in $\mathscr{E}(M)$ is the same as in $\mathscr{R}(M)$. Thus, according to Theorem 17, $\mathscr{E}(M)$ is a complete lattice.

Furthermore, if $u \equiv v\,(\Theta_\gamma)$, then $u \equiv v\,(\Sigma)$; that is Σ is an upper bound of $\{\Theta_\gamma\}$. Let Φ be any upper bound of $\{\Theta_\gamma\}$ and let $x \equiv y(\Sigma)$ $(x, y \in M)$. Then for the t's figuring in the definition of Σ, there holds $t_0 \equiv t_1 \equiv \ldots \equiv t_r(\Phi)$, and thus, $x \equiv y(\Phi)$. Hence, $\Phi \geqq \Sigma$, that is, $\Sigma = \sup_{\mathscr{E}(M)} \{\Theta_\gamma\}$.

In the next step of the proof we shall show that the lattice $\mathscr{E}(M)$ is relatively atomic. Let Θ and Ψ be two elements of $\mathscr{E}(M)$ such that $\Theta < \Psi$. Let us form that equivalence relation Θ of M, one class of which is the set union of two classes Θ included by the same Ψ-class, while the rest of the classes of Φ coincide with the rest of the classes of Θ. Clearly $\Theta \prec \Phi \leqq \Psi$.

Moreover the lattice $\mathscr{E}(M)$ satisfies the lower covering condition. To prove this assertion, let Θ and Φ be two elements of $\mathscr{E}(M)$ such that $\Theta \frown \Phi \prec \Phi$. Then the Φ-classes, disregarding a single class M^*, coincide with the classes of $\Theta \frown \Phi$, and M^* can be decomposed in exactly two $(\Theta \frown \Phi)$-classes; let the latter be denoted by M_1 and M_2. Let us further denote by M_j^Θ $(j = 1, 2)$ the Θ-class including M_j; clearly, $M_1^\Theta \neq M_2^\Theta$. (The above considerations are illustrated by Fig. 28 on the next page).However, if $x \in M_1^\Theta$, $y \in M_2^\Theta$, then, taking an arbitrary pair of elements t_1, t_2 $(t_1 \in M_1;\ t_2 \in M_2)$,

$$x \equiv t_1(\Theta), \qquad t_1 \equiv t_2(\Phi), \qquad t_2 \equiv y(\Theta)$$

that is, $x \equiv y(\Theta \smile \Phi)$. Hence, the Θ-classes M_1^Θ and M_2^Θ unite into a single $(\Theta \smile \Phi)$-class. At the same time, on the set $M - (M_1^\Theta \cup M_2^\Theta)$, the equivalence relation $\Theta \cap \Phi$ coincides with Φ, and hence, in this same set, $\Theta \cup \Phi$ coincides with Θ. The above two statements, however, imply the relation $\Theta \prec \Theta \cup \Phi$ which was to be proved.

By the results of the two preceding paragraphs and by Theorem 65, $\mathscr{E}(M)$ is semi-modular.

The proof of relative complementarity is left. Consider any elements Θ, Φ, Ψ $(\Theta \leq \Psi \leq \Phi)$ of $\mathscr{E}(M)$. Let $\{M_\varphi\}$ be the set of all Φ-classes. Clearly, every M_φ is the union of some Ψ-classes $M_{\varphi\psi}$, and every $M_{\varphi\psi}$ is the union of some Θ-classes.*

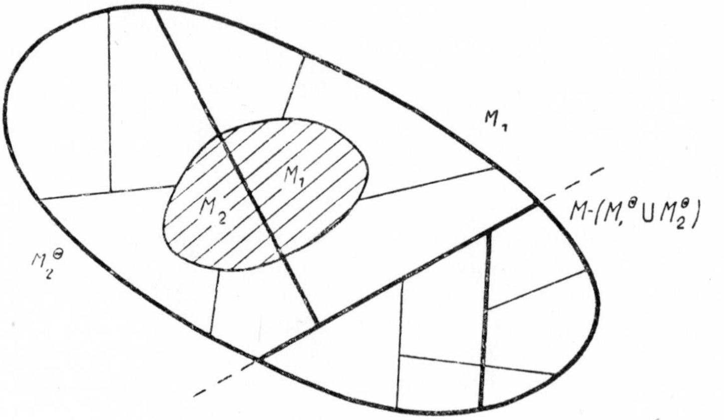

"Boundary" of Θ-classes
"Boundary" of $(\Theta \cap \Theta)$-classes

Fig. 28

Select one Θ-class from each $M_{\varphi\psi}$ and call it the "preferred Θ-class" of $M_{\varphi\psi}$. Then define the equivalence relation T as follows: Let the set union of all preferred Θ-classes included in the same Φ-class form a T-class and let the remaining T-classes coincide with the remaining Θ-classes. Clearly, $\Theta \leq \mathrm{T} \leq \Phi$, and hence, $\Theta \leq \Psi \cap \mathrm{T} \leq \Psi \cup \mathrm{T} \leq$ $\leq \Phi$. We shall show that both $\Theta \geq \Psi \cap \mathrm{T}$ and $\Psi \cup \mathrm{T} \geq \Phi$ are satisfied, i.e. that T is the relative complement of Ψ in $[\Theta, \Phi]$.

Let $u \equiv v(\Psi \cap \mathrm{T})$ $(u, v \in M)$, that is, $u \equiv v(\Psi)$ and $u \equiv v(\mathrm{T})$. Since in every Ψ-class there is precisely one preferred Θ-class, u and v must by the definition of T be in the same Θ-class. Hence, $\Psi \cap \mathrm{T} \leq \Theta$.

Now let $w \equiv z(\Phi)$ $(w, z \in M)$ and let $M_{\varphi\psi}$ and $M_{\varphi\bar{\psi}}$ denote the Ψ-class ncluding w and z; of course, $\psi = \bar{\psi}$ is not excluded. If t and $\bar{t}$ are any

* It can happen, of course, that some Φ- or Ψ-class consists of a single Ψ- or Θ-class; however, in the considerations to follow, this will cause no particular difficulty.

elements of the preferred Θ-class of $M_{\varphi\psi}$ and $M_{\varphi\bar{\psi}}$ respectively, then

$$w \equiv t(\Psi), \quad t \equiv \bar{t}(\mathsf{T}), \quad \bar{t} \equiv z(\Psi),$$

that is, $w \equiv z(\Psi \cup \mathsf{T})$, and hence, $\Phi \leq \Psi \cup \mathsf{T}$, completing the proof of the theorem.

To stress the significance of equivalence lattices, let us remark that every lattice is isomorphic with some sublattice of a suitably chosen equivalence lattice. (Whitman [214], Theorem 1). Hence, every lattice is isomorphic with some sublattice of a semimodular lattice. In particular for lattices of finite length the following stronger theorem was proved by Finkbeiner [62]: To every lattice L of finite length a semimodular lattice L^* can be constructed that is also of finite length, has as many atoms as L itself and possesses a sublattice isomorphic to L.

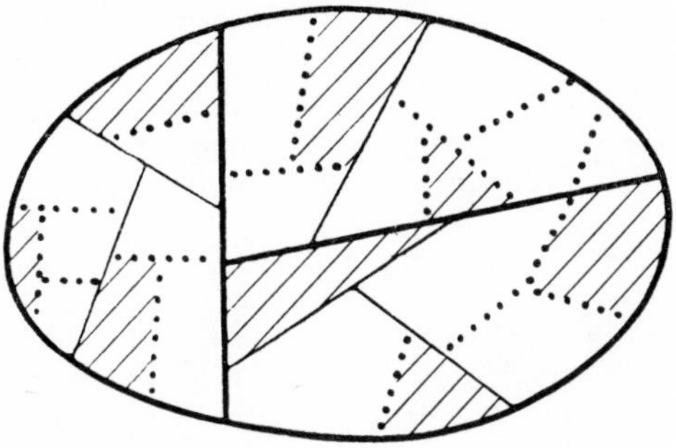

▬▬ "Boundary" of	Φ — classes	··· "Boundary" of	Θ — classes
—— "Boundary" of	Ψ — classes	///// Preferred	Θ — classes

Fig. 29.

Hartmanis [87] introduced the concept of partition of type n as follows: A partition of type n ($n \geq 1$), on a set M consisting of n or more elements is a collection of subsets of M such that any n distinct elements of M are contained in exactly one subset and every subset contains at least n distinct elements. He has shown that all the partitions of type n of a set M form a complemented complete lattice. Concerning the result of Hartmanis we remark that it can be deduced from Theorem 67. Namely, as can be verified by simple reasoning, the lattice of all the partitions of type n is isomorphic with $\chi(M^n)$, where M^n is the product set of M-s in number n.

51. Linear Dependence

In algebra and geometry the relation of linear dependence is frequently encountered. The essence of the concept is as follows. Consider the set $\mathscr{F}(M)$ of all finite subsets of a given set M and define in the product set $M \times \mathscr{F}(M)$ a relation Λ satisfying the following conditions (where $p, q, p_1, \ldots p_m, q_1, \ldots q_n$ denote certain elements of M):

$$\mathsf{A}_1. \quad p_j \Lambda \{p_1 \ldots, p_m\} \quad (j = 1, \ldots, m);$$

A_2. *If* $p \Lambda \{p_1, \ldots, p_m\}$ *and for every* j, $p_j \Lambda \{q_1, \ldots, q_n\}$, *then* $p \Lambda \{q_1, \ldots, q_n\}$;

A_3. *If* $p \Lambda \{p_1, \ldots, p_m, q\}$, *but* $p \Lambda' \{p_1, \ldots, p_m\}$, *then* $q \Lambda \{p_1, \ldots, p_m, p\}$.

The relation Λ having these properties is called a *linear dependence** defined on the set M, moreover, if $p \Lambda \{p_1, \ldots, p_m\}$, then p is said to *depend linearly* on the set $\{p, \ldots, p_m\}$ (or on the elements $p_1, \ldots, p_m$). If, on the other hand, $p \Lambda' \{p_1, \ldots, p_m\}$, p is said to be *linearly independent* of the set $\{p_1, \ldots, p_m\}$ (or of the elements $p_1, \ldots, p_m$).

We shall define — following Birkhoff [13] — a linear dependence on the set of the atoms of a semimodular lattice. This definition will contain as particular cases the concepts of linear dependence as usually meant in projective and affine spaces.

Let L be a lattice bounded below and let A denote the set of all atoms of L. Let us define between the elements and the finite subsets of A a relation Λ as follows: for any elements $p, p_1, \ldots, p_m$ of A, let

$$(1) \qquad p \Lambda \{p_1, \ldots, p_m\} \Leftrightarrow p \leqq p_1 \cup \ldots \cup p_m$$

It is obvious that the axioms A_1 and A_2 hold without any restrictions concerning L. However, Axiom A_3 is not always satisfied: for example, in the lattice shown as Fig. 30 (p. 157), $b \Lambda \{a, c\}$ and $b \Lambda' \{a\}$, but $c \Lambda' \{a, b\}$.

For semimodular lattices, however, the following theorem holds:

THEOREM 68. *On the set of atoms of a semimodular lattice bounded below, relation* (1) *defines a linear dependence.*

PROOF. We have only to show that if L is a semimodular lattice bounded below, then the relation under (1) also satisfies A_3. For this purpose, consider atoms $p, q, p_1, \ldots, p_m$ of the lattice L satisfying the two conditions included in A_3, that is, such that

$$(2) \qquad p \leqq p_1 \cup \ldots \cup p_m \cup q, \text{ but}$$

$$(3) \qquad p \nleqq p_1 \cup \ldots \cup p_m$$

These directly imply that

$$(4) \qquad q \nleqq p_1 \cup \ldots \cup p_m$$

since otherwise (2) would imply

$$p \leqq p_1 \cup \ldots \cup p_m \cup q = p_1 \cup \ldots \cup p_m$$

in contradiction with (3).

* The definition of linear independence as given by Kertész ([112], p. 260) generalizes the axioms $\mathsf{A}_1 - \mathsf{A}_3$ so that the finite subsets of M are there replaced by arbitrary subsets of it; at the same time, however, he brings in an additional axiom of finiteness.

Since p is an atom of L, we have $p \cap \bigcup_{j=1}^{m} p_j = o \prec p$ by (3). However, by Theorem 64, the lower covering condition holds in L, and hence

$$p_1 \cup \ldots \cup p_m \prec p_1 \cup \ldots \cup p_m \cup p \tag{5}$$

We obtain in a similar manner from (4)

$$p_1 \cup \ldots \cup p_m \prec p_1 \cup \ldots \cup p_m \cup q \tag{6}$$

At the same time, by (2),

$$p_1 \cup \ldots \cup p_m \cup p \leqq p_1 \cup \ldots \cup p_m \cup q \tag{7}$$

But, by (5) and (7), we get

$$p_1 \cup \ldots \cup p_m \prec p_1 \cup \ldots \cup p_m \cup p \leqq p_1 \cup \ldots \cup p_m \cup q$$

and by (6) this is possible only if the sign "$=$" is valid instead of "$\leqq$". But then, $q \leqq p_1 \cup \ldots \cup p_m \cup p$, that is, q depends linearly on $\{p_1, \ldots, p_m, p\}$, completing the proof of A_3.

Some finite set $\{p_1, \ldots, p_m\}$ of the atoms of a lattice L bounded below is called *linearly independent* if every p_j $(j = 1, \ldots, m)$ is linearly independent of $p - \{p_j\}$. An infinite set of the atoms of L is called linearly independent if every finite subset of the set is linearly independent.

An obvious fact but nevertheless an important one is that *every subset of a linearly independent set of atoms is also linearly independent.*

We have furthermore,

THEOREM 69. *From any non-void set of atoms of a semimodular lattice bounded below, it is possible to select a maximal linearly independent set of atoms and every linearly independent set of atoms of such a lattice can be extended into a maximal linearly independent set.*

Of course, a set M of atoms of the lattice L is called a maximal linearly independent set if M is linearly independent but every atom of L depends linearly on M.

PROOF. Let L be a semimodular lattice bounded below, M a set consisting of certain atoms of L and S an arbitrary linearly independent subset of M. Consider the set $\mathscr{H}$ of all linearly independent subsets of M containing S. We shall show that if $\{H_\gamma\}_{\gamma\in\Gamma}$ is an arbitrary subchain of $\mathscr{H}$, then $\bigcup_{\gamma\in\Gamma} H_\gamma$ is also included in $\mathscr{H}$. Firstly, $S \subseteq \bigcup_{\gamma\in\Gamma} H_\gamma \subseteq M$. Furthermore, also $\bigcup_{\gamma\in\Gamma} H_\gamma$ is linearly independent. Otherwise, there would exist in $\bigcup_{\gamma\in\Gamma} H_\gamma$ elements $x_0, x_1, \ldots, x_n$ such that $x_0 \leqq x_1 \cup \ldots \cup x_n$. However, every $x_j (j = 0, 1, \ldots, n)$ is included in some H_{γ_j} $(\gamma_j \in \Gamma)$; hence, if $H_{\bar\gamma} (\bar\gamma \in \Gamma)$ is the largest of the H_{γ_j}, then $x_0, x_1, \ldots, x_n \in H_{\bar\gamma}$. Since $H_{\bar\gamma} \in \mathscr{H}$, we have $x_0 \nleqq x_1 \cup \ldots \cup x_n$, in contradiction to the foregoing result.

By the above said, $\mathscr{H}$ satisfies the conditions of the Kuratowski—Zorn lemma, and by this lemma, $\mathscr{H}$ has a maximal element. Applying this result to the case $S = \{p\}$ $(p \in M)$, we obtain the first proposition of the theorem. If, on the other hand, M denotes the set of all atoms of L, we obtain (as a particular case) the second proposition of the theorem.

We shall now discuss finite linearly independent sets of atoms.

THEOREM 70. *The finite set* $\{p_1, \ldots, p_n\}$ *of atoms of a semimodular lattice* L *bounded below is linearly independent if, and only if,*

$$(p_1 \cup \ldots \cup p_{k-1}) \cap p_k = o \quad (k = 2, \ldots, n) \tag{8}$$

PROOF. Let $\{p_1, \ldots, p_n\}$ be a linearly independent set of the atoms of L. By the remark preceding Theorem 69, every p_k is linearly independent of $\{p_1, \ldots, p_{k-1}\}$. This means, by the definition, that $p_k \nleqq p_1 \cup \ldots \cup p_{k-1}$, which is equivalent to (8).

Conversely, let $\{p_1, \ldots, p_n\}$ be a set of the atoms of L which satisfy (8). In the case $n = 2$ this means that $p_1 \cap p_2 = o$, and thus, that $\{p_1, p_2\}$ is linearly independent. Hence, we can assume that our statement holds for every set consisting of at most $n - 1$ atoms of L where n is any integer greater than 1.

Applying (8) to $k = n$, we get directly that p_n is linearly independent of $p - \{p_n\}$. Let r be some index less than n; by the induction hypothesis p_r is linearly independent of $P - \{p_r, p_n\}$. Suppose for a moment that p_r depends linearly on $P - \{p_r\}$; then, by A_3, p_n would depend linearly on $P - \{p_n\}$, in contradiction to our foregoing remark. Hence, every p_r must be linearly independent of the set $P - \{p_r\}$ and this is exactly what has been stated above (in a different formulation).

In the case of semimodular lattices of finite length it is possible to give a condition very easy to work, for the linear independence of atoms by making use of the height of the elements:

THEOREM 71. *If* $p_1, \ldots, p_n$ *are arbitrary atoms of a Birkhoff lattice, then*

$$h(p_1 \cup \ldots \cup p_n) \leqq n$$

where $h(x)$ *is the height of the element* x *and equality prevails if, and only if, this set is linearly independent.*

COROLLARY. *In a Birkhoff lattice, every linearly independent set of atoms is finite.*

PROOF. If $p_1, \ldots, p_n$ are any atoms of the lattice, then for any p_k $(k = 1, \ldots, n)$, two cases may occur: either p_k is independent of the atoms of lesser index, or it is not. In the former case, $(p_1 \cup \ldots \cup p_{k-1}) \cap p_k = o \prec p_k$; that is, by the lower covering condition, $p_1 \cup \ldots \cup p_{k-1} \prec p_1 \cup \ldots \cup p_k$. In the latter case, $p_1 \cup \ldots \cup p_{k-1} \geqq p_k$, and hence, $p_1 \cup \ldots \cup p_{k-1} = p_1 \cup \ldots \cup p_k$. In any case,

$$o \prec p_1 \preceq p_1 \cup p_2 \preceq \ldots \preceq p_1 \cup \ldots \cup p_n \tag{9}$$

that is, the length of the maximal chain (9) between o and $p_1 \cup \cup \ldots \cup p_n$ is at most n. Consequently, since the Jordan—Dedekind chain condition is satisfied (by Theorem 41) $h(p_1 \cup \ldots \cup p_n) \leqq n$. If $\{p_1, \ldots, p_n\}$ is linearly independent, then in (9) the symbol "$\prec$ holds everywhere, and thus $h(p_1 \cup \ldots \cup p_n) = n$.

Conversely, assume that $h(p_1 \cup \ldots \cup p_n) = n$. In this case, the length of every maximal chain between the element o and $p_1 \cup \ldots \cup \cup p_n$ is n. However, the chain (9) is maximal, therefore its length is likewise n. Accordingly, now the symbol "$\prec$" holds everywhere in (9), wherefore the equations (8) hold for these atoms. Hence, the set $\{p_1, \ldots, p_n\}$ is linearly independent.

52. Complemented Semimodular Lattices

As yet, little is known about the structure of complemented semimodular lattices. In this Section, some simple results of this topic will be treated. However, let us verify first the following theorem of more general validity which is also important in itself:

THEOREM 72. *The join of all atoms of a semi complemented lattice of finite length equals the greatest element of the lattice* (Szász [190]).

COROLLARY. *Every element of a weakly complemented lattice of finite length can be represented as the join of atoms.*

Let us recall before starting the proof that every lattice of finite length is complete (see Theorem 18); that is, in a lattice of finite length, the join of all atoms exists.

PROOF. Let us denote by u the join of all atoms of the semi complemented lattice of finite length L, and let us suppose, in contradiction with the statement, that $u \neq i$. Then, u has (at least) one proper semicomplement x. Since L is of finite length, an atom p can be found such that $p \leqq x$; by the definition of x, there holds $u \cap p (\leqq u \cap x) = = o$. On the other hand, $u \geqq p$ by the definition of u. Consequently, the assumption $u \neq i$ leads to a contradiction, whence only $u = i$ is possible.

To prove the corollary, it is sufficient, by the theorem just proved, to show that any sublattice $[o, a]$ of a weakly complemented lattice L is semicomplemented. For this purpose, consider an arbitrary inner element b of $[o, a]$. (If $[o, a]$ has no inner element, it is evidently semicomplemented.) Since L is weakly complemented, b has a semicomplement x such that $y = a \cap x \neq o$. But $b \cap y = b \cap (x \cap a) = = (b \cap x) \cap a = o$, that is, y is a proper semicomplement of b.

Applying the above reasoning the following generalization of the theorem, and of the corollary can also be proved: 1. If in a semicomplemented, atomic lattice the join of all the atoms does exist, this is the greatest element of the lattice. 2. Every element of a weakly complemented, atomic lattice can be represented as a join of atoms.

For Birkhoff lattices, also the following converse of Theorem 72 holds:

THEOREM 73. *If the greatest element of a Birkhoff lattice can be represented as the join of atoms, it is complemented and if every one of its elements can be represented as the join of atoms, it is relatively complemented.*

COROLLARY 1. *A Birkhoff lattice is complemented (relatively complemented) if, and only if, its greatest element (all of its elements) can be represented as joins of atoms.*

COROLLARY 2. *If a Birkhoff lattice is semicomplemented, it is also complemented.*

The theorem and Corollary 1 were proved by Birkhoff and first published in § 76 of the first edition of [19]. Concerning Corollary 2, see Szász [190].

PROOF. Consider a Birkhoff lattice L. Let A_x denote the set of all atoms of $(x]$ $(x \in L)$, provided $x \neq o$, and let $A_o = \{o\}$. We shall show that if a, b, r are such (otherwise arbitrary) elements of L that

$$a \leqq r \leqq b,\ a = \bigcup_{p \in A_a} p,\ b = \bigcup_{p \in A_b} p \tag{1}$$

then r has a relative complement in $[a, b]$.

If $r = a$ or $r = b$, the proposition is trivial; hence, it is legitimate to assume $a < r < b$. Introduce the notation $A^* = A_b - A_r$; by $r < b$, A^* is non-void. Select from A^* a subset $\{p_1, p_2, \ldots\}$ in the following way: take as p_1 any element of A^*, and as p_k one of the elements of A^* such that

$$(r \cup p_1 \cup \ldots \cup p_{k-1}) \cap p_k = o$$

By the lower covering condition,

$$r \cup p_1 \cup \ldots \cup p_{k-1} \prec r \cup p_1 \cup \ldots \cup p_k \quad (k = 1, 2, \ldots) \tag{2}$$

Since L is of finite length, by (2) the described procedure of selection cannot be continued beyond a finite index n. In other words, there must exist a finite index n such that for every atom p of A^* the inequality $r \cup p_1 \cup \ldots \cup p_n \geqq p$ is true. But then, considering (1), we have

$$r \cup p_1 \cup \ldots \cup p_n \geqq \bigcup_{p \in A_a} p \cup \bigcup_{p \in A^*} p = \bigcup_{p \in A_b} p = b$$

and, on the other hand, by $r \leqq b$ and $p_1, \ldots, p_n \leqq b$ we have $r \cup p_1 \cup \ldots \cup p_n \leqq b$. By these two inequalities,

$$r \cup p_1 \cup \ldots \cup p_n = b \tag{3}$$

Now consider the element $s = a \cup p_1 \cup \ldots \cup p_n$. We shall show that s is precisely a relative complement of r in $[a, b]$. By (3), $r \cup s = b \cup a = b$. Furthermore, $r \cap s \geqq a$. Consequently, to prove our proposition, it is sufficient to show that the height of $r \cap s$ is at most as great as that of the element a (since then, we have necessarily $r \frown s = a$). By Theorem 42, the inequality (8) of Section 37 holds for the height of the elements in L; applying this inequality twice, we have

$$h(r \frown s) \leqq h(r) + h(s) - h(r \smile s) =$$

$$= h(r) + h(a \smile (p_1 \smile \ldots \smile p_n)) - h(b) \leqq$$

$$\leqq h(r) + h(a) + h(p_1 \smile \ldots \smile p_n) - h(b)$$

But by Theorem 71, $h(p_1 \smile \ldots \smile p_n) \leqq n$, and at the same time by (3) and (2), $h(b) = h(r) + n$. Hence,

$$h(r \frown s) \leqq h(r) + h(a) + n - (h(r) + n) = h(a)$$

Summarizing, *if* (1) *is satisfied for some triplet of elements a, b, r of L, then r has a relative complement in* $[a, b]$. This yields immediately the second statement of the theorem whereas the first is obtained by applying the above result to the case $a = o$, $b = i$.

Corollary 1 can be derived from Theorem 72, from its corollary and from the theorem just proved (taking into consideration that by Theorem 12 every relatively complemented lattice bounded below is weakly complemented as well). Now the proposition of Corollary 2 can be verified as follows: If L is a semicomplemented semimodular lattice of finite length, then by Theorem 72, the greatest element of L can be represented as the join of atoms; but then, by Theorem 73, L is complemented.

Corollary 2 to Theorem 73 gives rise to the problem as to what, possibly general, conditions are sufficient so that for semimodular lattices the property of being semicomplemented shall imply their also being complemented. Corollary 1 of Theorem 74 below will give a rather general sufficient (but not necessary) condition.

THEOREM 74. *If an element r of a semicomplemented semimodular lattice L has a maximal proper semicomplement m, then L has a greatest element, and m is the complement of r* (Szász [193]).

COROLLARY. *If every inner element of a semimodular lattice has a maximal proper semicomplement, then the lattice has a greatest element and is complemented.*

PROOF. Since the theorem is clearly true for the bound elements of the lattice, we can restrict the discussion to the case when r is an inner element of L.

The Theorem will be proved indirectly. In fact, we show the following: *If r is an inner element of L and f is a proper semicomplement of L such that d-$r \smile f$ is still an inner element of L, then r has a semicomplement greater than f.*

Accordingly, let r and f be two elements of L for which the above conditions hold. Assuming that d is an inner element of L, it has a proper semicomplement x; for this x,

$$x \cap f \leqq x \cap d = o \tag{4}$$

The statement to be proved will now be decomposed into two parts:

1. If some element z of L satisfies the conditions

$$o < z \leqq x \tag{5}$$

and

$$(z \cup f) \cap d = f \tag{6}$$

then $z \cup f$ is a proper semicomplement of r, and $z \cup f > f$.

2. If r is an inner element of L and f is a semicomplement of r such that $d = r \cup f$ is likewise an inner element, then there exists in L an element z satisfying conditions (5) and (6).

PROOF OF 1. By the meaning of d we have $r = r \cap d$, and thus by (6)

$$r \cap (z \cup f) = r \cap d \cap (z \cup f) = r \cap f = o$$

that is, $z \cup f$ is a semicomplement of r. Further, by (5) and (4), $z \cap f \leqq x \cap f = o < z$. Now $z \cap f < z$ is equivalent to $z \cup f > f$.

PROOF OF 2. Introduce the following notation:

$$v = (x \cup f) \cap d \tag{7}$$

Then $d \geqq f$ implies $v \geqq f$.

If $v = f$, then (6) is satisfied by the substitution $z = x$. However, for $z = x$ (5) is also satisfied, x being a proper semicomplement of d, there holds $o < x (\leqq x)$.

There remains the case $v > f$. We shall show that then

$$x \parallel v \quad \text{and} \quad x \cap v < f < v \tag{8}$$

Indeed, by (7) and (4),

$$x \cap v = x \cap (x \cup f) \cap d = x \cap d = o (< f)$$

and thus, neither $x \leqq v$ (since $x \neq o$), nor $x \geqq v$ (since $o < f < v$). Consequently $x \parallel v$. Hence, both statements of (8) are true.

We shall now make use of L being semimodular. By (8), there exists an element $t (\in L)$ such that

$$x \cap v < t \leqq x \tag{9}$$

and

$$f = (f \cup t) \cap v \tag{10}$$

By (9), $t \cup f \leqq x \cup f$ and hence, by (10) and (7)

$$f = (t \cup f) \cap v = (t \cup f) \cap (x \cup f) \cap d = (t \cup f) \cap d \tag{11}$$

Finally, from (9) and (11) we see, that (5) and (6) hold for $z = t$, completing the proof.

Attention is called to the fact that the theorem fails for non-semimodular lattices. For example, in the lattice shown in Fig. 30 c is a maximal semi-complement of b, and yet it is not a complement of it; moreover, b has no complement at all.

Exercises to Chapter VII

1. Verify that the lattice shown in Fig. 11 (p. 43) is the non-modular Birkhoff lattice having the least number of elements.
2. Define in a Birkhoff lattice L of length n an equivalence relation Θ as follows: let $x \equiv y(\Theta)$ $(x, y \in L)$ hold if, and only if, either $x = y$ or $h(x)$, $h(y) \geqq m$, where m is a positive integer less than n. Show that all Θ-classes of L form a Birkhoff lattice which is the join-homomorphic image of L.
3. Prove that in any bounded semimodular lattice, all elements of finite height form an ideal.
4. Draw the diagram of the partition lattice of the two-, three- and four-element set.
5. Prove that every equivalence lattice is atomic as well as dually atomic.
6. Show that the equivalence lattice of an infinite set satisfies neither the maximum nor the minimum condition.

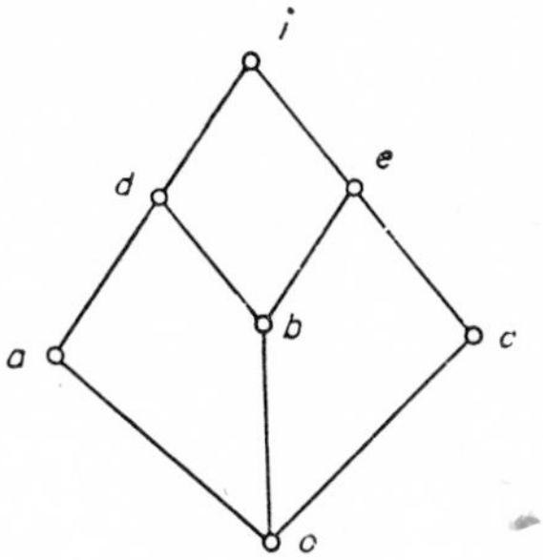

Fig. 30

7. Show that any equivalence lattice L has a sublattice R such that
   a) R is a Boolean algebra;
   b) Each element of L has a complement included by R.
8. Show that the equivalence lattice of a set including at least four elements cannot be modular.
9. Show that if the greatest element of a Birkhoff lattice can be represented as the join of atoms, then it can be represented also as the join of a finite number of atoms.
10. Show that if the greatest element of a Birkhoff lattice can be represented as the join of atoms, than every one of its intervals $[a, i]$ is a complemented sublattice.
11. Let M be a relatively complemented modular lattice of finite length and let u be any inner element of M. Prove that on deleting from M every element of $(u]$ other than o, the remaining elements

form a Birkhoff lattice L with respect to the original ordering relation.

12. Let L be a lattice bounded below and let x be an element of L which can be represented in the form $x = p_1 \cup \ldots \cup p_r$ where $\{p_1 \ldots p_r\}$ is a linearly independent set of atoms of L. Show that for every valuation v of L,

$$v(x) = \sum_{j=1}^{r} v(p_j) - (r-1)\, v(o)$$

13. Show that any set of atoms of a distributive lattice bounded below is linearly independent.

14. Let L be a semicomplemented semimodular lattice L of infinite length, every element of which is of finite height. Show that there can be found to every inner element a $(\in L)$ and to every positive integer r an x $(\in L)$ which is a semicomplement of a, of exactly height r.

15. Prove that if an atomic semicomplemented semimodular lattice bounded below has a finite number r of atoms, then the length of the lattice is at most r.

16. Prove that every subinterval and homomorphic image of a Birkhoff lattice is likewise a Birkhoff lattice.

17. Show that if a relatively complemented semimodular lattice satisfies the minimum condition, then the lattice is of locally finite length.

18. Give an example of a complemented semimodular lattice which is not relatively complemented.

19. Prove: If a semimodular semicomplemented lattice satisfies the maximum condition, the lattice is complemented as well.

20. Prove that if a semicomplemented lattice is infinitely meet-distributive, then it is bounded and complemented.

CHAPTER VIII

IDEALS OF LATTICES

53. Ideals and Dual Ideals. Ideal Chains

As stated at the end of Section 20, by an ideal of a lattice L is meant a non-void subset I of L which satisfies the following conditions:

I_1. *$a, b \in I$ implies $a \cup b \in I$.*

I_2. *$a \in I$ implies $a \cap x \in I$ for every element x* of L.

In this definition, the condition I_2 can be changed by the following:

I_3. *$a \in I$ and $y \leqq a$ imply $y \in I$.*

Indeed, if $a \in I$, $y \leqq a$ and if I_2 holds for I, then $y = y \cap a \in I$; conversely, if $a \in I$, $x \in L$ and I_3 holds for I, then $a \cap x \leqq a$ implies $a \cap x \in I$.

By the definition of ideals, it follows that the least element of a lattice bounded below forms an ideal, in itself. This ideal is called the *zero ideal* of the lattice in question.

By dualizing the ideal concept, the concept of the *dual ideal* is arrived at. Accordingly if a lattice theoretical statement involves ideals and dual ideals, these two concepts have to be interchanged in the course of dualizing the statement.

Let us remark that in this book, we shall usually mention ideals only, and the corresponding statements concerning dual ideals will not even be formulated.

There holds

THEOREM 75. *Every ideal and dual ideal of a lattice L is a convex sublattice of L. Conversely, every convex sublattice of L is the set intersection of an ideal and of a dual ideal.*

PROOF. It has already been shown in Section 16 that every ideal I is a sublattice. Let $a, b \in I$ and $a \leqq b$. Then, by I_3 $I \supseteq (b] \supseteq [a, b]$; that is, I is convex.

Conversely, let K be some convex sublattice of the lattice L. Consider the elements x of L to which there can be found in K an element v such that $x \leqq v$, and denote the set of all such x by I. It is clear that the set I has the property I_3; we shall show that it has also the property I_1. If $x, y \in I$, then by the definition of I there exist in K elements v and w such that $x \leqq v$ and $y \leqq w$. But then $x \cup y \leqq v \cup w$, and since K is a sublattice of L, $v \cup w \in K$. Hence, $x \cup y \in I$.

The dual of the definition of I defines a subset D of L, which is, by the dual of the above consideration, a dual ideal in L.

Clearly, $K \subseteq I \cap D$. But also $K \supseteq I \cap D$, since if $t \in I \cap D$, then (by the definitions of I and D) there exists in K a pair of elements u, v such that $u \leqq t \leqq v$, and thus, by the convexity of K, $t \in K$.

The concept of a lattice theoretical ideal was defined by Stone ([183], p. 197) analogous to the ideal concept in ring theory. The analogy is, however, rather superficial as is confirmed by a number of circumstances.

Thus, contrary to the well-known results of ring theory, a lattice L_0 can have homomorphisms φ_1: $L_0 \sim L_1$ and φ_2: $L_0 \sim L_2$ having the same kernel and L_1 can still be non-isomorphic to L_2. Consider for example the two- and three-element chains

$$C_1\colon o_1 \prec a \prec i_1 \qquad C_2\colon o_2 \prec i_2$$

The mapping

$$\iota\colon \iota(x) = x \ (x \in C_1)$$

of C_1 onto itself and the mapping

$$\psi : \psi(o_1) = o_2,\ \psi(a) = \psi(i_1) = i_2$$

of C_1 onto C_2 are both homomorphisms with the kernel (o_1); the homomorphic images generated by φ and ψ are nevertheless non-isomorphic.

In the next chapter we shall encounter further facts confirming that there are profound differences between the properties of lattice theoretical and ring theoretical ideals. However, the formal analogy permits the definition of some particular classes of lattice ideals, very important in lattice theory.

An ideal I of the lattice L is called a *prime ideal* if, and only if, at least one of an arbitrary pair of elements whose meet is in L is contained in I. As a matter of course, the dual prime ideal is defined by dualizing the concept of prime ideal.

Let a be any element of the lattice L. Clearly $(a]$ is an ideal, whereas $[a)$ is a dual ideal of L; they are called the *principal ideal* and the *dual principal ideal*, respectively, generated by a.

There holds

THEOREM 76. *For every ideal of a lattice to be principal, it is necessary and sufficient for the lattice to satisfy the maximum condition* (Dilworth [43], Lemma 2.1).

In other words, the lattice theoretical analogue of the "ring of principal ideals" is the lattice satisfying the maximum condition.

Before proving the theorem, some preparation is necessary.

By an *ideal chain* of a lattice L we shall mean a set of ideals in L in which one of every pair of ideals includes the other. Concerning ideal chains, we shall prove the following:

LEMMA. *The set union of any ideal chain of a lattice L is itself an ideal in L.*

PROOF. Let $\mathfrak{C}$ be a chain of ideals of L and let I denote the set union of all ideals of L in $\mathfrak{C}$; it is to be shown that I is an ideal in L. Let a and b be two arbitrary elements of I. There exist in $\mathfrak{C}$ ideals A and B such that $a \in A$, $b \in B$, and we can assume that $A \subseteq B$ (in the opposite case, only the roles of a and b need be interchanged). But then a, $b \in B$, and hence by the property I_1 (valid for B),

$a \cup b \in B \subseteq I$. Thus we have proved that I satisfies I_1. Let now x be any element of L. Then, by the property I_2, (valid for A), $a \cap x \in A \subseteq I$. This means, however, that I also satisfies I_2.

We are now in a position to prove the theorem itself.

If the maximum condition is satisfied in the lattice L, then it is also satisfied in every ideal I of L. Hence, by the Corollary of Theorem 10, I includes a greatest element a. But then, by the property I_3, $I = (a]$.

On the other hand, if a lattice L fails to satisfy the maximum condition, it has an infinite subchain of the form

$$C: c_o < c_1 < c_2 < \ldots$$

The set $J = \bigcup\limits_{n=0}^{\infty} (c_n]$, being the set-union of the elements of an ideal chain, is by the lemma itself an ideal. On the other hand, J cannot be a principal ideal since every one of its elements is definitely less than one of the elements c_n, wherefore J has no greatest element.

54. Ideal Lattices

If in a lattice L the meet-operation is replaced by the totality of operations

$$(1) \qquad f_a(x) = a \cap x \quad (a, x \in L; \; a \text{ being fixed})$$

then we obtain, obviously, the ideals of L as its "subalgebras". With regard to this, denoting by $\mathscr{I}(L)$ the set of all ideals of L and applying the reasonings of Section 26 we reach the following result:

Let $\overline{\mathscr{I}(L)}$ denote the set arising from $\mathscr{I}(L)$ by adding the meet of all ideals, then $\overline{\mathscr{I}(L)}$ forms — with respect to the set-inclusion — a complete lattice in which the meet coincides with the set theoretical meet.

Starting from this conclusion let us establish some important properties of $\mathscr{I}(L)$ itself considered as a subset of $\overline{\mathscr{I}(L)}$.

Let $\{I_\gamma\}_{\gamma \in \Gamma}$ an arbitrary subset of $\overline{\mathscr{I}(L)}$. Since the void set O (not belonging to $\mathscr{I}(L)$, but eventually contained in $\overline{\mathscr{I}(L)}$ does not take part in the formation of suprema in $\overline{\mathscr{I}(L)}$, therefore the supremum in $\mathscr{I}(L)$ of the set $\{\mathscr{I}_\gamma\}_{\gamma \in \Gamma}$ coincides with its supremum in $\overline{\mathscr{I}(L)}$. Let us determine this supremum.

Consider now an upper bound J in $\mathscr{I}(L)$ of the set $\{\mathscr{I}_\gamma\}_{\gamma \in \Gamma}$. By I_1, J must include — besides the elements of $\bigcup\limits_{\gamma} I_\gamma$ — every element of L of the form

$$(2) \qquad y_1 \cup \ldots \cup y_n \quad (y_j \in I_{\gamma_j}; \; \gamma_j \in \Gamma)$$

and by I_3, also every element y less than any element of the form

(2). Let I denote the set of all elements y of L to which there can be found elements $y_1, \ldots, y_n$ such that

$$y \leq y_1 \cup \ldots \cup y_n \quad (y_j \in I_{\gamma_j};\ \gamma_j \in \Gamma) \tag{3}$$

Clearly, $I_\gamma \subseteq I$ for every γ and $I \subseteq J$ for every upper bound J of $\{I_\gamma\}$. Moreover, it is apparent by the definition that I is an ideal of L, that is, $I \in \mathcal{J}(L)$. Hence I is the supremum of $\{I_\gamma\}$ in $\mathcal{J}(L)$.

For an arbitrary subset $\{I_\gamma\}_{\gamma \in \Gamma}$ of $\mathcal{J}(L)$, the infimum need not exist (see Exercise 5 and the hints added). If however $\bigcap_{\gamma \in \Gamma} I_\gamma$ is non-void, then this same itself belongs to $\mathcal{J}(L)$, according to the first paragraph of Section 26, and it represents obviously the greatest lower bound of $\{I_\gamma\}$, i.e.

$$\inf_{\mathcal{J}(L)} \{I_\gamma\}_{\gamma \in \Gamma} = \bigcap_{\gamma \in \Gamma} I_\gamma, \quad \text{if } \bigcap_{\gamma \in \Gamma} I_\gamma \neq O \tag{4}$$

Summing up we have the

THEOREM 77. *The set $\mathcal{J}(L)$ of all ideals of a lattice L forms a lattice with respect to the set inclusion. This latter lattice is conditionally complete and join-complete. The join of the elements of some subset $\{I_\gamma\}_{\gamma \in \Gamma}$ of $\mathcal{J}(L)$ consists of the elements y of L satisfying* (3), *while their intersection is formed by the elements of $\bigcap_{\gamma \in \Gamma} y_\gamma$. provided that this set intersection is non void.*

The lattice $\mathcal{J}(L)$ is called the *ideal lattice of lattice L*. Regarding the meet and join of its elements in finite number we have

THEOREM 78. *The meet $I_1 \cap \ldots \cap I_n$ in $\mathcal{J}(L)$ of the ideals (in finite number) $I_1, \ldots, I_n$ of the lattice L consists of the elements x of the form*

$$x = a_1 \cap \ldots \cap a_n \quad (a_j \in I_j;\ j = 1, \ldots, n) \tag{5}$$

while their join $I_1 \cup \ldots \cup I_n$ in $\mathcal{J}(L)$ *consists of the elements y of L satisfying an inequality of the form*

$$y \leq a_1 \cup \ldots \cup a_n \quad (a_j \in I_j;\ j = 1, \ldots, n)$$

(Stone [186], Theorems 18 and 31).

COROLLARY 1. *The set $\mathcal{J}_0(L)$ of all principal ideals of a lattice L is a sublattice of $\mathcal{J}(L)$, isomorphic to L.*

COROLLARY 2. *If a lattice satisfies the maximum condition then it is isomorphic to the subalgebra lattice of a suitably chosen algebra.*

PROOF. By the preceding theorem $\bigcap_{j=1}^{n} I_j = \bigcap_{j=1}^{n} I_j$. However, as stated above, every element of the form (5) is included in the set intersection of the ideals $I_1, \ldots, I_n$. But each element of this intersection is of the form (5) since if $x \in \bigcap_{j=1}^{n} I_j$, then performing the substitution

$x_1 = \ldots = x_n = x$ in (5) we get exactly x. Thus $\bigcap_{j=1}^{n} I_j$ consists precisely of all elements of the form (5).

The proposition concerning the joins of Theorem 78 follows immediately, in view of I_3, from the corresponding proposition of Theorem 77.

In order to prove Corollary 1, it has to be shown that the formulae

$$(a] \frown (b] = (a \frown b] \tag{6}$$

$$(a] \smile (b] = (a \smile b] \tag{7}$$

hold for every pair of elements a, b of L, since then the mapping $x \to (x]$ is already an isomorphism between L and $\mathcal{I}_0(L)$. By Theorem 78, $(a] \frown (b]$ consists of all elements of the form $a_1 \frown b_1$ $(a_1 \leqq a,$ $b_1 \leqq b)$, and for any one of these, $a_1 \frown b_1 \leqq a \frown b$, that is, $a_1 \frown b_1 \in$ $\in (a \frown b]$. Hence, $(a] \frown (b] \subseteq (a \frown b]$. Conversely, again by the theorem, $(a] \frown (b] \ni a \frown b$, and thus, by the property I_3 of ideals, $(a] \frown (b] \supseteq (a \frown b]$, completing the proof of (6). Now (7) can be verified as follows: $x \in (a \smile b]$ if, and only if, $x \leqq a \smile b$; that, however, is equivalent, by Theorem 78, to $x \in (a] \smile (b]$.

Corollary 2 can be proved as follows. If the lattice L satisfies the maximum condition, then, with regard to Theorem 76, $\mathcal{I}(L) =$ $= \mathcal{I}_0(L)$. Hence we get — taking into account Corollary 1 — $\mathcal{I}(L) \approx L$. On the other hand, as we have already seen above, $\mathcal{I}(L)$ may be considered as the "subalgebra lattice" of L, supposing that we take as "operations in L" the join and all the functions of form (1).

If the lattice L is distributive, the join in $\mathcal{I}(L)$ can be defined in a simpler manner than in the above general case. We have

THEOREM 79. *If the* I_γ $(\gamma \in \Gamma)$ *are arbitrary ideals of a distributive lattice* L *then all the elements of the form* (2) *constitute an ideal in* L. *Consequently, in this case* $\bigcup_{\gamma \in \Gamma} I_\gamma$ *consists of all elements of the form* (2).

This theorem is essentially identical with Theorem 17 of Stone [186].

PROOF. By the foregoing theorem, all elements y of the form (3) constitute an ideal in any L. Particularly, if L is distributive, (3) implies that

$$y = y \frown (y_1 \smile \ldots \smile y_n) = (y \frown y_1) \smile \ldots \smile (y \frown y_n)$$

and by I_2, $y \frown y_j \in I_{\gamma_j} (j = 1, \ldots, n)$. Hence, the element y can also be represented in the form (2).

The converse of Theorem 79 is also true: If for any subset $\{I_\gamma\}_{\gamma \in \Gamma} \subseteq \mathcal{I}(L)$ the elements of the form (2) constitute an ideal in L, then L is distributive (see Exercise 10).

The close structural relation between lattices and their ideal lattices is emphasized by

THEOREM 80. *The ideal lattice* $\mathcal{I}(L)$ *of a lattice* L *is modular (distributive) if, and only if,* L *is modular (distributive).*

The statement concerning modular lattices was proved by Dilworth ([43], Lemma 2.2), that concerning distributive lattices by Stone ([187], Theorem 1). Let us call attention to the following result by Hashimoto ([89], p. 165): The ideal lattice $\mathcal{J}(L)$ of a lattice L is a Boolean algebra if, and only if, L is bounded below, relatively complemented, distributive and satisfies the minimum condition.

The theorem readily yields a corollary stronger than the Corollary of Theorem 27:

COROLLARY. *Every lattice is isomorphic to some sublattice of a complete lattice; moreover, every modular (distributive) lattice is isomorphic to some sublattice of a suitably chosen modular (distributive) complete lattice.*

PROOF. If $\mathcal{J}(L)$ is modular, then by Theorem 31 and by Corollary 1 of Theorem 78, $\mathcal{J}_0(L)$ also is modular and $\mathcal{J}_0(L) \approx L$. We get in a similar manner — replacing Theorem 31 by Theorem 29 — that if $\mathcal{J}(L)$ is distributive, so is L. Hence, the condition is necessary.

The proof of the sufficiency of the condition necessitates a more involved line of thought. Consider first the case when the lattice L is modular. With regard to the modular inequality it is sufficient to prove that if the ideals X, Y, Z of the lattice L satisfy the condition $X \subseteq Z$, then there holds in $\mathcal{J}(L)$ the inequality

$$(X \cup Y) \cap Z \leqq X \cup (Y \cap Z) \tag{8}$$

Consider for this purpose any element t of the ideal on the left side of the inequality. By Theorem 78, $t \in Z$ and $t \in X \cup Y$, that is there exists a pair of elements x_0, y_0 ($x_0 \in X$; $y_0 \in Y$) for which $t \leqq x_0 \cup y_0$ holds. Since $X \subseteq Z$, x_0 is also an element of Z, and hence, the element $z_0 = x_0 \cup t$ is included in Z. Besides, by the definition of the elements x_0, y_0, z_0, there holds $t \leqq (x_0 \cup y_0) \cap z_0$. Since L is modular and x_0 is less than or equal to z_0 the last inequality may be rewritten in the form

$$t \leqq x_0 \cup (y_0 \cap z_0)$$

Applying Theorem 78 again, we have $y_0 \cap z_0 \in Y \cap Z$, and further, $t \in X \cup (Y \cap Z)$, proving (8).

Now let X, Y, Z be three arbitrary ideals of a distributive lattice. It is sufficient to prove that

$$X \cap (Y \cup Z) \leqq (X \cap Y) \cup (X \cap Z)$$

For this purpose, consider any element t of the ideal on the left side of the inequality. By Theorem 78, $t \in X$ and $t \in Y \cup Z$, and hence, by Theorem 79, there can be found elements $y (\in Y)$, $z (\in Z)$ such that $t = y \cup z$. Hence, using Theorem 78 again, we have

$$t = t \cap t = t \cap (y \cup z) = (t \cap y) \cup (t \cap z) \in (X \cap Y) \cup (X \cap Z)$$

so proving the statement which was to be verified.

The statement of the corollary is now immediately obtained by considering Corollary 1 to Theorem 78 and the results of Section 24. $\mathcal{J}(L)$ is either complete by itself, or it can be made complete by adjoining a least element to the void set O.

THEOREM 81. *If for an ideal A and element a of a lattice L there holds $A < (a]$ in $\mathcal{J}(L)$, then there exists an ideal B in L such that $A \leq B \prec (a]$ in $\mathcal{J}(L)$.*

PROOF. Let us take all the elements I of $\mathcal{J}(L)$ for which $A \leq \leq I < (a]$ holds. For the set $\mathfrak{J}$ of all these I-s the conditions of the Kuratowski—Zorn lemma are satisfied: namely, if $\{I_\lambda\}_{\lambda \in \Lambda}$ is an arbitrary subchain of $\mathfrak{J}$, then by the lemma of the preceding section $\mathfrak{J}^* = \bigcup_{\lambda \in \Lambda} I_\lambda$ is also an ideal of L, moreover obviously $A \leq \mathfrak{J}^* < (a]$ (therefore $I^* \in \mathfrak{J}$) and $\mathfrak{J}^*$ is an upper bound of $\{I_\lambda\}_{\lambda \in \Lambda}$. Applying the Kuratowski—Zorn lemma we obtain that $\mathfrak{J}$ has some maximal element; let one of them be denoted by B.

By the definition of B we have $A \leq B < (a]$. Let us suppose that L has an ideal J such that $B < J < (a]$. Then J should also belong to the set $\mathfrak{J}$ of ideals, in contradiction to that B is a maximal element of $\mathfrak{J}$. Therefore, such J does not exist, thus $B \prec (a]$.

The set $\mathcal{D}(L)$ of all dual ideals of a lattice L is also partly ordered by set-inclusion. Accordingly, writing $\mathcal{D}(L)$ instead of $\mathcal{J}(L)$ in Theorems 78—81 and dualizing the concepts referring to L but not those referring to $\mathcal{J}(L)$ we get again true theorems.*

In [43], Dilworth discussed lattices, whose dual ideal lattices satisfy the lower covering condition. (The generalization of the concept of Birkhoff lattices given by Dilworth — mentioned in Section 49 — involves precisely lattices of this type.) He has proved, among other things, that every semimodular lattice satisfying the minimum condition is of this type and that conversely, if $\mathfrak{J}(L)$ satisfies the lower covering condition, L is semimodular.

55. Distributive Lattices and Rings of Sets

We have seen (as Example 21) that every ring of sets is a distributive lattice. We shall show in the present section that the converse statement is also true: every distributive lattice is isomorphic to a ring of sets. As a preliminary we have the following theorem, which is also highly significant in itself:

THEOREM 82. *A lattice is distributive if, and only if, for any two distinct elements of the lattice there exists a prime ideal which includes one of the elements without including the other.*

The necessity of the condition was proved by Stone ([186], Theorem 64, and [187], Theorem 8) its sufficiency by Iséki [97].

* For example, the dualizing of Theorem 78 yields that in the lattice $\mathcal{D}(L)$ $D_1 \cap \ldots \cap D_n$ consists of all elements x of L of the form $x = a_1 \cup \ldots \cup a_n$ ($a_j \in D_j$; $j = 1, \ldots, n$) whereas $D_1 \cup \ldots \cup D_n$ consists of all elements y of L satisfying some inequality $y \geq b_1 \cap \ldots \cap b_n$ ($b_j \in D_j$; $j = 1, \ldots, n$).

PROOF. We shall give, first, an indirect proof of the sufficiency of the condition. Let L be any non-distributive lattice. By Theorem 33, L has a sublattice $\{u, x, y, z, v\}$ the diagram of which coincides with one of the diagrams shown in Fig. 31. Consider a prime ideal P of L including x. Since $y \cap z \leq x$, by the property l_3 of ideals there holds $y \cap z \in P$ and thus since P is prime, either $y \in P$ or $z \in P$. However, if $z \in P$, then by the property l_1 of ideals $v = x \cup z \in P$, and thus, a fortiori, $y \in P$. Summarizing, every prime ideal of L including x also includes y.

To show the necessity of the condition, consider a distributive lattice L and a pair of elements x, $y(x \neq y)$ of the same. We can assume

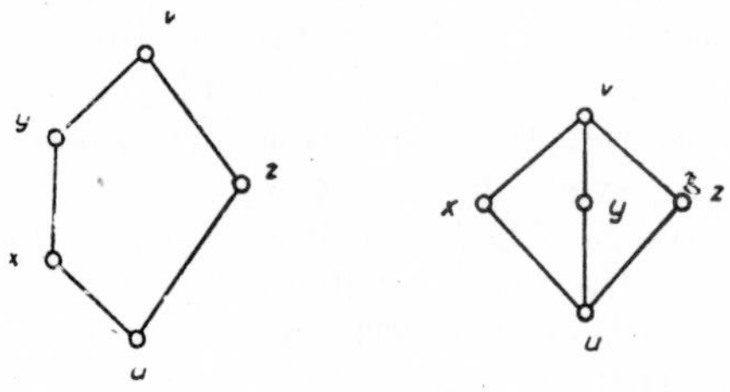

Fig. 31   Fig. 32

without loss of generality that $y \not\leq x$. Let $\mathscr{I}$ denote the set of all ideals of L which include x but not y. Thus $\mathscr{I}$ satisfies the hypothesis of the Kuratowski—Zorn lemma:

1. $\mathscr{I}$ is non-void, since by $y \not\leq x$ the principal ideal $(x]$ does not include y, and hence $(x] \in \mathscr{I}$.

2. If $\mathscr{K}$ is some subchain of $\mathscr{I}$, then the set union K of the elements of $\mathscr{K}$ is by the lemma of Section 53 itself an ideal, and clearly, $x \in K$, $y \notin K$.

Thus, by the Kuratowski—Zorn lemma, $\mathscr{I}$ has a maximal element. That is, an ideal P exists such that, on the one hand, $x \in P$, $y \notin P$, and on the other, every ideal properly including P also includes y.

We shall show that P is prime. Consider an arbitrary pair of elements a, b of L such that, $a, b \notin P$ and let $I_a = P \cup (a]$ and $I_b = P \cup (b]$ where the joins are to be understood in $\mathscr{I}(L)$. By the assumption $a, b \notin P$, $I_a, I_b \supseteq P$ and hence both I_a and I_b include the element y. But then, by Theorem 79, elements

(1) $p, q \in P, \ u \in (a], \ v \in (b]$

exist such that $y = p \cup u = q \cup v$.

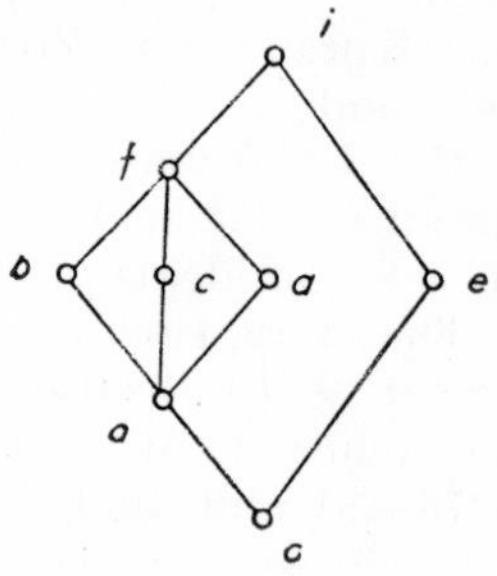

Hence,

$$y \leqq (y \cup a) \cap (y \cup b) = (p \cup u \cup a) \cap (q \cup v \cup b) =$$

$$= (p \cup a) \cap (q \cup b) = (p \cap q) \cup (a \cap q) \cup (p \cap b) \cup (a \cap b)$$

It is clear from the above equation that $a \cap b \notin P$, since on the one hand, by (1) the elements $p \cap q$, $a \cap q$ and $p \cap b$ are included in P, and on the other, $y \notin P$ by assumption. Hence, P is prime indeed, thus completing the proof of the theorem.

THEOREM 83. *Every distributive lattice is isomorphic to a ring of sets, and so is every Boolean algebra to a field of sets.*

The first proposition of the theorem was proved by Birkhoff ([10], Theorem 25. 2), the second by Stone [183]. Concerning a refinement in a certain sense of the second proposition see the papers [126] by Loomis, and [178] by Sikorski. (See also Sikorski [179], § 24.)

PROOF. Let L be a lattice, arbitrary for the time being, and let $\mathscr{P}(x)$ $(x \in L)$ denote the set of all proper dual prime ideals (that is, those different from L) which include x.* We show that for arbitrary elements a, b of L

$$\mathscr{P}(a \cap b) = \mathscr{P}(a) \cap \mathscr{P}(b) \tag{2}$$

and

$$\mathscr{P}(a \cup b) = \mathscr{P}(a) \cup \mathscr{P}(b) \tag{3}$$

In fact, considering only the definition of $\mathscr{P}(x)$ and of the dual prime ideals,

$$P \in \mathscr{P}(a \cap b) \Longleftrightarrow a \cap b \in P \Longleftrightarrow a, b \in P \Longleftrightarrow P \in \mathscr{P}(a) \cap \mathscr{P}(b)$$

and

$$P \in \mathscr{P}(a \cup b) \Longleftrightarrow a \cup b \in P \Longleftrightarrow (\text{either } a \in P \text{ or } b \in P) \Longleftrightarrow$$

$$\Longleftrightarrow \big(\text{either } P \in \mathscr{P}(a) \text{ or } P \in \mathscr{P}(b)\big) \Longleftrightarrow P \in \mathscr{P}(a) \cup \mathscr{P}(b).$$

Hence, the set $\mathfrak{P} = \{\mathscr{P}(x)\}_{x \in L}$ constitutes a ring of sets and the mapping

$$x \longrightarrow \mathscr{P}(x) \quad (x \in L; \quad \mathscr{P}(x) \in \mathfrak{P}) \tag{4}$$

is a homomorphism of L onto $\mathfrak{P}$.**

Particularly, if L is distributive, the mapping (4) is one-to-one by the dual of the foregoing theorem and hence $L \approx \mathfrak{P}$.

* As an example, consider the lattice of Fig. 31. The proper dual prime ideals of this lattice are $A = [a)$, and $E = [e)$. Accordingly $\mathscr{P}(o) = O$ $\mathscr{P}(a) = \mathscr{P}(b) = \mathscr{P}(c) = \mathscr{P}(d) = \mathscr{P}(f) = \{A\}$, $\mathscr{P}(e) = \{E\}$, $\mathscr{P}(i) = \{A, E\}$.

** The lattice of Fig. 32 is mapped by (4) onto a lattice isomorphic to the lattice L_1 of Fig. 15 (p. 53). It is interesting to note that the mapping (4) carries the non-distributive sublattices of Fig. 31 into distributive sublattices.

Consider finally the special case when L is complemented as well. If $\mathscr{D}$ denotes the set of all proper dual prime ideals of L, then obviously O and $\mathscr{D}$ are the bound elements of $\mathfrak{P}$ and $\mathscr{P}(o) = O$, $\mathscr{P}(i) = \mathscr{D}$. Furthermore, if $\mathscr{P}(x)$ is any element of $\mathfrak{P}$ and y is the complement of x in L, then, by (2) and (3), $\mathscr{P}(y)$ is the complement of $\mathscr{P}(x)$ in $\mathfrak{P}$. Hence, in the case under consideration $\mathfrak{P}$ is indeed a field of sets.

The second proposition of Theorem 83 is of fundamental significance for the modern Kolmogorov theory of probability. The starting point of this theory is that every algebra of events is isomorphic to a field of sets. Since every algebra of events is a Boolean algebra, the theorem just proved shows that this concept introduces no arbitrary restriction (see, for example, [225], Chapter I, § 1).

Let us here call attention to Copeland's paper [27], in which he introduces the concept of "implicative Boolean algebras" and shows that such an algebra forms an adequate basis for the theory of probability.

For the foundation of the theory of probability see also [19], Chapter 12, Section 9, or [179] § 46.

Exercises to Chapter VIII

1. Show that a subset R of a lattice L is an ideal in L if, and only if, for any elements a, b of L, $a \cup b \in R \Longleftrightarrow a, b \in R$.
2. Prove that a subset R of a lattice L is an ideal if, and only if, L has a join-homomorphism of which R is the kernel.*
3. Prove that to any prime ideal I of a lattice L there can be found a homomorphism of which I is the kernel.
4. Let R be a proper sublattice of L. Prove that R is a prime ideal in L if, and only if, $L - R$ is a dual prime ideal.
5. Show that the ideal lattice of a lattice L is complete if, and only if, L is bounded below.
6. An ideal M of a lattice L is called a *maximal ideal* if, in the ideal lattice $\mathscr{I}(L)$, it is covered by L. Show that an ideal I of a Boolean algebra B is maximal if, and only if, for any element x of B, either x or x' but not both, is included in I.
7. Prove that every maximal ideal of a distributive lattice is prime and that an ideal of a Boolean algebra is prime if, and only if, it is maximal**.
8. Let B be a Boolean algebra, J an ideal and c an element of B. Show that $J \cup (c] = B$ (where $\cup$ means the join in the ideal lattice of B) implies $c' \in J$.
9. Show that a principal ideal $(a]$ of a distributive lattice is prime if, and only if, the element a is meet-irreducible; in particular, that a lattice is a chain if, and only if, every one of its ideals is prime.
10. Verify the statement formulated in the paragraph after the proof of Theorem 79 (p. 163).

* The kernel of a join-homomorphism is defined analogously to that of a homomorphism.

** Concerning the latter proposition see Nachbin [143].

11. Let a, b be an arbitrarily selected pair of elements of a distributive lattice L. Denote by $I(a, b)$ the set of the elements x $(\in L)$ such that $a \frown x = b \frown x$, and by $D(a, b)$ the set of the elements y $(\in L)$ such that $a \smile y = b \smile y$. Verify that every $I(a, b)$ is an ideal, every $D(a, b)$ a dual ideal of L, and either $I(a, b) = D(a, b) = L$, or $I(a, b) \cap \cap D(a, b) = O$.

12. Let J be an ideal of a complete lattice. Show that if the supremum of J is compact, then J is a principal ideal.

13. Show by an example that the mapping defined by (4) of Section 55 is not necessarily a complete isomorphism even for complete lattices.

14. Show that every distributive lattice is isomorphic to some sublattice of a Boolean algebra.*

* The statement of the exercise is a simple corollary of Theorem 83. It is all the more interesting that Peremans should have found a proof of this statement (see [157]), which is based neither directly nor indirectly on the Axiom of Choice.

CHAPTER IX

CONGRUENCE RELATIONS

56. Congruence Relations of an Algebra

By a *congruence relation* of an algebra $A = A(\{f_\gamma\}_{\gamma \in \Gamma})$ we mean an *equivalence relation* Θ defined on the set A which satisfies the following:

SUBSTITUTION PROPERTY: *For every operation* $f_\gamma (\gamma \in \Gamma)$ *of the algebra* A *and for any elements* $x_1, \ldots, x_{n(\gamma)}, y_1, \ldots, y_{n(\gamma)}$ of A, $x_1 \equiv y_1, \ldots, x_{n(\gamma)} \equiv y_{n(\gamma)}(\Theta)$ *imply* $f_\gamma(x_1, \ldots, x_{n(\gamma)}) \equiv f(y_1, \ldots, y_{n(\gamma)})\ (\Theta)$ (Birkhoff—MacLane [219]).

If Θ is a congruence relation of A and $x \equiv y(\Theta)$, then x and y are said to be *congruent with respect to the congruence relation* Θ or, briefly, that they are *congruent modulo* Θ.

Let Θ be any congruence relation of the algebra $A = A(\{f_\gamma\}_{\gamma \in \Gamma})$. Consider the set $\bar{A}$ of all Θ-classes of A and denote by $\bar{x}$ $(x \in A)$ the Θ-class including the element x. The element x is called the *representant* of the class $\bar{x}$.

It is natural to define operations on the set $\bar{A}$ by the aid of the operations on A. Consider an arbitrary operation f_γ of A and assign to every system $\bar{x}_1, \ldots, \overline{x_{n(\gamma)}} \in \bar{A}$ the Θ-class $\bar{f}_\gamma(\bar{x}_1, \ldots, \overline{x_{n(\gamma)}})$ of A including the element $f_\gamma(x_1, \ldots, x_{r(\gamma)})$; in symbols,

$$\text{(1)} \qquad \bar{f}_\gamma(\overline{x_1}, \ldots, \overline{x_{n(\gamma)}}) = \overline{f_\gamma(x_1, \ldots, x_{r(\gamma)})}$$

It is obvious that $\bar{f}_\gamma(\bar{x}_1, \ldots, \overline{x_{r(\gamma)}})$ depends solely on the classes $\overline{x_1}, \ldots, \bar{x}_{n(\gamma)}$ being independent of the choice of their representants: if $\bar{x}_j = \bar{y}_j$ $(j = 1, \ldots, n(\gamma))$, then by the Substitution Property of Θ, $\overline{f_\gamma(x_1, \ldots, x_{r(\gamma)})} = \overline{f_\gamma(y_1, \ldots, y_{n(\gamma)})}$. Hence, by (1) operations on $\bar{A}$ have, indeed, been defined.

Under the operations defined by (1), $\bar{A}$ becomes an algebra similar to A, whence by our agreement in Section 10, we shall simply write f_γ instead of $\bar{f}_\gamma$. The algebra $\bar{A} = A\{f_\gamma\}_{\gamma \in \Gamma}$ will be called the *factor algebra* of A with respect to the congruence relation Θ (or, the factor algebra of A modulo Θ) and the symbolism $\bar{A} = A/\Theta$ will be employed. Clearly, if an identity, for example, commutativity or associativity of an operation, or distributivity of one operation with respect to another, holds in A, then it also holds in every factor algebra of A.

The factor algebra A/Θ is a homomorphic image of A, since by (1) the mapping

$$\varphi_\Theta\colon \varphi_\Theta(x) = \bar{x} \quad (x \in A,\ \bar{x} \in A/\Theta) \tag{2}$$

satisfies for any γ the condition

$$\varphi_\Theta\big(f_\gamma(x_1, \ldots, x_{n(\gamma)})\big) = \overline{f_\gamma(x_1, \ldots, x_n)} =$$
$$= f_\gamma(\overline{x_1}, \ldots, \overline{x_{n(\gamma)}}) = f_\gamma\big(\varphi(x_1), \ldots, \varphi(x_{n(\gamma)})\big)$$

The homomorphism φ_Θ is called the *natural homomorphism belonging to the congruence relation* Θ.

By the above, to every congruence relation there corresponds a (natural) homomorphism. Conversely, every homomorphism gives rise to a congruence relation. Let $\varphi\colon A \sim A'$ and define in A a relation Θ_φ as follows:

$$x \equiv y(\Theta_\varphi) \longleftrightarrow \varphi(x) = \varphi(y) \qquad (x, y \in A) \tag{3}$$

It is immediately clear that Θ_φ is an equivalence relation. Moreover, if $x_j \equiv y_j(\Theta_\varphi)$ $\big(j = 1, \ldots, n(\gamma)\big)$, then by (3)

$$\varphi\big(f_\gamma(x_1, \ldots, x_{n(\gamma)})\big) = f_\gamma\big(\varphi(x_1), \ldots, \varphi(x_{n(\gamma)})\big) =$$
$$= f_\gamma\big(\varphi(y_1), \ldots, \varphi(y_{n(\gamma)})\big) = \varphi\big(f_\gamma(y_1, \ldots, y_{n(\gamma)})\big)$$

that is, Θ_φ also has the Substitution Property. The congruence relation Θ_φ defined by (3) is called the *congruence relation generated by the homomorphism* φ. By the argument applied above it can be shown that $A/\Theta_\varphi \approx A'$, the isomorphism being established by the mapping $\bar{x} \to \varphi(x)$ $(x \in A)$. This means that one can find for every homomorphism φ of A a congruence relation Θ of A, so that the image algebra generated by the natural homomorphism φ_Θ on the one hand and by the homomorphism φ on the other are isomorphic. Hence, from the point of view of abstract algebra, every homomorphism essentially coincides with a natural homomorphism belonging to a suitable congruence relation. Therefore, for the study of the structure of an algebra it is a matter of indifference whether its homomorphisms or its congruence relations are considered. In this book, we shall do the latter.

The set of all congruence relations of an algebra A will be denoted by $\mathscr{K}(A)$. For this set, there holds

THEOREM 84. *The set $\mathscr{K}(A)$ of the congruence relations of an algebra $A = A(\{f_\gamma\}_{\gamma\in\Gamma})$ is a complete sublattice of the lattice $\mathscr{E}(A)$ of all equivalence relations on A* (Birkhoff [12], Theorem 24; see also Krishnan [122]).

PROOF. The statement of the theorem means precisely that if $\{\Theta_\delta\}_{\delta\in\Delta}$ is an arbitrary subset of $\mathscr{K}(A)$, then the meet $\bigcap_{\delta\in\Delta} \Theta_\delta$ and the join $\bigcup_{\delta\in\Delta} \Theta_\delta$ of the Θ_δ considered in $\mathscr{E}(A)$ are also congruence relations.

Let $x_1, \ldots, x_{n(\gamma)}, y_1, \ldots, y_{n(\gamma)}$ be elements of A such that

$$x_j \equiv y_j\ (\bigcap_{\delta\in\Delta} \Theta_\delta)\ \ (j = 1, \ldots, n(\gamma))$$

that is, $x_j \equiv y_j(\Theta_\delta)$ for every δ and every j. This implies by the Substitution Property of the Θ_δ that for every γ,

$$f_\gamma(x_1, \ldots, x_{n(\gamma)}) \equiv f_\gamma(y_1, \ldots, y_{n(\gamma)})\ (\Theta_\delta) \qquad (\delta \in \Delta)$$

and consequently

$$f_\gamma(x_1, \ldots, x_{n(\gamma)}) \equiv f_\gamma(y_1, \ldots, y_{n(\gamma)})\ (\bigcap_{\delta\in\Delta} \Theta_\delta) \qquad (\gamma \in \Gamma)$$

Hence, the Substitution Property also holds for $\bigcap_{\delta\in\Delta} \Theta_\delta$.

Now let $x_1, \ldots, x_{n(\gamma)}, y_1, \ldots, y_{n(\gamma)}$ be elements of A such that

$$x_j \equiv y_j\ (\bigcup_{\delta\in\Delta} \Theta_\delta)\ \ (j = 1, \ldots, n(\gamma))$$

Then, writing for the moment simply n instead of $n(\gamma)$, there exist in A finite sequences of elements

$$(4) \qquad \begin{cases} x_1 = z_{10}, z_{11}, \ldots, z_{1r_1} = y_1 \\ \quad\vdots \\ x_n = z_{n0}, z_{n1}, \ldots, z_{nr_n} = y_n \end{cases}$$

such that to any pair of indices j, k $(j = 1, \ldots, n;\ k = 1, \ldots, r_j)$ there can be found (at least one) Θ_{jk} for which

$$z_{j,k-1} \equiv z_{jk}(\Theta_{jk})\ \ (\Theta_{jk} \in \{\Theta_\delta\}_{\delta\in\Delta})$$

Hence, it follows immediately that for any γ

$$\begin{aligned} f_\gamma(z_{10}, z_{20}, \ldots, z_{n0}) &\equiv f_\gamma(z_{11}, z_{20}, \ldots, z_{n0})\ (\Theta_{11}) \\ f_\gamma(z_{11}, z_{20}, \ldots, z_{n0}) &\equiv f_\gamma(z_{12}, z_{20}, \ldots, z_{n0})\ (\Theta_{12}) \\ &\ \,\vdots \\ f_\gamma(z_{1,r-1}, z_{20}, \ldots, z_{n0}) &\equiv f_\gamma(z_{1r_1}, z_{20}, \ldots, z_{n0})\ (\Theta_{1r_1}) \end{aligned}$$

Considering these relations and the similar one concerning the remaining sequences in (4), we obtain

$$f_\gamma(z_{10}, z_{20}, \ldots, z_{n0}) \equiv f_\gamma(z_{1r_1}, z_{20}, \ldots, z_{n0}) \left(\bigcup_{k=1}^{r_1} \Theta_{1k} \right)$$

$$f_\gamma(z_{1r_1}, z_{20}, \ldots, z_{n0}) \equiv f_\gamma(z_{1r_1}, z_{2r_2}, z_{30}, \ldots, z_{n0}) \left(\bigcup_{k=1}^{r_2} \Theta_{2k} \right)$$

$$\vdots$$

$$f_\gamma(z_{1r_1}, \ldots, z_{n-1,r_{n-1}}, z_{n0}) \equiv f_\gamma(z_{1r_1}, \ldots z_{n-1,r_{n-1}}, z_{nr_n}) \left(\bigcup_{k=1}^{r_n} \Theta_{nk} \right)$$

Hence — returning to the symbol $n(\gamma)$ instead of n — for every index γ

$$f_\gamma(x_1, \ldots, x_{n(\gamma)}) \equiv f_\gamma(y_1, \ldots, y_{n(\gamma)}) \left(\bigcup_{j=1}^{n(\gamma)} \bigcup_{k=1}^{r_j} \Theta_{jk} \right)$$

and, a fortiori,

$$f_\gamma(x_1, \ldots, x_{n(\gamma)}) \equiv f_\gamma(y_1, \ldots, y_{n(\gamma)}) \left(\bigcup_{\delta \in \Delta} \Theta_\delta \right) \qquad (\gamma \in \Gamma)$$

proving that $\bigcup_{\delta \in \Delta} \Theta_\delta$ is also a congruence relation.

From this theorem we shall in the following make use only of the fact that *the set $\mathscr{K}(A)$ of all congruence relations of an algebra $A = A(\{f_\gamma\}_{\gamma \in \Gamma})$ is a complete lattice with respect to the operations described in the Supplement of Theorem 67*. This lattice will be called the *congruence lattice* of the algebra A.

By Theorem 84, the bound elements of $\mathscr{K}(A)$ coincide with the bound elements of $\mathscr{E}(A)$, that is, the least element of $\mathscr{K}(A)$ is the equality relation and its greatest element is the congruence relation I, with $x \equiv y$ (I) for any pair of elements x, y of A. These two congruence relations (which exist in every A) are called the *trivial congruence relations* of A, and if A has no other congruence relation, it is called a *simple algebra*.

As an example, we mention that the equivalence lattice of any set is simple (Ore [153], Chapter IV, Theorem 8). For further examples see Exercises 16, 17 and 18.

Consider again an algebra $A = A(\{f_\gamma\}_{\gamma \in \Gamma})$ and let H be some subset of A. Congruence relations occur in A — for example, I — under which any two elements of H are congruent. Theorem 84 guarantees the existence of the meet of all congruence relations of A having this property; let this meet be denoted Θ_H. By its definition, Θ_H has the following two characteristic properties:

1. For any elements x, y of H, $x \equiv y(\Theta_H)$;

2. If for a congruence relation of A and for any pair of elements x, y of H, $x \equiv y(\Theta)$, then $\Theta \geq \Theta_H$.

Accordingly, Θ_H is called the *minimal congruence relation belonging to the subset H*. Instead of $\Theta_{\{ab\}}$ we write briefly Θ_{ab}.

With the help of the concept introduced above we can prove

THEOREM 85. *The congruence lattice of any algebra is compactly generated* (Birkhoff—Frink [20], Theorem 6).

PROOF. At first we show that for an arbitrary congruence relation Θ of an algebra A

$$\Theta = \bigcup_{\substack{a,\, b \\ a \equiv b\, (\Theta)}} \Theta_{ab} \tag{4}$$

(that is Θ is the join of all the Θ_{ab}-s, for which $a \equiv b(\Theta)$. Aiming at this let us denote for the moment the right side of (4) by Σ. It is obvious that for any pair x, y of elements of A, $x \equiv y(\Theta)$ implies $x \equiv y(\Sigma)$; that means: $\Theta \leqq \Sigma$. Conversely, if $u \equiv v(\Sigma)$ $(u, v \in A)$, then there are in A finite sequences of elements

$$u = x_0, x_1, \ldots, x_n = v$$

$$a_1, a_2, \ldots, a_n$$

and

$$b_1, b_2, \ldots, b_n$$

such that for $j = 1, 2, \ldots, n$

$$x_{j-1} \equiv x_j \ (\Theta_{a_j b_j}) \tag{5}$$

and $a_j \equiv b_j(\Theta)$. Owing to the latter every $\Theta_{a_j b_j} \leqq \Theta$. Consequently from (5) we have

$$x_{j-1} \equiv x_j(\Theta) \ (j = 1, 2, \ldots, n)$$

which implies $u \equiv v(\Theta)$. Therefore $\Sigma \leqq \Theta$ is also true. Thus the validity of (4) is proved.

Now we have yet to prove the statement, interesting in itself, that *for any algebra A every congruence relation $f\,\Theta_{ab}$ $(a, b \in A)$ is compact in $\mathscr{K}(A)$.*

Let us take a set $\{\Theta_\lambda\}_{\lambda \in \Lambda}$ of congruence relations of A for which

$$\Theta_{ab} \leqq \bigcup_{\lambda \in \Lambda} \Theta_\lambda$$

Then in particular $a \equiv b(\bigcup_{\lambda \in \Lambda} \Theta_\lambda)$, therefore there exists a finite sequence $a = y_0, y_1, \ldots, y_r = b$ in A such that

$$y_{j-1} \equiv y_j(\Theta_{\lambda_j}) \ (\lambda_j \in \Lambda\ ;\ j = 1, \ldots, r)$$

Consequently $a \equiv b(\bigcup_{j=1}^{r} \Theta_{\lambda_j})$, and thus according to the meaning of Θ_{ab} we have

$$\Theta_{ab} \leqq \bigcup_{j=1}^{r} \Theta_{\lambda_j}$$

Thus the compactness of Θ_{ab} is demonstrated.

It is worth mentioning that the refinement of the theorem — due to Grätzer and Schmidt ([84], Theorem 10) — is as follows: A lattice L is compactly generated if, and only if, there exists an algebra A such that $L = \mathcal{K}(A)$.

Another interesting lattice theoretical property of $\mathcal{K}(A)$ is dealt with in the paper by Dwinger [54].

57. Permutable Equivalence Relations

Let M be an arbitrary set and let Θ, Φ be equivalence relations of M. In keeping with the general definition of the product of relations, we mean by the product $\Theta\Phi$ of the equivalence relations that relation under which $x\Theta\Phi y$ $(x, y \in M)$ if, and only if, there exists in M a t such that $x \equiv t(\Theta)$ and $t \equiv y(\Phi)$.

The product of equivalence relations is not an equivalence relation in general. Consider for example the equivalence relations Θ and Φ of the set $M = \{a, b, c\}$ which belong to the partitions $\mathfrak{c}(\Theta) = (a, b)(c)$ and $\mathfrak{c}(\Phi) = (a, c)(b)$. Then, $b\Theta\Phi c$ [since $b \equiv a(\Theta)$ and $a \equiv c(\Phi)$] and yet $c(\Theta\Phi)' b$; hence, the relation $\Theta\Phi$ is not symmetrical.

The following theorem gives a sufficient condition for the product of two equivalence relations to be itself an equivalence relation:

THEOREM 86. *If Θ and Φ are permutable equivalence relations of a set M, then their product is also an equivalence relation of M, and* $\Theta\Phi = \Theta \cup \Phi$ (Ore [153], Chapter 1, Theorem 18).*

SUPPLEMENT. *In the particular case if Θ and Φ are permutable congruence relations of A, then their product is itself a congruence relation of A.*

PROOF. Clearly it is sufficient to prove the equation in the theorem. By the appropriate definitions, $\Theta\Phi \leqq \Theta \cup \Phi$ for every Θ and Φ. Hence, it is sufficient to verify that if Θ and Φ are permutable, then the reverse inequality

$$\Theta\Phi \geqq \Theta \cup \Phi$$

also holds.

Let a, b be a pair of elements of M such that $a \equiv b(\Theta \cup \Phi)$. This means that there exists in M a finite sequence of elements

$$(1) \qquad (a =)\, x_0, x_1, \ldots, x_{r-1}, x_r\, (= b),$$

such that for any one of the indices $j = 1, \ldots, r$, either $x_{j-1} \equiv x_j(\Theta)$, or $x_{j-1} \equiv x_j(\Phi)$ or, eventually, both. Now let us apply induction on r. If $r = 0$, then $a = b$ and thus, trivially, $a\Theta\Phi b$. Consider in the following the case $m \geqq 1$ and suppose that the statement to be proved holds for $r = m - 1$. Let a, b be a pair of elements of M such that $a \equiv b(\Theta \cup \Phi)$ with $r = m$ in (1). Then, by the induction hypothesis, $a\, \Theta\Phi x_{r-1}$; that is, there exists a $u \in M$ such that

$$(2) \qquad a \equiv u(\Theta) \text{ and } u \equiv x_{r-1}(\Phi)$$

* A simple necessary and sufficient condition for the permutability of equivalence relations is to be found on p. 18 of Dubreil's book [222].

At the same time, by $a \equiv b(\Theta \cup \Phi)$, at least one of $x_{r-1} \equiv b(\Phi)$ and $x_{r-1} \equiv b(\Theta)$ holds. In the former case, by (2) $u \equiv b(\Phi)$ holds, whence $a\Theta\Phi b$. In the latter case, again by (2) $u\Phi\Theta b$, and hence, by the permutability of Θ and Φ also $u\Theta\Phi b$; that is, there exists $v \in M$ such that $u \equiv v(\Theta)$ and $v \equiv b(\Phi)$. Hence, by (2) $a \equiv u \equiv v(\Theta)$ and $v \equiv b(\Phi)$, from which, again, $a\Theta\Phi b$, completing the proof.

It is known that on assigning to every congruence relation Θ of a group G its kernel N_Θ, a one-to-one correspondence between the set of all congruence relations of G and the set of all its normal subgroups is arrived at. Further, for some congruence relation Θ of G, $x \equiv y(\Theta)$ holds for a pair of elements x, $y(\in G)$ if, and only if, $xy^{-1} \in N_\Theta$.

Let Φ be another congruence relation of G, having the kernel N_Φ. Consider a pair of elements a, b of G such that $a\Theta\Phi b$. Then, by what has been expounded above, G has an element u such that $au^{-1} \in N_\Phi$ and $ub^{-1} \in N_T$. Hence, $ab^{-1} = (au^{-1})(ub^{-1}) \in N_\Theta N_\Phi$ (for the meaning of $N_\Theta N_\Phi$, see Example 20). Since the multiplication of normal subgroups (regarded as complexes) is commutative, $N_\Theta N_\Phi = N_\Phi N_\Theta$ (see, for example, [228], Theorems 74 and 68). Hence, elements $b^*(\in N_\Phi)$ and $a^*(\in N_\Theta)$ exist such that $ab^{-1} = b^* a^*$. Let y denote the element of G for which $ay^{-1} = b^*$. Then $(ay^{-1})(yb^{-1}) = ab^{-1} = b^* a^*$ which, implies $yb^{-1} = a^*$. Hence $a = y(\Phi)$ and $y = b(\Theta)$, that is, $a\Phi\Theta b$.

By the same argument (with changes only in notation and nomenclature) a similar result can be obtained concerning the congruence relations Θ, Φ of a ring R. That is, if Θ and Φ are arbitrary congruence relations of a group G or a ring R, and $a\Theta\Phi b$ ($a, b \in G$, resp. $a, b \in R$), then also $a\Phi\Theta b$. Interchanging Θ and Φ we have the converse statement; hence, *the congruence relations of a group (or of a ring) are pairwise permutable.*

We have shown in Section 32 that the set of all normal subgroups of a group is a modular lattice under set inclusion as ordering relation. Hence, considering the connection between the congruence relations and the normal subgroups of groups, it can be inferred that the congruence lattice of a group is modular. This result is a particular case of the more general

THEOREM 87. *Let Θ_1, Θ_2 and Φ be three equivalence relations of a set M. If Θ_1 is less than or equal to Θ_2, and if it is permutable with Φ, then*

$$\Theta_1 \cup (\Phi \cap \Theta_2) = (\Theta_1 \cup \Phi) \cap \Theta_2$$

A somewhat weaker theorem is that of Ore [153], Chapter 1, Theorem 8. Concerning the statement just proposed see Hermes [91], Theorem 18.3.

COROLLARY. *If the congruence relations of an algebra A are pairwise permutable then the congruence lattice of A is modular.*

PROOF. In order to prove the theorem, it is sufficient by the modular inequality to show that

$$(3) \qquad (\Theta_1 \cup \Phi) \cap \Theta_2 \leq \Theta_1 \cup (\Phi \cap \Theta_2)$$

Consider for this purpose a pair of elements a, b of M such that $a \equiv b((\Theta_1 \cup \Phi) \cap \Theta_2)$. Then,

$$(4) \qquad a \equiv b(\Theta_2)$$

and, since $\Theta_1 \cup \Phi = \Theta_1 \Phi = \Phi\Theta_1$ by the foregoing theorem, $a \equiv b(\Phi\Theta)$. By the latter there exists an element x of M for which

(5) $$a \equiv x(\Phi)$$

and

(6) $$x \equiv b(\Theta_1)$$

Since $\Theta_1 \leq \Theta_2$, assumption (6) implies immediately $x \equiv b(\Theta_2)$ and this means, together with (4), that $a \equiv x(\Theta_2)$. Hence, by (5) $a \equiv$ $\equiv x(\Phi \frown \Theta_2)$. Applying (6) again, we get $a \equiv b(\Theta_1 \smile (\Phi \frown \Theta_2))$. Hence, the inequality (3) and consequently also the theorem is proved. The corollary is a trivial consequence of the theorem.

Let us remark in connection with the corollary that the condition of the pairwise permutability of congruence relations is a sufficient but not necessary condition for the lattice of congruence relations to be modular. For example, by Theorem 90 below, the congruence lattice of every lattice is distributive, although lattices occur (for example, any chain with at least three-elements) whose congruence relations are not pairwise permutable.

Let us observe as a supplement to the foregoing remark that any two congruence relations of a relatively complemented lattice are permutable (Dilworth [47], Theorem 4.2), and that in the case of distributive lattices, the congruence relations are pairwise permutable if, and only if, the lattice is relatively complemented (Grätzer—Schmidt [80], Theorem 10). Concerning a generalization of this latter result see Jakubik [101].

58. The Schreier Refinement Theorem in Arbitrary Algebras

A well-known, classical theorem of group theory is the Schreier refinement theorem for normal series. In the following, we shall discuss the generalization of this theorem to any algebra. However, to facilitate a more profound understanding of the generalized theorem, we shall first describe the original Schreier theorem itself.

Let G be a group and its unit denoted by e. The finite series $H_0, H_1, \ldots, H_r$ of the subgroups of G is called a normal series of G provided

(1) $$\{e\} = H_0 \subseteq H_1 \subseteq \ldots \subseteq H_r = G$$

and every H_j $(j = 0, 1, \ldots, r-1)$ is a normal subgroup in H_{j+1}. The groups H_{j+1}/H_j are called the factor groups of the normal series (1). A further normal series of G is called a refinement of (1) if it includes every term of (1). Schreier's refinement theorem declares that any two normal series of G can be refined so that the factor groups of the refined normal series — taken in a suitable order — are pairwise isomorphic. That is, if

(2) $$\{e\} = H'_0 \subseteq H'_1 \subseteq \ldots \subseteq H'_s = G$$

is a normal series of G, other than (1), then all subgroups $H_{jk} = H_{j-1}(H_j \cap H_k)$ resp. $H'_{kj} = H'_{k-1}(H'_k \cap H'_j)$ $(j = 1, \ldots, r;\ k = 1, \ldots, s)$ directly furnish refinements of (1) respectively (2) for which there hold the isomorphisms

(3) $$H_{jk}/H_{j,\,k-1} \approx H'_{kj}/H'_{k,\,j-1}$$

Passing from groups to arbitrary algebras, the role of the normal subgroups in forming the factor algebra is assumed by the congruence relations of the algebra considered. Accordingly, it is to be expected that the generalization of the Schreier theorem refer to chains of relations whose elements establish congruence relations on certain subalgebras of the algebra considered.

We introduce some preliminary definitions.

Let M be a set, and let

(4) $$\Theta_1 \leqq \Theta_2 \leqq \ldots \leqq \Theta_m$$

be a subchain of the equivalence lattice $\mathscr{E}(M)$ of a set M, then by the *refinement* of (4) is meant every subchain of $\mathscr{E}(M)$ which includes all the Θ_j $(j = 1, \ldots, m)$.

Let A be an algebra and R a subset of A. Clearly, every equivalence relation Φ of A also establishes an equivalence relation on R in the following sense: the relation which holds for any pair of elements x, y of R if, and only if, $x \equiv y(\Phi)$ is an equivalence relation of R. We retain the symbol Φ to denote the equivalence relation established by Φ on R. Of course, the case may be that Φ itself is not a congruence relation (on A), whereas the equivalence relation established by it on R is nevertheless a congruence relation.

In the rest of this section we always assume that the algebra $A = A(\{f_\gamma\}_{\gamma \in \Gamma})$ contains an element e with the special property that the one-element set $\{e\}$ forms a subalgebra of A (that is, that $f_\gamma(e, \ldots, e) = e$ for every $\gamma \in \Gamma$). The set of all elements x of A for which $x \equiv e(\Phi)$ holds under a given equivalence relation Φ will be denoted $K(\Phi)$. Clearly, $\Phi_1 \geqq \Phi_2$ implies $K(\Phi_1) \supseteq K(\Phi_2)$. Moreover it is easily seen that $K(\Phi) \cap K(\Psi) = K(\Phi \frown \Psi)$ for any equivalence relations Φ and Ψ of A.

THEOREM 88. *Let $A = A(\{f_\gamma\}_{\gamma \in \Gamma})$ be an algebra having a single-element subalgebra $\{e\}$ $(e \in A)$. Consider two subchains*

(5) $$\mathsf{E} = \Phi_0 \leqq \Phi_1 \leqq \ldots \leqq \Phi_r = \mathsf{I}$$

(6) $$\mathsf{E} = \Psi_0 \leqq \Psi_1 \leqq \ldots \leqq \Psi_s = \mathsf{I}$$

of the equivalence lattice $\mathscr{E}(A)$ of the set A satisfying the following conditions (A)—(C):

(A) *Every $K(\Phi_j)$ $(j = 1, \ldots, r)$ and every $K(\Psi_k)$ $(k = 1, \ldots, s)$ is a subalgebra of A;*

(B) *Every Φ_{j-1} establishes a congruence relation on $K(\Phi_j)$ and every Ψ_{k-1} establishes one on $K(\Psi_k)$;*

(C) *Every Φ_j is permutable with every Ψ_k.*

Then there exists a refinement $\{\Phi_{jk}\}$ of (5) *and a refinement $\{\Psi_{kj}\}$ $(j = 0,1,\ldots)r$; $k = 0,1,\ldots,s)$ of* (6) *for which the following propositions hold:*

(D) *Every $K(\Phi_{jk})$ and $K(\Psi_{kj})$ is a subalgebra of A;*

(E) *Every $\Phi_{j,\,k-1}$ establishes a congruence relation on $K(\Phi_{jk})$ and every $\Psi_{k,\,j-1}$ establishes one on $K(\Psi_{kj})$;*

(F) $K(\Phi_{jk}) / \Phi_{j,\,k-1} \approx K(\Psi_{kj}) / \Psi_{j,\,k-1}$

(Châtelet [26], pp. 354—356).

PROOF. Clearly, if j runs through the numbers $0, 1, \ldots, r$ and k through the numbers $0, 1, \ldots, s$, then

$$\Phi_{jk} = \Phi_{j-1} \smile (\Phi_j \frown \Psi_k)$$

is a refinement of (5), and

$$\Psi_{kj} = \Psi_{k-1} \cup (\Psi_k \cap \Phi_j)$$

is a refinement of (6). We shall show that these refinements have the properties (D)—(F).

First of all, by Theorem 87 and by the assumption (C), $\Phi_{j-1} \cup \cup (\Psi_k \cap \Phi_j) = (\Phi_{j-1} \cup \Psi_k) \cap \Phi_j$, and hence, by Theorem 86,

$$(7) \qquad \Phi_{jk} = \Phi_{j-1} \Psi_k \cap \Phi_j$$

Making use of this equation, we now prove

(G) *To every element a of $K(\Phi_{jk})$ there can be found an element a^* in $K(\Phi_j \cap \Psi_k)$ such that $a \equiv a^*(\Phi_{j-1})$ and the analogous statement also holds for $K(\Psi_{kj})$.*

Indeed, if $a \in K(\Phi_{jk})$, then by (7) $a \equiv e(\Phi_j)$ and there exists an $a^*(\in A)$ such that $a \equiv a^*(\Phi_{j-1})$, and $a^* \equiv e(\Psi_k)$. Since $\Phi_{j-1} \leqq \Phi_j$, these imply also $a^* \equiv a \equiv e(\Phi_j)$. But then $a^* \in K(\Psi_k) \cap K(\Phi_j) = = K(\Psi_k \cap \Phi_j)$.

Observe further that in the assumptions and in the propositions (D), (E) the Φ_j and Ψ_k occur in symmetric positions; hence, it is sufficient to prove the statements (D) and (E) with respect to the Φ_{jk} only. Accordingly, in the course of proving these two statements we shall write for short K_j instead of $K(\Phi_j)$ and K_{jk} instead of $K(\Phi_{jk})$.

PROOF OF (D). Consider some operation f_γ of A and any elements $x_1, \ldots, x_{n(\gamma)}$ of K_{jk}. By (7),

$$x_l \equiv e(\Phi_j) \qquad (l = 1, \ldots, n(\gamma))$$

and there exist in A elements $t_1, \ldots, t_{n(\gamma)}$ such that

$$x_l \equiv t_l(\Phi_{j-1}) \text{ and } t_l \equiv e(\Psi_k) \qquad (l = 1, \ldots, n(\gamma))$$

Since $\Phi_{j-1} \leq \Phi_j$, hence $t_l \equiv x_l \equiv e(\Phi_j)$ for every l; that is, $t_l, x_l \in K_j$. But then we have, on the one hand, by (B),

$$f_\gamma(x_1, \ldots, x_{n(\gamma)}) \equiv f_\gamma(t_1, \ldots, t_{n(\gamma)}) \, (\Phi_{j-1})$$

and on the other hand by (A),

$$f_\gamma(x_1, \ldots, x_{n(\gamma)}) \equiv e(\Phi_j)$$

and

$$f_\gamma(t_1, \ldots, t_{n(\gamma)}) \equiv e(\Psi_k)$$

Thus

$$f_\gamma(x_1, \ldots, x_{n(\gamma)}) \equiv e(\Phi_{j-1} \Psi_k \cap \Phi_j)$$

that is, $f_\gamma(x_1, \ldots, x_{n(\gamma)}) \in K_{jk}$.

PROOF OF (E). Obviously each K_j is precisely one of the Φ_j-classes. Therefore, applying (7) to the case $k-1$ instead of to k, we see at once that

(H) *$\Phi_{j,k-1}$ and $\Phi_{j-1}\Psi_{k-1}$ establish the same equivalence relation on K_j.*

Since, again by (7), $K_{jk} \subseteq K_j$, it is sufficient to prove with regard to (H) that the equivalence relation $\Phi_{j-1}\Psi_{k-1}$ establishes a congruence relation on K_{jk}. For this purpose consider some operation f_γ of A and elements $x_1, \ldots, x_{n(\gamma)}, y_1, \ldots, y_{n(\gamma)}$ of K_{jk} such that

$$(8) \qquad x_l \equiv y_l \ (\Phi_{j-1}\Psi_{k-1}) \qquad (l = 1, \ldots, n(\gamma))$$

By (G), there exist elements x_l^*, y_l^* such that

$$(9) \qquad x_l^* \equiv e\ (\Phi_j \frown \Psi_k), \qquad y_l^* \equiv e\ (\Phi_j \frown \Psi_k)$$

and

$$(10) \qquad x_l \equiv x_l^*\ (\Phi_{j-1}), \quad y_l^* \equiv y_l\ (\Phi_{j-1})$$

But then, by (B),

$$(11) \qquad \begin{cases} f_\gamma(x_1, \ldots, x_{n(\gamma)}) \equiv f_\gamma(x_1^*, \ldots, x_{n(\gamma)}^*)\ (\Phi_{j-1}) \\ f_\gamma(y_1^*, \ldots, y_{n(\gamma)}^*) \equiv f_\gamma(y_1, \ldots, y_{n(\gamma)})\ (\Phi_{j-1}) \end{cases}$$

However, by the reflexive property of equivalence relations, (10) implies also that

$$x_l^* \equiv x_l\ (\Phi_{j-1}\Psi_{k-1}) \text{ and } y_l \equiv y_l^*\ (\Phi_{j-1}\Psi_{k-1})$$

Since by assumption (C) and by Theorem 86, $\Phi_{j-1}\Psi_{k-1}$ is also an equivalence relation and hence transitive, we obtain with regard to (8)

$$x_l^* \equiv y_l^*\ (\Phi_{j-1}\Psi_{k-1}) \ (l = 1, \ldots, n(\gamma))$$

There exist consequently t_l's such that

$$x_l^* \equiv t_l\ (\Phi_{j-1}),\ t_l \equiv y_l^*\ (\Psi_{k-1})$$

A fortiori, $t_l \equiv x_l^*(\Phi_j)$ and thus by (9) every t_l (and every x_l^*) is included in K_j. Hence, by (B),

$$f_\gamma(x_1^*, \ldots, x_{n(\gamma)}^*) \equiv f_\gamma(t_1, \ldots, t_{n(\gamma)})\ (\Phi_{j-1})$$

Similarly,

$$f_\gamma(t_1, \ldots, t_{n(\gamma)}) \equiv f_\gamma(y_1^*, \ldots, y_{n(\gamma)}^*)\ (\Psi_{k-1})$$

From these two identities,

$$f_\gamma(x_1^*, \ldots, x_{n(\gamma)}^*) \equiv f_\gamma(y_1^*, \ldots, y_{n(\gamma)}^*)\ (\Phi_{j-1}\Psi_{k-1})$$

But then, by (11), $f_\gamma(x_1, \ldots, x_{r(\gamma)}) \equiv f_\gamma(y_1, \ldots, y_{r(\gamma)})\ (\Phi_{j-1}\Psi_{k-1})$ and thus we have shown that $\Phi_{j-1}\Psi_{k-1}$ establishes a congruence relation on K_{jk}.

PROOF OF (F). Now let us return from the notation K_{jk} to the notation $K(\Phi_{jk})$ and let us show first of all that

$$K(\Phi_{kj})/\Phi_{j-1}\Psi_{k-1} \approx K(\Phi_j \frown \Psi_k)/\Phi_{j-1}\Psi_{k-1} \tag{12}$$

Since $K(\Phi_{jk}) \supseteq K(\Phi_j \frown \Psi_k)$ for (12) to be true it is sufficient that every congruence class belonging to the factor algebra on the left possesses a representative in $K(\Phi_j \frown \Psi_k)$; this is, however, directly implied by (G). Then, by (H) and (12),

$$K(\Phi_{jk})/\Phi_{j,\, k-1} \approx K(\Phi_{jk})/\Phi_{j-1}\Psi_{k-1} \approx K(\Phi_j \frown \Psi_k)/\Phi_{j-1}\Psi_{k-1}$$

Similarly,

$$K(\Psi_{kj})/\Psi_{k,j-1} \approx K(\Psi_k \frown \Phi_j)/\Psi_{k-1}\, \Phi_{j-1}$$

By the permutability of Φ_{j-1} and Ψ_{k-1},

$$K(\Phi_j \frown \Psi_k)/\Phi_{j-1}\Psi_{k-1} \approx K(\Psi_k \frown \Phi_j)/\Psi_{k-1}\, \Phi_{j-1}$$

By the isomorphisms enumerated, (F) holds.

To conclude our line of thought we shall show, returning to the case of groups, how the Schreier theorem can be inferred from the theorem just proved. Let (1) and (2) be two normal series of the group G. Let us define the relations Φ_j $(j = 1, \ldots, r)$ and Ψ_k $(k = 1, \ldots, s)$ as follows:

$$x \equiv y(\Phi_j) \Longleftrightarrow xy^{-1} \in H_j \quad (x, y \in G)$$

$$x \equiv y(\Psi_k) \Longleftrightarrow x^{-1}y \in H'_k \quad (x, y \in G)$$

It can be easily verified that these relations are equivalence relations on G. Since both (1) and (2) are normal series, condition (B) clearly holds. So does (A), since $K(\Phi_j) = H_j$ $K(\Psi_k) = H'_k$. Now let us show that (C) also holds. Observe first of all that for every element z of G

$$x \equiv y(\Phi_j) \Longrightarrow xz \equiv yz(\Phi_j) \tag{13}$$

$$x \equiv y(\Psi_k) \Longrightarrow zx \equiv zy(\Psi_k) \tag{14}$$

Now let $a \equiv b(\Phi_j\, \Psi_k)$ $(a, b \in G)$. In this case there exists a c such that $a \equiv c(\Phi_j)$, $c \equiv b(\Psi_k)$. Consider the element $d = ac^{-1}b$. By (14), $a = ac^{-1}c \equiv ac^{-1}b = d(\Psi_k)$, and by (13), $d = ac^{-1}b \equiv cc^{-1}b = b(\Phi_j)$. Consequently $a \equiv b(\Psi_k\, \Phi_j)$. Hence, $\Phi_j\, \Psi_k \leq \Psi_k\, \Phi_j$. It can be verified in the same way that $\Phi_j\, \Psi_k \geq \Psi_k\, \Phi_j$.

In summary, the assumptions of the theorem are satisfied by the above equivalence relations, and hence $\mathscr{E}(G)$ has one subchain $\{\Phi_{jk}\}$ and one subchain $\{\Psi_{kj}\}$ for which (D) — (F) hold. Introduce the symbols $H_{jk} = K(\Phi_{jk})$, $H'_{jk} = K(\Psi_{kj})$. Then, by (D) and (E), the H_{jk} and the H'_{kj} form refinements of the normal series (1) and (2), respectively; and from (F), (3) results by the well-known relation between the congruence relations and the normal subgroups of a group.

The lattice-theoretical generalization of the Schreier theorem and the Jordan—Hölder theorem concerning composition series of groups has been studied by many. Among them, let us mention Ore [151], Uzkov [204], Kořínek [120], Livshitz [125], Benado [7], [8], Fujiwara [73], Vilhelm [207] and Felscher [61].

59. Congruence Relations of Lattices

Specializing the definition of congruence relations of algebras to the case of a lattice, we mean by a congruence relation of a lattice L an equivalence relation Θ of L having the following property: If $a \equiv b(\Theta)$ and $c \equiv d(\Theta)$ for some elements a, b, c, d of L, then $a \frown c \equiv b \frown d(\Theta)$ and $a \smile c \equiv b \smile d(\Theta)$.

The following lemma will prove to be useful:

Lemma. *Let Θ be a congruence relation of L. Then, for any pair a, b of elements of L, the following conditions* (A)—(C) *are equivalent*:

(A) $a \equiv b(\Theta)$
(B) $a \frown b \equiv a \smile b(\Theta)$
(C) $x, y \in [a \frown b, a \smile b] \Longrightarrow x \equiv y(\Theta)$

Proof. (A) *implies* (B), since if $a \equiv b(\Theta)$, then by the Substitution Property

$$a \frown b \equiv a \frown a = a = a \smile a \equiv a \smile b(\Theta)$$

(B) *implies* (C), since if $x, y \in [a \frown b, a \smile b]$, then

$$x = x \smile (a \frown b) \equiv x \smile (a \smile b) = a \smile b(\Theta)$$

and similarly, $y \equiv a \smile b(\Theta)$; but then, $x \equiv y(\Theta)$. Finally, (C) *implies* (A) under the substitution $x = a$, $y = b$.

The Lemma directly implies

Theorem 89. *Let Θ be a congruence relation of a lattice L. Then, every Θ-class is a convex sublattice of L.*

Proof. Let K be any Θ-class. If $a, b \in K$, then by the Lemma also $a \frown b$, $a \smile b \in K$; hence, K is a sublattice. Furthermore, if $u, v \in K$, $u \leq v$ and $x \in [u, v]$, then $x, u \in [u \frown v, u \smile v]$ and thus, again by the Lemma, $x \equiv u(\Theta)$, that is, $x \in K$. Hence, K is convex.

By Theorem 84, the set $\mathscr{K}(L)$ of all congruence relations of a lattice L constitutes a complete lattice. A further essential property of this lattice is expressed by

Theorem 90. *The congruence lattice of any lattice is distributive; moreover, it is infinitely meet-distributive* (Funayama—Nakayama [76]).

Proof. By Theorem 28, it is sufficient to prove the second proposition of the theorem. Consider for this purpose some subset $\{\Phi, \Theta_\gamma\}_{\gamma \in \Gamma}$ of the congruence lattice $\mathscr{K}(L)$ of the lattice L. Clearly,

$$\Phi \frown \bigcup_{\gamma \in \Gamma} \Theta_\gamma \geq \bigcup_{\gamma \in \Gamma} (\Phi \frown \Theta_\gamma)$$

there remains to be shown that the reverse inequality also holds.

If $a \equiv b(\Phi \frown \bigcup_{\gamma \in \Gamma} \Theta_\gamma)$ for some elements a and b of L, then

$$a \equiv b\ (\Phi) \tag{1}$$

and there can be found in L a finite sequence of elements $x_0, x_1, \ldots, x_{r-1}, x_r$ such that $x_0 = a$, $x_r = b$ and

$$x_{j-1} \equiv x_j(\Theta_{\gamma j}) \ (\gamma_j \in \Gamma;\ j = 1, \ldots, r)$$

Let us form the elements

(2) $$y_j = ((a \frown b) \smile x_j) \frown (a \smile b) \ (j = 0, 1, \ldots, r)$$

It follows by direct calculation that

(3) $$y_0 = a, \quad y_r = b$$

By applying the Substitution Property twice, we have

(4) $$y_{j-1} \equiv y_j\,(\Theta_{\gamma j}) \ (j = 1, \ldots, r)$$

Moreover, (2) implies that $a \frown b \leq y_j \leq a \smile b$ $(j = 0, 1, \ldots, r)$ and thus by (1) and the Lemma

(5) $$y_{j-1} \equiv y_j\,(\Phi) \quad (j = 1, \ldots, r)$$

However, (3)—(5) together imply precisely that $a \equiv b(\bigcup_{\gamma\in\Gamma} (\Phi \frown \Theta_\gamma))$, that is, $\Phi \frown (\bigcup_{\gamma\in\Gamma} \Theta_\gamma) \leq \bigcup_{\gamma\in\Gamma} (\Phi \frown \Theta_\gamma)$.

The following statement by Dilworth, but first proved by Grätzer and Schmidt in a generalized form ([19], p. 140, Ex. 6 and [83], Theorem 1) may be taken as a converse of the theorem concerning finite lattices: Every finite distributive lattice is isomorphic to the congruence lattice of some lattice.

It is an interesting problem as to what conditions $\mathscr{K}(L)$ must satisfy to be a Boolean algebra. By a result of Tanaka [199] it is necessary and sufficient that the lattice L have a subdirect decomposition* into simple lattices in which any two distinct elements of L differ only in a finite number of components. See also Dilworth [47], Theorems 4.4 and 3.2, Wang [210], Grätzer—Schmidt [79], Theorem 11, Crawley [29] and Finkbeiner [63].

Hasimoto has shown ([89)], Theorem 8.4 that the congruence relations of a distributive lattice form a Boolean algebra if, and only if, the lattice is of locally finite length.

Grätzer and Schmidt have proved [81] that $\mathscr{K}$(L) is a Boolean algebra if, and only if, L is cempletely join-distributive.

60. Minimal Congruence Relations of Some Subsets of a Distributive Lattice

THEOREM 91. *The minimal congruence relation Θ_{ab} belonging to the subset $\{a, b\}$ $(a \geq b)$ of L can be described as follows: for any elements x, y of L, $x \equiv y(\Theta_{ab})$ if, and only if,*

(1) $$a \smile (x \frown y) \geq x \smile y$$

* For the concept see Section 63.

and

$$(2) \qquad b \cap (x \cup y) \leq x \cap y$$

(Grätzer—Schmidt [79], Theorem 2).

Proof. Let us define in L the relation Θ so that $x\Theta y$ if, and only if, (1) and (2) hold for the elements x, y and let us prove $\Theta = \Theta_{ab}$.

The relation Θ is clearly reflexive and symmetric. Let us verify that Θ has the substitution property.

For any elements x, y, z, t of L,

$$a \cup \big((x \cup z) \cap (y \cup t)\big) \geq a \cup (x \cap y)$$

and

$$a \cup \big((x \cup z) \cap (y \cup t\big) \geq a \cup (z \cap t)$$

Hence

$$(3) \qquad a \cup \big((x \cup z) \cap (y \cup t)\big) \geq \big(a \cup (x \cap y)\big) \cup \big(a \cup (z \cap t\big)$$

Let now $x\Theta y$ and $z\Theta t$. Then by (3) and (1)

$$a \cup \big((x \cup z) \cap (y \cup t)\big) \geq (x \cup y) \cup (z \cup t) = (x \cup z) \cup (y \cup t)$$

On the other hand, by the distributivity of L and by (2)

$$b \cap \big((x \cup z) \cup y \cup t)\big) = b \cap \big((x \cup y) \cup (z \cup t)\big) =$$
$$= \big((b \cap (x \cup y)\big) \cup \big(b \cap (z \cup t)\big) \leq$$
$$\leq (x \cap y) \cup (z \cap t) \leq (x \cup z) \cap (y \cup t)$$

Hence, $(x \cup z)\,\Theta(y \cup t)$. By dualizing we see that also $(x \cap z)\,\Theta(y \cap t)$.

The transitivity of Θ will be shown first for the case of comparable elements. Let $u\Theta v$, $v\Theta w$ and $u \geq v \geq w$. Then, by the definition of Θ,

$$a \cup v \geq u, \qquad a \cup w \geq v$$

and

$$b \cap u \leq v, \qquad b \cap v \leq w$$

Hence

$$a \cup (u \cap w) = a \cup w \geq a \cup v \geq u = u \cup w$$

and similarly, $b \cap (u \cup w) \leq u \cap w$; that is, $u\Theta w$.

Now let x, y, z be any elements of the lattice L such that $x\Theta y$ and $y\Theta z$. By the reflexivity, symmetry and substitution property, already proved for Θ,

$$(x \cup y)\,\Theta(x \cup x) = x, \text{ and } \quad x = (x \cap x)\,\Theta(x \cap y)$$

Hence, in agreement with the result of the foregoing section $(x \cup$

$\cup y)\,\Theta(x \cap y)$. Similarly, $(y \cup z)\,\Theta(y \cap z)$. Hence, applying the substitution property twice,

$$x \cup y \cup z = \big((x \cup y) \cup (y \cup z)\big)\,\Theta\,\big((x \cup y) \cup (y \cap z)\big) = x \cup y$$

$$(x \cup y)\,\Theta(x \cap y)$$

$$x \cap y = \big((x \cap y) \cap (y \cup z)\big)\,\Theta\big((x \cap y) \cap (y \cap z)\big) = x \cap y \cap z$$

Since $x \cup y \cup z \geqq x \cup y \geqq x \cap y \geqq x \cap y \cap z$, by applying the result of the foregoing paragraph twice, we get $(x \cup y \cap z)\,\Theta(x \cap \cap y \cap z)$. This implies, however, by the substitution property,

$$x \cup z = \{\big((x \cup y \cup z) \cap (x \cup z)\big) \cup (x \cap z)\}\,\Theta$$

$$\{\big((x \cap y \cap z) \cap (x \cup z)\big) \cup (x \cap z)\} = x \cap z$$

that is, $(x \cup z)\,\Theta(x \cap z)$. Hence, by the definition of Θ, (1) and (2) must be satisfied if the x and y figuring in them are substituted by $x \cup z$ and $x \cap z$, respectively. But then

$$a \cup (x \cap z) \geqq x \cup z$$

and

$$b \cap (x \cup z) \leqq x \cap z$$

implying that also $x\Theta z$ holds, completing the proof of transitivity.

By the above, Θ is a congruence relation, therefore, in the remaining part of the proof we shall denote Θ by the usual notation of congruence relations. It can be shown by direct calculation and by using the assumption $a \geqq b$ that $a \equiv b(\Theta)$, whence $\Theta \geqq \Theta_{ab}$. We shall also show that $\Theta_{ab} \geqq \Theta$. If $x \equiv y(\Theta)$, then by the definition of Θ and by the substition property of Θ_{ab},

$$\begin{aligned} x \cap y &= \big(b \cap (x \cup y)\big) \cup (x \cap y) = \\ &= \big(b \cup (x \cap y)\big) \cap \big((x \cup y) \cup (x \cap y)\big) = \\ &= \big(b \cup (x \cap y)\big) \cap (x \cup y) \equiv \big(a \cup (x \cap y)\big) \cap (x \cup y) = \\ &= x \cup y(\Theta_{ab}) \end{aligned}$$

and hence, by Theorem 89, $x \equiv y(\Theta_{ab})$.

THEOREM 92. *Let L be distributive lattice bounded below and I an ideal of L. Then for the minimal congruence relation Θ_I belonging to I, $a \equiv b(\Theta_I)$ $(a, b \in L)$ if, and only if, there exists a $v \in I$ satisfying the equation*

(4) $$a \cup v = b \cup v$$

COROLLARY. *For some element u of L, $u \equiv o\ (\Theta_I)$ if, and only if, $u \in I$.*

As a preliminary to the proof we have

LEMMA. *If I is an ideal of a lattice L bounded below, then* $\Theta_I = \bigcup_{u \in I} \Theta_{ou}$ (where the join is taken, as a matter of course, in $\mathscr{K}(L)$).

PROOF. For any element u of I, there holds $u \equiv o\ (\Theta_I)$. Hence by the definition of Θ_{ou}, $\Theta_I \geqq \Theta_{ou}$. Consequently, $\Theta_I \geqq \bigcup_{u \in I} \Theta_{ou}$. On the other hand, for any pair of elements x, y of I, $x \equiv o\ (\Theta_{ox})$ and $o \equiv y(\Theta_{oy})$, that is, $x \equiv y\ (\bigcup_{u \in I} \Theta_{ou})$. This means by the definition of Θ_I that $\Theta_I \leqq \bigcup_{u \in I} \Theta_{ou}$.

Let us now proceed to prove the theorem.

If I has an element v satisfying (4), then

$$a = a \cup o \equiv a \cup v = b \cup v \equiv b \cup o = o\ (\Theta_I)$$

Hence, the condition is sufficient. Conversely, if for any elements a, b of a lattice L bounded below, $a \equiv b\ (\Theta_I)$, then by the Lemma it is legitimate to write $a \equiv b\ (\bigcup_{u \in I} \Theta_{ou})$; hence elements $x_0, x_1, \ldots, x_r$ exist in L and $u_1, \ldots, u_r$ in I such that $x_{j-1} \equiv x_j(\Theta_{ou_j})$ $(j = 1, \ldots, r)$. Let $v = \bigcup_{j=1}^{r} u_j$; then clearly, $v \in I$. Since $v \equiv o\ (\Theta_{ov})$, we have by Theorem 89 also $u_j \equiv o\ (\Theta_{ov})$ $(j = 1, \ldots, r)$.

Hence $\Theta_{ov} \geqq \Theta_{ou_j}$ for every j, and thus $x_{j-1} \equiv x_j(\Theta_{ov})$; consequently, $a \equiv b(\Theta_{ov})$. Applying Theorem 91 to the elements v, o, a, b (substituting them in that order for a, b, x, y there) we obtain that $v \cup (a \cap b) \geqq a \cup b$. Hence, by the distributivity of L

$$(v \cup a) \cup (v \cup b) = v \cup (a \cup b) = v \cup (a \cap b) \cup (a \cup b) =$$

$$= v \cup (a \cap b) = (v \cup a) \cap (v \cup b)$$

consequently, $v \cup a = v \cup b$.

As regards the corollary, $u \equiv o\ (\Theta_I)$ is satisfied according to the theorem if, and only if, I has an element v such that $u \cup v = o \cup v = v$. However, in that case, $u \leqq v$ and $v \in I$, whence $u \in I$. Conversely, if $u \in I$, then $u \equiv o\ (\Theta_I)$ by the definition of Θ_I.

A topic related to that of the present paragraph is discussed in Krishnan's paper [121].

61. The Connection between Ideals and Congruence Relations of a Lattice

Let Θ be any congruence relation of a lattice L and θ the natural homomorphism belonging to the same. If θ has a kernel, the latter is also called the *kernel of the congruence relation* Θ. By Theorem 16 this is an ideal of L.

If the lattice L is bounded below then so is every one of its homomorphic images. Moreover, the least element o^* of the homomorphic image L^* is the homomorphic image of the least element o of the lattice L. Hence, o is included in the kernel of every congruence relation of L, whence the kernel of the congruence relation Θ is that Θ-class of L which includes o. In other words, *the kernel of any congruence relation Θ of a lattice L bounded below consists of those elements x of L which satisfy $x \equiv o(\Theta)$.*

It is known that there can be established between the set of congruence relations and the set of ideals of a ring a one-to-one correspondence by assigning to each congruence relation its own kernel. The example given in Section 53 — paraphrased to the terminology of congruence relations — shows that for lattices, no such statement holds in general.

It was Birkhoff who raised the problem as to what necessary and sufficient conditions can be given for every congruence relation of a lattice to have a kernel and for every ideal of the lattice to be the kernel of precisely one congruence relation.

The answer to the first part of the problem is simple: clearly it is sufficient if the lattice L has a least element. However, this condition is also necessary, since otherwise the least element of $\mathscr{K}(L)$, the relation E, would have no kernel.

A partial solution of the second part of the problem preparing the way for the complete solution to be given later is proposed by Theorems 93 and 94.

THEOREM 93. *In order that every ideal of a lattice L be the kernel of at least one congruence relation of L, it is necessary and sufficient that L be distributive* (Hashimoto [89], Theorem 2.2).

PROOF. The sufficiency of distributivity is directly obtained by considering the result stated as the Corollary to Theorem 92. Let us now prove the necessity of distributivity. Let L^* be a non-distributive lattice. Then, by Theorem 33, it has a sublattice $\{u, x, y, z, v\}$ whose diagram coincides with one of the diagrams of Fig. 30 (p. 166). We shall show that the principal ideal $(x]$ is not the kernel of a congruence relation of L^*. Indeed, even for the minimal congruence relation $\Theta_{(x]}$ belonging to $(x]$,

$$y = y \frown (x \smile z) \equiv y \frown (u \smile z) \equiv u\ (\Theta_{(x]})$$

that is, y is also included in the kernel of $\Theta_{(x]}$, although $y \notin (x]$, completing the proof.

As a preliminary to Theorem 94, we prove the following

LEMMA. *Let Θ be a congruence relation of a section complemented lattice L. For any pair of elements x, y of L, $x \equiv y(\Theta)$ if, and only if, every relative complement of $x \frown y$ in $[o, x \smile y]$ is included in the kernel of Θ.*

PROOF. Let z denote a relative complement of $x \frown y$ in $[o, x \smile y]$. If $x \equiv y(\Theta)$, then by the Lemma in Section 59, $o = (x \frown y) \frown z \equiv$ $\equiv (x \smile y) \frown z \equiv z\ (\Theta)$. Conversely, if $z \equiv o\ (\Theta)$, then $x \smile y =$ $= (x \frown y) \smile z \equiv (x \frown y) \smile o \equiv x \frown y(\Theta)$, and hence $x \equiv y(\Theta)$.

From the lemma, there follows as a simple corollary

THEOREM 94. *In a section complemented lattice, every ideal constitutes the kernel of at most one congruence relation.*

Indeed, if the congruence relations Θ_1 and Θ_2 of a section complemented lattice L have the same ideal as their kernel, then by the lemma, $x \equiv y(\Theta_1) \longleftrightarrow x \equiv y(\Theta_2)$ for every pair of elements x, y.

The complete answer to Birkhoff's problem is given by

THEOREM 95. *For any lattice L, the following two conditions are equivalent* (Hashimoto [89], Theorem 7.2):

(A) *Every ideal of L is the kernel of exactly one congruence relation and every congruence relation of L has a kernel;*

(B) *L is bounded below, distributive and relatively complemented.*

Hashimoto obtained this result as a particular consequence of more general considerations. Concerning the direct proof to be expounded below see Grätzer—Schmidt [79], p. 146. In [80] pp. 277—278 the latter authors give a still shorter proof, making use of more profound theorems; for a sharpening of the theorem see Grätzer—Schmidt [79], Theorem 3.

For distributive lattices bounded below Areshkin [1] has found that proposition (A) is true if, and only if, the congruence lattice of the lattice is weakly complemented.

PROOF.

(B) *implies* (A). Provided the assumptions of (B) are satisfied, every ideal of L is, by Theorem 93, the kernel of at least one, by Theorem 94, of at most one congruence relation; moreover, by the existence of the element o, every congruence relation in L has a kernel.

(A) *implies* (B). We have already learned above (prior to Theorem 93) that if every congruence relation of a lattice L has a kernel, then L is necessarily bounded below. Further, in order that every ideal of L be the kernel of precisely one congruence relation, it is necessary, by Theorem 93, that L be distributive. Hence, it is sufficient to prove the following: If L is a distributive lattice bounded below, in which every ideal is the kernel of exactly one congruence relation, then L is relatively complemented.

Let therefore L be a lattice satisfying the condition stated above. Consider two elements a, b of L such that $a \geqq b$ (otherwise arbitrary) and let the kernel of the minimal congruence relation Θ_{ab} belonging to the set $\{a, b\}$ be denoted by I. Since I is also the kernel of Θ_I we have $\Theta_{ab} = \Theta_I$ by our assumptions. But then, $a \equiv b\ (\Theta_I)$, and thus, by Theorem 92, there exists in I an element v such that

$$a \cup v = b \cup v \tag{1}$$

Furthermore, again by $\Theta_I = \Theta_{ab}$, we have $v \equiv o(\Theta_{ab})$, and hence, applying Theorem 91,

$$a \geqq v \tag{2}$$

and

$$b \cap v = o \tag{3}$$

From (1), with regard to (2), there follows $b \cup v = a$. Now this means together with (3) that v is a relative complement of b in $[o, a]$. This means that L is section complemented, and thus by Theorem 50, a relatively complemented lattice, indeed.

Exercises to Chapter IX

1. Show that under the multiplication $xy = x$ $(x, y \in F)$ the set F is a semigroup, every equivalence relation of which is a congruence relation as well.

2. Let $\Theta_1, \ldots, \Theta_r$ and Φ be equivalence relations defined on a given set. Prove that if Φ is permutable with every Θ_j $(j = 1, \ldots, r)$ then it is also permutable with their join. Show by an example that the dual statement is not true.

3. Find non-permutable congruence relations on a finite chain with three or more elements.

4. Prove that an equivalence relation defined on a lattice L is a congruence relation if, and only if, for any elements a, b, c of L, $a \equiv b(\Theta)$ implies $a \cap c \equiv b \cap c(\Theta)$ and $a \cup c \equiv b \cup c(\Theta)$. Generalize this condition to equivalence relations of arbitrary algebras.

5. Show that if $A_1 = A(\{f_\gamma\}_{\gamma \in \Gamma})$ and $A_2 = A(\{f_\delta\}_{\delta \in \Delta})$ are algebras defined on the same set A and $\Gamma \supseteq \Delta$, then the lattice $\mathcal{K}(A_1)$ is a complete sublattice of $\mathcal{K}(A_2)$.

6. Show that the congruence lattice of any finite chain is a Boolean algebra. Discuss the connection between the length of the lattice and the number of its congruence relations.

7. Define in a modular lattice L the relation Θ as follows: let $x\Theta y$ $(x, y \in L)$ if, and only if, there exists a finite maximal chain connecting the elements $x \cap y$ and $x \cup y$. Show that Θ is a congruence relation of L.

8. Let u, v, a, b be elements of a modular lattice such that $a \parallel b$, $u \prec a < v$ and $u < b \prec v$. Prove that under a congruence relation Θ of the lattice, $u \equiv a(\Theta)$ if, and only if, $b \equiv v(\Theta)$.

9. Show that a lattice L is distributive if, and only if, each interval $[a, b]$ $(a, b \in L)$ is a congruence class under the congruence relation Θ_{ab}.

10. Show that a lattice L is distributive if, and only if, for each ideal I, and for each pair of elements x, y $(x \geq y)$ of L there holds $x \equiv y(\Theta_I)$ if, and only if, there exists an element v in I such that $x = y \cup v$.

11. Prove that under a congruence relation Θ of a Boolean algebra B the following statements concerning any pair of elements a, b of B are equivalent:

(A) $x \equiv y(\Theta)$; (B) $x' \equiv y'(\Theta)$;

(C) $x \cap y' \equiv x' \cap y(\Theta)$.

12. Let I be an ideal of a Boolean algebra B. Prove that the relation defined by

$$a \equiv b\ (\Theta) \longleftrightarrow (a' \frown b) \smile (a \frown b') \in I$$

is precisely that congruence relation of B whose kernel is I.

13. Prove that a relation Θ defined on a Boolean algebra B is a congruence relation if, and only if, Θ is a congruence relation in the ring-theoretical sense of the Boolean ring $\mathfrak{R}(B)$ belonging to B. (For the definition of $\mathfrak{R}(B)$ see Section 44.)

14. Show that in a weakly complemented lattice the zero ideal cannot be the kernel of any congruence relation different from the equality relation.

15. Show that every distributive lattice consisting of at least three elements has a proper congruence relation.

16. Determine the congruence relations of the lattices shown in Figs 17a and 17b (p. 90).

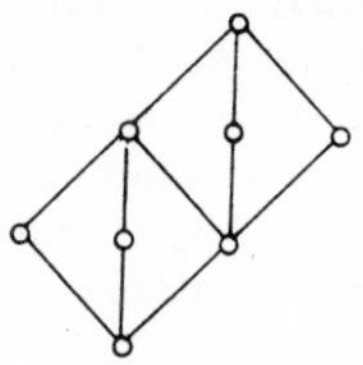

Fig. 33/a

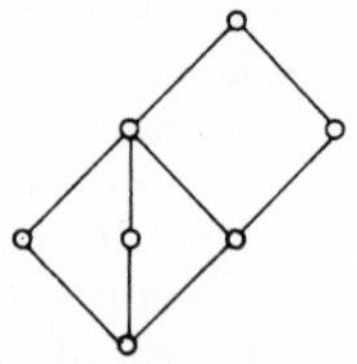

Fig. 33/b

17. Show that the lattice in Fig. 33a is simple, and that in Fig. 33b is not simple.

18. Show that if to any two distinct atoms p, q of a relatively complemented semimodular lattice of finite length there can be found a third atom r such that $r \leqq p \smile q$, then the lattice is simple.

CHAPTER

DIRECT AND SUBDIRECT DECOMPOSITIONS

62. Direct Unions and Decompositions of Algebras

Let $A_1, \ldots, A_r$ ($r \geqq 1$) be similar algebras with the operations $\{f_\gamma\}_{\gamma \in \Gamma}$. Consider the product set $A_1 \times \ldots \times A_r$, that is, the set of all sequences of the form

(1) $$(a_1 \ \ldots \ a_r) \qquad (a_j \in A_j; \ \ j = 1, \ldots, r)$$

In this set, let us define by means of every f_γ an operation — to be denoted similarly by f_γ — such that

(2) $$f_\gamma\big((a_{11}, \ldots, a_{1r}), \ldots, (a_{n(\gamma)1}, \ldots, a_{n(\gamma)r})\big) =$$
$$= \big(f_\gamma(a_{11}, \ldots, a_{n(\gamma)1}), \ldots, f_\gamma(a_{1r}, \ldots, a_{n(\gamma)r})\big)$$

The algebra thus obtained is called the *direct union* of $A_1, \ldots, A_r$ and is symbolized $A_1 \otimes \ldots \otimes A_r$. In particular, every algebra is a "direct union" of itself.

The number of all direct unions of the algebras $A_1, \ldots, A_r$, to be formed in the manner just described, equals the number of permutations of the indices $1, \ldots, r$. However, these direct unions are not different from the point of view of abstract algebra, since if $\pi(1), \ldots, \pi(r)$ denotes some permutation of the indices $1, \ldots, r$, then the mapping $(a_1, \ldots, a_r) \rightarrow (a_{\pi(1)}, \ldots, a_{\pi(r)})$ is an isomorphism of $A_1 \otimes \ldots \otimes A_r$ onto $A_{\pi(1)} \otimes \ldots \otimes A_{\pi(r)}$.

The algebras $A_1, \ldots, A_r$ are called the *components of the direct union* $A_1 \otimes \ldots \otimes A_r$; in particular, A_j is called the jth *component*. It is also frequently said that, in (1), a_j is the jth *component* (or the component in A_j) *of the element* $(a_1, \ldots, a_r)$. Accordingly, the rule of operation (2) can be verbally expressed as follows: *In a direct union, the operations are to be performed component by component.*

By the definition, every direct union is an algebra similar to its components. From (2) it follows that if an identity (commutativity, associativity, distributivity) holds in $A_1, \ldots, A_r$, then it also holds in $A_1 \otimes \ldots \otimes A_r$. Furthermore, if R_j ($j = 1, \ldots, r$) is a subalgebra of A_j, then the set of all elements of the form $(a_1, \ldots, a_r)$ ($a_j \in R_j$) — incidentally equalling the direct union $R_1 \otimes \ldots \otimes R_r$ defined by the operation (2) — is a subalgebra of $A_1 \otimes \ldots \otimes A_r$. Furthermore, the mapping

(3) $$\varphi_k(a_1, \ldots, a_k, \ldots, a_n) = a_k$$

is a homomorphism of $A_1 \otimes \ldots \otimes A_r$ onto A_k, since for every operation f_γ

$$\varphi_k\{f_\gamma((\ldots, a_{1k}, \ldots), \ldots, (\ldots, a_{n(\gamma)k}, \ldots))\} =$$
$$= \varphi_k\{\ldots, f_\gamma(a_{1k}, \ldots, a_{n(\gamma)k}), \ldots\} = f_\gamma(a_{1k}, \ldots, a_{n(\gamma)k}) =$$
$$= f_\gamma(\varphi_k(\ldots, a_{1k}, \ldots), \ldots, \varphi_k(\ldots, a_{n(\gamma)k}, \ldots))$$

In the foregoing we have formed the direct union of given algebras $A_1, \ldots, A_r$. From the point of view of research in the algebras, the converse procedure is also important: Given an algebra A, find some algebras $A_1, \ldots, A_r$ such that $A \approx A_1 \otimes \ldots \otimes A_r$. If the A_j $(j = 1, \ldots, r)$ satisfy this condition, we say that A can be represented as the direct union of the algebras $A_1, \ldots, A_r$; $A_1 \otimes \ldots \otimes A_r$ itself is then called a *direct decomposition* of A.

If there exists the isomorphism $A \approx A_1 \otimes \ldots \otimes A_r$, established by the mapping

$$\varphi : x \rightarrow (x_1, \ldots, x_r) \quad (x \in A;\ x_j \in A_j,\ \ j = 1, \ldots, r)$$

then — similarly to (3) — every

$$\varphi_k : \varphi_k(x) = x_k \ (x \in A)$$

is a homomorphism of A onto A_k. The φ_k are called *decomposition homomorphisms;* the set $\{\varphi_1, \ldots, \varphi_r\}$ is called a *complete system of decomposition homomorphisms* (belonging to the decomposition in question). The congruence relations

$$x \equiv y(\Phi_k) \longleftrightarrow \varphi_k(x) = \varphi_k(y) \ (x, y \in A)$$

generated by the decomposition homomorphisms on A are called *decomposition congruences;* the set $\{\Phi_1, \ldots, \Phi_r\}$ of these is called a *complete system of decomposition congruences.* Of course, the use of these terms is permitted in the previous case $A = A_1 \otimes \ldots \otimes A_r$, too.

Lemma. *Let $\{\Phi_1, \ldots, \Phi_r\}$ be a complete system of decomposition congruences belonging to a direct decomposition. Then*

(A) $\Phi_j \Phi_k = \Phi_k \Phi_j = \mathsf{I}$ (if $j \neq k$)

(B) $\Phi_j \cup \Phi_k = \mathsf{I}$ (if $j \neq k$)

(C) $\Phi_1 \cap \ldots \cap \Phi_r = \mathsf{E}$

Proof. If, in the decomposition considered, $x \rightarrow (x_1, \ldots, x_r)$ and $y \rightarrow (y_1, \ldots, y_r)$ then

$$(x_1, \ldots, x_j, \ldots, x_r) \equiv (y_1, \ldots, y_{j-1}, x_j, y_{j+1}, \ldots, y_r)\ (\Phi_j)$$

and

$$(y_1, \ldots, y_{r-1}, x_j, y_{j+1}, \ldots, y_r) \equiv (y_1, \ldots, y_r)\ (\Phi_k)$$

Hence $\Phi_j \Phi_k = \mathsf{I}$. In the same way, $\Phi_k \Phi_j = \mathsf{I}$. Thus (A) is verified. Now, by (A), $\mathsf{I} = \Phi_j \Phi_k \leqq \Phi_j \cup \Phi_k \leqq \mathsf{I}$, implying (B). Finally, (C) is evident.

Every algebra $A = A(\{f_\gamma\}_{\gamma \in \Gamma})$ has a trivial direct decomposition as follows. Consider the single-element set $\{e\}$ and define on it the operations f_γ so that $f_\gamma(e, \ldots, e) = e$ for every $\gamma \in \Gamma$. Clearly, in this case $A \approx A \otimes \{e\}$. However, now the first decomposition homomorphism is an isomorphism.

An algebra A is called *directly decomposable* or *directly reducible* if A has a direct decomposition under which no decomposition homomorphism is an isomorphism.* If A has no direct decomposition of this sort, it is called *directly indecomposable* or *directly irreducible*.

THEOREM 96. *An algebra A is directly decomposable if, and only if, it has two non-trivial congruence relations which are permutable and which are complements of each other in the congruence lattice of A.*

SUPPLEMENT. *If A has congruence relations Θ_1, Θ_2 with these properties, then $A \approx (A/\Theta_1) \otimes (A/\Theta_2)$.*

PROOF. Assume that $\varphi : A \approx A_1 \otimes A_2$, or, in more detail

$$\varphi(x) = (x_1, x_2) \quad (x \in A; x_1 \in A_1, x_2 \in A_2)$$

is an isomorphism of A onto $A_1 \otimes A_2$. The decomposition congruences Θ_1 and Θ_2 belonging to this decomposition are, by the lemma, permutable and complements of each other. If none of the decomposition homomorphisms $\varphi_1(x) = x_1$ and $\varphi_2(x) = x_2$ is an isomorphism, then neither Θ_1, nor Θ_2 equals E; hence, $\Theta_1 \neq \mathsf{I}$ and $\Theta_2 \neq \mathsf{I}$. Thus the necessity of the condition is shown.

The sufficiency of the condition will be proved by verifying the supplement of the theorem. Let A_k $(k = 1, 2)$ denote the factor algebra A/Θ_k, and x_k the Θ_k-class including the element $x (\in A)$. The mapping

$$\psi : x \to (x_1, x_2) \quad (x \in A)$$

is obviously a homomorphism of A into $A_1 \otimes A_2$. However, it is also an isomorphism, since if $x_1 = y_1$ and $x_2 = y_2$ for some elements x, y of A, then $x \equiv y(\Theta_1)$ and $x \equiv y(\Theta_2)$ and thus by $\Theta_1 \cap \Theta_2 = \mathsf{E}$, also $x = y$. We show that every element of $A_1 \otimes A_2$ figures among the image elements of ψ. For this purpose, consider an arbitrary element (x_1, y_2) of $A_1 \otimes A_2$, and $x \in x_1$, $y \in y_2$. By hypothesis and by Theorem 86, $\Theta_1 \Theta_2 = \Theta_1 \cup \Theta_2 = \mathsf{I}$, and hence there exists a t in A such that $x \equiv t(\Theta_1)$ and $t \equiv y(\Theta_2)$. But then, $t_1 = x_1$ and $t_2 = y_2$, that is, $\psi(t) =$

* Or if there holds the equivalent statement that none of the decomposition congruences coincides with the equality relation.

$=(x_1, y_2)$. Finally, since Θ_1 and Θ_2 were assumed to be non-trivial congruences, neither of the decomposition homomorphisms

$$x \longrightarrow x_1 \quad (x \in A;\ x_1 \in A_1)$$

and

$$x \longrightarrow x_2 \quad (x \in A;\ x_2 \in A_2)$$

is an isomorphism. Thereby, the proof of the theorem is completed.

The concept of direct union can also be extended to an infinite number of components. Let $\{A_\lambda\}_{\lambda \in \Lambda}$ be an infinite set of similar algebras and let $\{f_\gamma\}_{\gamma \in \Gamma}$ denote the set of operations defined on the A_γ' s. Let us construct all sets of the form

$$\{a_\lambda\}_{\lambda \in \Lambda} \quad (a_\lambda \in A_\lambda;\ \lambda \in \Lambda)$$

(that is, all sets which contain exactly one element of each A_λ), and let us denote this set of sets by A. Now let us define operations in A by taking

$$f_\gamma(\{a_{1\lambda}\}_{\lambda \in \Lambda}, \ldots, \{a_{n(\gamma),\lambda}\}_{\lambda \in \Lambda} = \{f_\gamma(a_{1\lambda}, \ldots, a_{n(\gamma),\lambda}\}_{\lambda \in \Lambda}$$

that is, every operation is performed component by component. The algebra thus obtained is called the *direct union* of the algebra A_λ and denoted $\prod_{\lambda \in \Lambda} A_\lambda$.

In the literature the algebra $\prod_{\lambda \in \Lambda} A_\lambda$ is frequently referred to as the "complete direct union" of the A_λ and distinguished from the "discrete direct union of the A_λ". The latter can be defined only when every A_λ includes a one-element subalgebra $\{e_\lambda\}$. In this case, those elements of the set A in which $a_\lambda = e_\lambda$ except for a finite number of λ, constitute a subalgebra $\prod^*_{\lambda \in \Lambda} A_\lambda$ of $\prod_{\lambda \in \Lambda} A_\lambda$; this subalgebra is called the discrete direct union of the A_λ. For finite $\Lambda = \{1, \ldots, r\}$ clearly $\prod_{\lambda \in \Lambda} A_\lambda = \prod^* A_\lambda = A_1 \otimes \ldots \otimes A_r$. A common generalization of complete and discrete direct unions is defined and discussed by Hashimoto [90].

The concepts introduced in connection with finite direct unions also retain their utility in this more general case and it is easy to see that the statements concerning them remain true.

63. Subdirect Unions and Decompositions of Algebras

By a *subdirect union* of the algebras $A_\lambda (\lambda \in \Lambda)$ is meant a subalgebra R of the direct union $\prod_{\lambda \in \Lambda} A_\lambda$ having the property that to every $a_\lambda (\in A_\lambda)$ there exists at least one element in R whose component in A_λ is equal to a_λ. In other words, a subalgebra R of $\prod_{\lambda \in \Lambda} A_\lambda$ is called a subdirect union of the A_λ if $\varphi(R) = A_\lambda$ holds for every decomposition homomorphism φ_λ of $\prod_{\lambda\in\Lambda} A_\lambda$. It is immediately seen that $\prod_{\lambda\in\Lambda} A_\lambda$ itself is a subdirect union of the algebras A_λ.

It is said that the algebra A can be represented as the subdirect union of the algebras A_λ if A is isomorphic to a subdirect union of the A_λ; this subdirect union is called the *subdirect decomposition* of A. Accordingly, an algebra A is called *subdirectly decomposable* or *subdirectly reducible* if A has a subdirect decomposition, no decomposition homomorphism of which is an isomorphism. In the opposite case, A is called *subdirectly indecomposable* or *subdirectly irreducible.*

THEOREM 97. *Let A be an algebra and Λ an arbitrary index set. The algebra A can be represented as a subdirect union of some algebras $A_\lambda(\lambda \in \Lambda)$ if, and only if, A has congruence relations $\Theta_\lambda(\lambda \in \Lambda)$ such that*

$$\bigcap_{\lambda\in\Lambda} \Theta = \mathrm{E} \tag{1}$$

(Birkhoff [19], first edition, Theorem 3.20).

SUPPLEMENT. If (1) *is satisfied, then A is isomorphic to a subdirect union of the factor algebras A/Θ_λ $(\lambda \in \Lambda)$.*

PROOF. If A can be represented as a subdirect union of the algebras A_λ, then, by the Lemma in Section 62, (1) holds for the complete system of decomposition congruences belonging to the decomposition considered; hence, the condition is necessary.

The sufficiency of the condition will be proved in the sharper form proposed in the supplement. Assume that (1) is satisfied by the congruence relations Θ_λ $(\lambda \in \Lambda)$ of A. Let ϑ_λ denote the natural homomorphism belonging to Θ_λ and σ that mapping of A into $\prod_\lambda A/\Theta_\lambda$ for which

$$\sigma(x) = \{\vartheta_\lambda(x)\}_{\lambda\in\Lambda} \qquad (x \in A;\ \vartheta_\lambda(x) \in A/\Theta_\lambda;\ \lambda \in \Lambda)$$

Clearly σ is a homomorphism. Furthermore, if $\vartheta_\lambda(x) = \vartheta_\lambda(y)$ $(x, y \in A)$ for every λ, then by (1), $x = y$; hence, σ is one-to-one. So, σ is an isomorphism of A onto the subalgebra $R = \{\sigma(x)\}_{x\in A}$ of $\prod_\lambda A/\Theta_\lambda$. Consider finally some element $\bar{x}$ of A. element x of A included in the Θ-class $\bar{x}$, then the component in A/Θ_λ of $\sigma(x)$ is precisely $\bar{x}$; hence, the R is a subdirect union of the A/Θ_λ.

It is known that there exist algebras (in particular groups) which cannot be decomposed into direct unions of directly irreducible algebras. On the contrary, there holds

THEOREM 98. *Every algebra can be represented as the subdirect union of subdirectly irreducible algebras* (Birkhoff [18], Theorem 2).

PROOF. Let a, b $(a \neq b)$ be any pair of elements of the algebra A. Let us denote by $\mathscr{K}^{ab}$ the set of all congruence relations of A under which a and b are incongruent.* Of course, the set $\mathscr{K}^{ab}$ is partly

* The superfixes are employed in order to avoid incompatibility with the notation introduced in Section 59.

ordered by the relation defined in (1) of Section 45. We shall show that this set has a maximal element with respect to this ordering.

Consider for this purpose some subchain $\mathfrak{C}$ of $\mathscr{K}^{ab}$ and define on A a relation Φ as follows: let $x \equiv y(\Phi)$ $(x, y \in A)$ if, and only if, A has a congruence relation Θ in $\mathfrak{C}$ such that $x \equiv y(\Theta)$. Clearly, Φ is reflexive and symmetric. But Φ is also transitive. Assume that for any elements x, y, z of A, $x \equiv y(\Phi)$ and $y \equiv z(\Phi)$. Then by the definition of Φ, there exist congruences Θ_1 and Θ_2 in $\mathfrak{C}$ such that $x \equiv y(\Theta_1)$ and $y \equiv z(\Theta_2)$; a fortiori, $x \equiv y \equiv z$ $(\Theta_1 \cup \Theta_2)$. Since $\mathfrak{C}$ is a chain, $\Theta_1 \cup \Theta_2 \in \mathfrak{C}$ and hence $x \equiv z(\Phi)$. It can be verified in the same manner that Φ also satisfies the substitution property. By the above Φ is a congruence relation, and clearly Φ is the upper bound of $\mathfrak{C}$ in $\mathscr{K}^{ab}$. Now $\mathscr{K}^{ab}$ is non-void (since $\mathsf{E} \in \mathscr{K}^{ab}$), and hence, by the Kuratowski—Zorn lemma, it has a maximal element, which we shall denote by Σ^{ab}.

Now consider the factor algebra A/Σ^{ab} and denote by $\bar{x}$ the Σ^{ab}-class including the element $x (\in A)$. Clearly, $\bar{a} \neq \bar{b}$. If A/Σ^{ab} is simple, it follows immediately by the foregoing theorem that it is also subdirectly irreducible. Consider the case when A/Σ^{ab} has non-trivial congruence relations, and let $\{\overline{\Psi}_\mu\}_{\mu \in M}$ be the set of all non-trivial congruence relations of A/Σ^{ab}. For every μ, we have necessarily $\bar{a} \equiv \bar{b}(\overline{\Psi}_\mu)$, since otherwise $a \not\equiv b(\Psi_\mu)$ would hold for the congruence relation Ψ_μ of A defined by

$$x \equiv y(\Psi_\mu) \Longleftrightarrow \bar{x} \equiv \bar{y}(\overline{\Psi}_\mu)$$

which is evidently greater than Σ^{ab}. Hence $\bar{a} \equiv \bar{b}(\bigcap_{\mu \in M} \overline{\Psi}_\mu)$, that is, $\bigcap_{\mu \in M} \overline{\Psi}_\mu > \overline{\mathsf{E}}$, where $\overline{\mathsf{E}}$ denotes the least element of $\mathscr{K}(A/\Sigma^{ab})$. Then, by the foregoing theorem, A/Σ^{ab} is subdirectly irreducible.

Now let a and b run through all pairs of distinct elements of A and let us construct for every pair of elements the factor algebra A/Σ^{ab}. Then for each of these pairs of elements, $a \not\equiv b(\Sigma^{ab})$, consequently $\bigcap_{\substack{a,b \in A \\ a \neq b}} \Sigma^{ab} = \mathsf{E}$, and hence, by the supplement of the foregoing theorem, A is the subdirect union of all the A/Σ^{ab}.

In his paper [70], Fuchs raised the problem as to how all subdirect unions of given algebras A and B can be described. He solved the problem for groups, rings and Boolean algebras.

64. Direct and Subdirect Union of Lattices

In agreement with the definition of the direct union of algebras, we mean by the direct union of the lattices $L_1, \ldots, L_n$, denoted by $L_1 \otimes \ldots \otimes L_n$, the algebra defined on the product set $L_1 \times \ldots \times L_n$, in which

(1) $$(a_1, \ldots, a_n) = (b_1, \ldots, b_n) \Longleftrightarrow a_j = b_j \ (j = 1, \ldots, n)$$

and the operations are defined by the formulae

$$(2) \qquad (a_1, \ldots, a_n) \cap (b_1, \ldots, b_n) = (a_1 \cap b_1, \ldots, a_n \cap b_n)$$

$$(3) \qquad (a_1, \ldots, a_n) \cup (b_1, \ldots, b_n) = (a_1 \cup b_1, \ldots, a_n \cup b_n)$$

The lattices $L_1, \ldots, L_n$ are the components of the direct union $L_1 \otimes \ldots \otimes L_n$.

It follows by direct calculation that *the direct union* $L_1 \otimes \ldots \otimes L_n$ *is itself a lattice*. Moreover, (2) and (3) imply that *if every* L_j $(j = 1, \ldots n)$ *is modular or distributive, then the resulting* $L_1 \otimes \ldots \otimes L_n$ *is also modular or distributive, respectively.*

Furthermore, *the ordering of the lattice* $L_1 \otimes \ldots \otimes L_n$ *is described by the formula*

$$(4) \qquad (a_1, \ldots, a_n) \leqq (b_1, \ldots, b_n) \longleftrightarrow a_j \leqq b_j \; (j = 1, \ldots, n)$$

Indeed, by (2) and (1), $(a_1, \ldots, a_n) \cap (b_1, \ldots, b_n) = (a_1, \ldots, a_n)$ if, and only if, $a_j \cap b_j = a_j$ for every one of the indices $j = 1, \ldots, n$.

(4) implies that *the direct union of complete lattices is also complete.* Furthermore, $L_1 \otimes \ldots \otimes L_n$ *is bounded (or bounded above, or bounded below) if, and only if, every* L_j *is also.* If the least element of L_j is o_j, and its greatest element i_j, then the least element of $L_1 \otimes \ldots \otimes L_n$ is $(o_1, \ldots, o_n)$ and its greatest element is $(i_1, \ldots, i_n)$.

In the direct union $L_1 \otimes \ldots \otimes L_n$ of the bounded lattices $L_1, \ldots, L_n$ the set of all complements of the element $(a_1, \ldots, a_n)$ consist of those elements $(x_1, \ldots, x_n)$ in which every x_j is the complement of a_j in L_j. In fact, if every x_j is the complement of a_j in L_j, then by (2) and (3)

$$(a_1, \ldots, a_n) \cap (x_1, \ldots, x_n) = (a_1 \cap x_1, \ldots, a_n \cap x_n) = (o_1, \ldots, o_n)$$

$$(a_1, \ldots, a_n) \cup (x_1 \ldots, x_n) = (a_1 \cup x_1, \ldots, a_n \cup x_n) = (i_1, \ldots, i_n)$$

Conversely, if $(x_1, \ldots, x_n)$ is a complement of $(a_1, \ldots, a_n)$ then

$$(a_1, \ldots, a_n) \cap (x_1, \ldots, x_n) = (o_1, \ldots, o_n)$$

$$(a_1, \ldots, a_n) \cup (x_1, \ldots, x_n) = (i_1, \ldots, i_n)$$

whence, by (1)—(3), $a_j \cap x_j = o_j$, $a_j \cup x_j = i_j$ $(j = 1, \ldots, n)$. The result can be paraphrased as follows: *In the direct union* $L_1 \otimes \ldots \otimes L_n$ *of the bounded lattices* $L_1, \ldots, L_n$ *the complements of the elements can be formed component by component.*

It follows by a similar consideration that also *the semicomplements and the relative complements may be formed component by component.* However, this implies that $L_1 \otimes \ldots \otimes L_n$ is complemented (semicomplemented, relatively complemented) if, and only if, each of its components is so.

Now let us turn again to arbitrary lattices. Of particular importance is the following:

THEOREM 99. *Let $L_1, \ldots, L_n$ be arbitrary lattices and $L = L_1 \otimes \ldots \otimes L_n$ their direct union. Then, to each L_j $(j = 1, \ldots, n)$ there can be found a sublattice of L which is isomorphic to L_j*

PROOF. Let r_j be some fixed element of L_j $(j = 1, \ldots, n)$ and consider the set H_k of all elements of the form

$$(r_1, \ldots, r_{k-1}, x_k, r_{k+1}, \ldots, r_n) \qquad (x_k \in L_k)$$

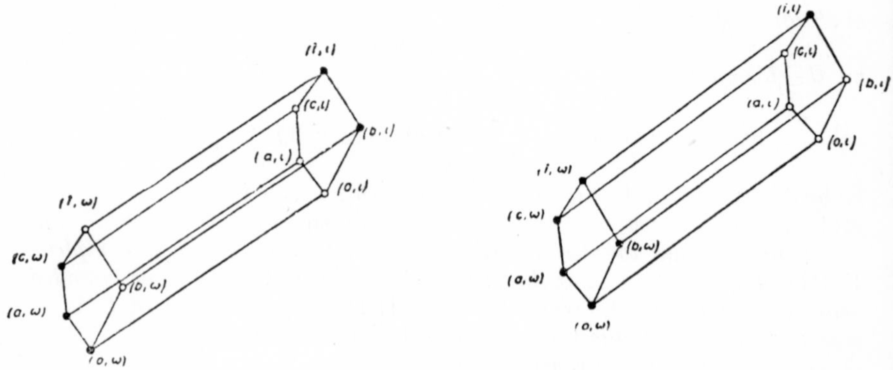

Fig. 34

Since every r_j itself constitutes a sublattice of L_j, H_k is a sublattice in $L_1 \otimes \ldots \otimes L_n$; moreover, it is easily shown that

$$(5) \qquad (r_1, \ldots, r_{k-1}, x_k, r_{k+1}, \ldots, r_n) \to x_k$$

is an isomorphism of $L_1 \otimes \ldots \otimes L_n$ onto L_k. This fact is usually expressed by saying that each of the $L_1, \ldots, L_n$ can be "embedded" into $L_1 \otimes \ldots \otimes L_n$.

The statement of this theorem and its proof is also valid, more generally, for the discrete direct union of arbitrary (similar) algebras.

The definition of the direct union $\prod_{\lambda \in \Lambda} L_\lambda$ of lattices $L_\lambda (\lambda \in \Lambda)$ with an arbitrary Λ will not be formulated here; this can be accomplished by the reader taking into consideration the general definition given in Section 62 and the above arguments. However, let us remark that the above propositions are also valid for the direct union of an infinite number of lattices.

In accordance with the general definition given in Section 63, we mean by a subdirect union of the lattices L_λ $(\lambda \in \Lambda)$ every sublattice R of $\prod_{\lambda \in \Lambda} L_\lambda$ satisfying the condition that every a_λ $(\in L_\lambda)$ is the component in L_λ of at least one element of R. Let us remark that — contrary to the direct union — the subdirect union need not include sublattices which would be isomorphic to any one of the components.

Since the direct union and any sublattice of distributive lattices are distributive, so is any subdirect union of distributive lattices.

Similarly, the subdirect union of modular lattices is also modular.

Finally, let us cite concrete examples of the direct and subdirect unions of lattices. In Fig. 34 the direct union of the lattice shown in Fig. 17a (p. 90) and of the two-element chain $\{\omega, \iota\}$ is represented in two drawings: the full circles constitute in each drawing a subdirect union of the two lattices. It is at once clear that the subdirect union of these two complemented lattices which is shown in the diagram on the right is non-complemented.

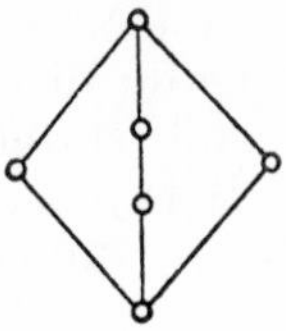

Fig. 35

65. Direct and Subdirect Decompositions of Lattices

In this section, some simple theorems concerning the direct and subdirect decomposition of lattices will be proved.

The problem of the existence of the subdirect decomposition was completely clarified by Theorems 97 and 98: no further general statement can be added to them. However, for distributive lattices there holds

THEOREM 100. *Disregarding the single-element lattice, every distributive lattice can be represented as the subdirect union of two-element chains* (Birkhoff [18]).

PROOF. With regard to Theorem 98, we have only to prove that every distributive lattice L having an inner element is subdirectly reducible. Let, for the moment, d be any element of L. The mappings

$$\varphi : \varphi(x) = d \cap x \text{ and } \psi : \psi(x) = d \cup x \quad (x \in L)$$

are endomorphisms of L. Let us construct from them the mapping

$$\sigma : x \longrightarrow (\varphi(x), \psi(x)) \qquad (x \in L)$$

It is at once clear that σ is a homomorphism of L into the direct union $(d] \otimes [d)$. Furthermore, if for a pair of elements x, y $(\in L)$, $\varphi(x) = \varphi(y)$ and $\psi(x) = \psi(y)$, then by Corollary 2 to Theorem 33, $x = y$; hence, the mapping σ is one-to-one. That is, σ is an isomorphism of L onto a sublattice S of $(d] \otimes [d)$. However, if $u \in (d]$, then $\varphi(u) = u$; hence, by σ, every element of $(d]$ occurs as a first component in S. Since the corresponding statement holds also for $[d)$, S is the subdirect union of the lattices $(d]$ and $[d)$. Hence, we have obtained a subdirect decomposition of L, with φ and ψ as decomposition homomorphisms.

If d is an inner element of L, then there exists in L an element t

such that $t \nleq d$. Clearly, $t \cup d > d$ and $\varphi(t \cup d) = \varphi(d)$. That means that the decomposition homomorphism φ is not an isomorphism; in a similar manner it can be verified that neither is ψ. This proves Theorem 100.

In the following we shall discuss the direct decompositions of lattices.

First of all we note that each component in a direct decomposition of a modular lattice is itself modular and the similar proposition is true for distributive, bounded, or complete lattices. (The proof of this simple statement is left to the reader: see also Exercise 8.)

It is possible for a lattice L to have different direct decompositions. Let us suppose that L can be represented by the direct decompositions

$$L \approx A_1 \otimes \ldots \otimes A_r \tag{1}$$

and also by

$$L \approx B_1 \otimes \ldots \otimes B_s \tag{2}$$

We say that these two representations have a common refinement if there can be found lattices L_{jk} $(j = 1, \ldots, r;\ k = 1, \ldots, s)$ such that L is isomorphic to the direct union of all the L_{jk}, and,

$$A_j \approx L_{j1} \otimes \ldots \otimes L_{js} \quad (j = 1, \ldots, r) \tag{3}$$

$$B_k \approx L_{1k} \otimes \ldots \otimes L_{rk} \quad (k = 1, \ldots, s) \tag{4}$$

THEOREM 101. *Any two different direct decompositions of a lattice have a common refinement.*

This theorem is a special case of a theorem by Nakayama [147]; we shall also adopt here his method of proof. Maeda [131] gave a proof based on some deeper properties of decomposition congruences. Concerning bounded lattices, Birkhoff had proved the statement of the theorem already somewhat earlier ([12]; see also Birkhoff [17]).

PROOF. Let (1) and (2) be two direct decompositions of a lattice L. Under the isomorphism (1) there corresponds to every element x of L an element $(x_{1A}, \ldots, x_{rA})$ of $A_1 \otimes \ldots \otimes A_r$, and under the isomorphism (2) an element $(x_{1B}, \ldots, x_{sB})$ of $B_1 \otimes \ldots \otimes B_s$.

Select — arbitrarily — some element e of L. Let the set of all elements y such that $y_{pA} = e_{pA}$ except for the index $p = j$ be denoted Y_j $(j = 1, \ldots, r)$. Similarly, let the set of all elements z of L such that $z_{qB} = e_{qB}$ $(q \neq k)$ be denoted Z_k $(k = 1, \ldots, s)$. Clearly, every Y_j and Z_k is a sublattice of L; moreover

$$Y_j \approx (j\ Y_j = 1, \ldots, r) \quad \text{and} \quad Z_k \approx B_k \ (k = 1, \ldots, s) \tag{5}$$

Furthermore, the Y_j and Z_k are convex, since, for example, if y' and y "are elements of Y_j and that $y' \leq y \leq y''$, then

$$e_{pA} = y'_{pA} \leq y_{pA} \leq y''_{pA} = e_{pA} \qquad (p \neq j)$$

and hence, $y \in Y_j$.

Introduce the notation $L_{jk} = Y_j \frown Z_k$ ($j = 1, \ldots, r$; $k = 1, \ldots, s$); it is proposed that these L_{jk} satisfy (3) and (4). To prove the proposition, it is sufficient by (5) to show that (3) is true of the Y_j instead of the A_j, and that (4) is true of the Z_k instead of the B_k

Consider a Y_j (to be fixed in the following). Let y be any element of Y_j. Let us denote by $y^{(k)}$ ($k = 1, \ldots, s$) that element of L for which

$$y_{qB}^{(k)} = \begin{cases} y_{kB}, & \text{if} \quad q = k \\ e_{qB}, & \text{if} \quad q \neq k \end{cases}$$

Clearly, $y^{(k)} \in Z_k$; we shall show that every $y^{(k)}$ is also included in Y_j. It is obvious that $y_{qB} \frown e_{qB} \leqq y_{qB}^{(k)} \leqq y_{qB} \smile e_{qB}$ ($q = 1, \ldots, s$); hence, by (2)

$$(6) \qquad y \frown e \leqq y^{(k)} \leqq y \smile e$$

Since $y, e \in Y_j$ and Y_j is a convex sublattice of L, (6) indeed implies $y^{(k)} \in Y_j$. That is, $y^{(k)} \in L_{jk}$ ($k = 1, \ldots, s$).

Now let y run through every element of Y_j. Then the mapping

$$(7) \qquad y \longrightarrow (y^{(1)}, \ldots, y^{(s)})$$

is an orderisomorphism of Y_j into $L_{j1} \otimes \ldots \otimes L_{js}$ since for any pair of elements $y, \bar{y}$ of Y_j

$$\begin{aligned} y \leqq \bar{y} &\Longleftrightarrow y_{qB} \leqq \bar{y}_{qB} && (q = 1, \ldots, s) \Longleftrightarrow \\ &\Longleftrightarrow y_{qB}^{(k)} \leqq \bar{y}_{qB}^{(k)} && (q, k = 1, \ldots, s) \Longleftrightarrow \\ &\Longleftrightarrow y^{(k)} \leqq \bar{y}^{(k)} && (k = 1, \ldots, s) \Longleftrightarrow \\ &\Longleftrightarrow (y^{(1)}, \ldots, y^{(s)}) \leqq (\bar{y}^{(1)}, \ldots, \bar{y}^{(s)}) \end{aligned}$$

We shall show that (7) is onto $L_{j1} \otimes \ldots \otimes L_{js}$. For this purpose consider any element $(w^{(1)}, \ldots, w^{(s)})$ ($w^{(k)} \in L_{jk}$) of that direct union. By definition, the components $w^{(1)}, \ldots, w^{(s)}$ are carried by the isomorphism (2) one by one into elements of the form

$$\begin{aligned} \mathfrak{w}_1 &= (w_1, e_{2B}, e_{3B}, \ldots, e_{sB}) \quad (w_1 \in B_1) \\ \mathfrak{w}_2 &= (e_{1B}, w_2, e_{3B}, \ldots, e_{sB}) \quad (w_2 \in B_2) \\ &\vdots \\ \mathfrak{w}_s &= (e_{1B}, \ldots, e_{s-1,B}, w_s) \quad (w_s \in B_s) \end{aligned}$$

in that order, of $B_1 \otimes \ldots \otimes B_s$. Let w denote the element of L

carried under the isomorphism (2) precisely into the element $\mathfrak{w} = (w_1, \ldots, w_s)$. Since in $B_1 \otimes \ldots \otimes B_s$

$$\bigcap_{k=1}^{s} \mathfrak{w}_k \leq \mathfrak{w} \leq \bigcup_{k=1}^{s} \mathfrak{w}_k$$

hence in L

$$\bigcap_{k=1}^{s} w^{(k)} \leq w \leq \bigcup_{k=1}^{s} w^{(k)}$$

However, $w^{(k)} \in (L_{jk} \subseteq) Y_j$ $(k = 1, \ldots, s)$ and hence, the first and last term of the last series of inequalities are elements of Y_j. But then, by the convexity of Y_j, $w \in Y_j$. Now it is obvious that under the isomorphism (7), w is carried precisely into $(w^{(1)}, \ldots, w^{(s)})$.

In this way, (3) has been proved by taking (5) into consideration; (4) can be obtained in the same manner.

We have already mentioned the fact that not every algebra can be represented as a direct union of directly irreducible components. The statement is true in particular also of lattices.

Consider as an example the ring of sets $\mathcal{F}(M)$ of all finite subsets of a set M. If $O \subset R \subset M$, then the mapping

$$X \to (X \cap R, X \cap (M - R)) \qquad (X \in \mathcal{F}(M))$$

is an isomorphism of $\mathcal{F}(M)$ onto $\mathcal{F}(R) \otimes \mathcal{F}(M - R)$ (the verification of the details being left to the reader) and none of the decomposition homomorphisms is an isomorphism. Hence $\mathcal{F}(M)$ is directly irreducible if, and only if, M is a single-element set, that is, if $\mathcal{F}(M)$ is a two-element chain. Let now M be infinite. Then $\mathcal{F}(M)$ is not bounded above; consequently, it can not be a direct union of two-element chains. Hence, in this case $\mathcal{F}(M)$ is directly reducible and yet it cannot be represented as the direct union of directly irreducible lattices.

On the other hand, it is not difficult to see that every lattice of finite length can be represented as the direct union of directly irreducible lattices. If L is a lattice of finite length and $L \approx A \otimes B$, but neither A nor B is isomorphic to L, then the length of both is less than the length of L (Exercise 4). Hence, the statement is obtained by induction.

Clearly every simple lattice is directly irreducible; however, not every directly irreducible lattice is simple. (Consider for example the three-element chain or the lattice shown in Fig. 17a.) Consequently, it is of interest to know whether a lattice can be represented as the direct union of simple lattices. With respect to this problem, we shall prove the following theorem:

THEOREM 102. *Every relatively complemented lattice of finite length can be represented as the direct union of a finite number of simple relatively complemented lattices.*

COROLLARY. *Every complemented modular lattice of finite length can be represented as the direct union of a finite number of simple complemented modular lattices.*

Let us note that the statement of the theorem holds even if the lattice itself is not of finite length but satisfies the maximum condition. In this more general form the theorem was presented by Dilworth ([47], Theorem 4.4); the above theorem was published by Birkhoff ([19], Chapter 2, Theorem 8), with reference to Dilworth.

By a result due to Jakubík, "relatively complemented" may be exchanged in the text of the theorem for "completely distributive".

Dilworth has also proved ([47], Theorem 3.1) that a directly reducible lattice L can be represented as the direct union of a finite number of simple lattices if, and only if, the congruence relations of L are pairwise permutable and if $\mathscr{K}(L)$ is a finite Boolean algebra.

The statement of the corollary was also known earlier by the name "Birkhoff–Menger Theorem" (Birkhoff [14], Theorem 2; see also Menger [139], p. 473).

PROOF. By Theorem 48, and the remark before Theorem 101 the Corollary follows from the Theorem trivially; thus we can restrict ourselves to proving the theorem.

Let L be a relatively complemented lattice of finite length and let Θ be some congruence relation of L. Since L is of finite length, each of its ideals is a principal ideal (see Theorem 76); hence, the kernel of Θ is likewise a principal ideal $(a]$. We show that for any element x, y of L

$$x \equiv y(\Theta) \Longleftrightarrow x \cup a = y \cup a \tag{8}$$

Clearly $x \cup a = y \cup a$ implies $x \equiv y(\Theta)$. Conversely, if $x \equiv y(\Theta)$, then by the lemma in Section 61, any relative complement w in $[o, x \cup y]$ of the element $x \cap y$ is included in $(a]$. Hence,

$$\left.\begin{matrix} x \cup a \\ y \cup a \end{matrix}\right\} \geqq (x \cap y) \cup a = (x \cap y) \cup w \cup a = x \cup y \cup a \geqq \left\{\begin{matrix} x \cup a \\ y \cup a \end{matrix}\right\}$$

that is, $x \cup a = (x \cap y) \cup a = y \cup a$.

Since, by Theorem 83, every Θ-class is a sublattice of L, in the present case, every Θ-class has a greatest element. Let us denote the Θ-class including x by $\bar{x}$, and the greatest element of $\bar{x}$ by i_x. Then $i_x \equiv x(\Theta)$ and thus, by (8), $i_x \cup a = x \cup a \equiv x(\Theta)$. Hence, $i_x \cup a = i_x$. That is, the mapping

$$\varphi : \varphi(x) = x \cup a \qquad (x \in L)$$

carries every element x of L into the maximal element of $\bar{x}$.

We shall show that this mapping is an endomorphism. Let x, y be an arbitrary pair of elements of L. Clearly, $(x \cap y) \cup a \equiv (x \cup a) \cap \cap (y \cup a)$ (Θ), and hence, by (8)

$$(x \cap y) \cup a = \big((x \cup a) \cap (y \cup a)\big) \cup a = (x \cup a) \cap (y \cup a)$$

the last equality holding by $(x \cup a) \cap (y \cup a) \geqq a$. Hence, φ is a meet-homomorphism. On the other hand, φ is obviously a join-homomorphism as well.

Consider now the set of the elements congruent with i. Dualizing the above we get that this set is a dual principal ideal $[b)$, and the mapping

$$\psi : \psi(x) = x \frown b \qquad (x \in L)$$

is an endomorphism of L which carries every element x into the least element of the Θ-class $\bar{x}$.

In particular, $\varphi(b) = i$ and $\psi(a) = o$, that is, b is a complement of a. We shall show that

$$L \approx (a] \otimes (b] \tag{9}$$

Consider for this purpose the above ψ and the mapping

$$\tau : \tau(x) = a \frown x \qquad (x \in L)$$

and construct from these the mapping

$$\sigma : \sigma(x) = \big(\tau(x), \psi(x)\big) \qquad (x \in L)$$

Clearly σ is a meet-homomorphism of L into $(a] \otimes (b]$. Let x be any element of L and let t be a relative complement of $b \frown x$ in $[o,x]$. Then $b \frown t = b \frown (x \frown t) = (b \frown x) \frown t = o = b \frown o$, and thus, by the dual of (8), $t \equiv o(\Theta)$. Consequently, $t \leqq a$. Hence, by the definition of t,

$$x \geqq (a \frown x) \smile (b \frown x) \geqq t \smile (b \frown x) = x$$

that is, $x = \tau(x) \smile \psi(x)$. Hence, the mapping σ is one-to-one as well, wherefore it is a meet isomorphism of L onto a sublattice S* of $(a] \otimes (b]$; in other words, σ: $L^{\frown} \approx S^{\frown}$. This, however, implies, by the Supplement of Theorem 9, that σ: $L \approx S$.

Now it is no more difficult to show that $S = (a] \otimes (b]$. For any elements u and v of L, there holds, by the definition of σ,

$$\sigma(u \smile v) = (\tau(u \smile v), \psi(u \smile v))$$

On the other hand, since σ is an isomorphism,

$$\begin{aligned}\sigma(u \smile v) &= \sigma(u) \smile \sigma(v) = (\tau(u), \ \psi(u)) \smile (\tau(v), \ \psi(v)) = \\ &= (\tau(u) \smile \tau(v), \ \psi(u) \smile \psi(v))\end{aligned}$$

Comparing the appropriate components, we have

$$\begin{cases} \tau(u \smile v) = \tau(u) \smile \tau(v) = (a \frown u) \smile (a \frown v) \\ \psi(u \smile v) = \psi(u) \smile \psi(v) = (b \frown u) \smile (b \frown v) \end{cases} \tag{10}$$

Now let u and v be chosen so that (u, v) be in $(a] \times (b]$, that is, let

* S is, in fact, a lattice, since it is an order isomorphic image of the lattice L.

$u \leq a$ and $v \leq b$. Then also $a \frown v \leq a \frown b = o$ and $b \frown u \leq b \frown a = o$. By all these and by (10), $\tau(u \smile v) = u$ and $\psi(u \smile v) = v$, that is, $\sigma(u \smile v) = (u, v)$. This means that every element of $(a] \otimes (b]$ belongs to the image elements of σ, completing the proof of (9).

If now Θ is a non-trivial congruence relation, then both $(a]$ and $(b]$ differ from L, whence the length of both is less than that of L. Thus, we get the following result: if the lattice L itself is non-simple, it can be decomposed into the direct union of two lattices of smaller length. If these components are already simple, the proof is complete; if not, the foregoing argument has to be repeated. Since the length of L is finite we obtain in a finite number of steps a representation $L \approx L_1 \otimes \ldots \otimes L_r$ (with finite r) in which every lattice L_j ($j = 1, \ldots, r$) is simple and of at least two elements. The relative complementarity of these L_j is trivial by the definition of direct union.

Let us note in connection with the above proof that in [137] McLaughlin gave a necessary and sufficient condition for the elements a, b of a relatively complemented lattice of finite length to satisfy $L \approx (a] \otimes (b]$.

66. The Neutral Elements and the Centre of a Lattice

Let a, b be any pair of elements of a lattice L, and according to Section 26, let $\langle a, b\rangle$ denote the sublattice generated by these elements in L. Then

$$\langle a, b\rangle = \begin{cases} \{a\}, \text{ if } a = b; \\ \{a, b\}, \text{ if either } a < b \text{ or } a > b; \\ \{a, b, a \frown b, a \smile b\}, \text{ if } a \parallel b. \end{cases}$$

Hence, the sublattice $\langle a, b\rangle$ consists in any case of less than five elements, and therefore, by Theorem 33, it is distributive.

This consideration yields the result that *the sublattice $\langle a, b\rangle$ generated by an arbitrary pair of elements a, b of a lattice is distributive in any lattice.*

A lattice is clearly distributive if, and only if, every one of the sublattices generated by three elements is distributive. Therefore, it is promising to study those elements d of any lattice L for which there holds that every sublattice $\langle d, x, y\rangle$ $(x, y \in L)$ of L is distributive. The elements having this property are termed the *neutral elements** of the lattice L.

Making use of the statement made in the preceding paragraph, it is very simple to prove that *the bound elements of any lattice are neutral*

* Let us note that this term is neither expressive nor appropriate. However, it is almost exclusively used in lattice-theoretical literature. An exception is e.g. [49], where one finds the term "élément distribuant", much more appropriate but hard to translate. Also the reader must be warned that this concept has nothing to do with the concept "neutral element" as defined, for example, in [228].

The definition of neutral elements as well as all theorems in this section are due to Birkhoff [16].

The following theorem gives necessary and sufficient conditions for an element of a lattice to be neutral.

THEOREM 103. *Concerning any element d of a lattice L, the following conditions are equivalent:*

(A) *d is a neutral element;*

(B) *The mappings $\varphi_d(x) = d \frown x$ and $\psi_d(x) = d \smile x$ $(x \in L)$ are endomorphisms of L such that $\varphi_d(x) = \varphi_d(y)$ and $\psi_d(x) = \psi_d(y)$ hold simultaneously only if $x = y$;*

(C) *L has a sublattice A bounded above and a sublattice B bounded below such that L can be represented as a subdirect union of A and B, wherein the two components of d are precisely the greatest element of A and the least element of B.*

COROLLARY. *An element d of a modular lattice L is neutral if, and only if, either φ_d or ψ_d is an endomorphism of L.*

PROOF.

(A) *implies* (B). For any elements d, x, y of a lattice L, $d \frown (x \frown y) = (d \frown x) \frown (d \frown y)$, that is, $\varphi_d(x \frown y) = \varphi_d(x) \frown \varphi_d(y)$ Let d be neutral. Then

$$\varphi_d(x \smile y) = d \frown (x \smile y) = (d \frown x) \smile (d \frown y) = \varphi_d(x) \smile \varphi_d(y)\,,$$

and hence, φ_d is an endomorphism of L. By dualizing, the same is seen to hold for ψ_d. Finally, if $\varphi_d(x) = \varphi_d(y)$ and $\psi_d(x) = \psi_d(y)$, for some pair of elements x, y $(\in L)$ then

$$\begin{aligned} x = x \frown \psi_d(x) &= x \frown \psi_d(y) = (x \frown y) \smile (x \frown d) = \\ &= (x \frown y) \smile \varphi_d(x) = (x \frown y) \smile \varphi_d(y) = \\ &= (x \frown y) \smile (d \frown y) = \psi_d(x) \frown y = \psi_d(y) \frown y = y \end{aligned}$$

(B) *implies* (C). Assume that the premises of (B) are satisfied by d. Then, $\varphi_d(x) \leqq d$, that is φ_d carries L into the principal ideal $(d]$. However, for every element y of $(d]$ there holds $\varphi_d(y) = y$, that is, every element of $(d]$ occurs among the image elements. Hence, φ_d is a homomorphism of L onto $(d]$. By the dual consideration, ψ_d is a homomorphism of L onto the dual principal ideal $[d)$.

Consider now the direct union $D = (d] \otimes [d)$, and the mapping

$$\sigma\colon \sigma(x) = (\varphi_d(x), \psi_d(x)) \quad (x \in L)$$

of the lattice L into D. By the first premise of (B) σ is a homomorphism, and by the second, it is one-to-one; hence, σ is an isomorphism of L onto a sublattice D^* of D (the image set D^* is a lattice since it is the isomorphic image of a lattice). Considering also what has been said in the previous paragraph, L is isomorphic to the subdirect union

D^* of the lattice $(d]$ bounded below and the lattice $[d)$ bounded below, this being the first proposition of (C). In this subdirect union, d is assigned to the pair of elements $(\varphi_d(d), \psi_d(d)) = (d, d)$, and d is the greatest element in $(d]$ and the least in $[d)$. Hence, also the second proposition of (C) is true.

(C) *implies* (A). Suppose that L can be represented as a subdirect union D^* of the sublattice A bounded above and sublattice B bounded below in which d corresponds to the element (i_A, o_B). Since i_A is neutral in A and o_B is neutral in B, and the meet and join are formed component-by-component in the subdirect union, (i_A, o_B) is a neutral element of D^*. By the isomorphism $L \approx D^*$ this already implies that d is a neutral element in L.

PROOF OF THE COROLLARY. The theorem implies immediately that the condition is necessary. To prove its sufficiency let us suppose d to be an element of the modular lattice L such that φ_d is an endomorphism of L. Then we have for any pair x, y of elements of L

$$d \frown (x \smile y) = (d \frown x) \smile (d \frown y)$$

therefore by Theorem 35, the lattice $\langle d, x, y\rangle$ is distributive. The validity of the statement concerning ψ follows by the duality principle.

THEOREM 104. *The set N of the neutral elements of any lattice L is a distributive sublattice of L; that is, N is the set intersection of all maximal distributive sublattices of L.*

As a matter of course, by a maximal distributive sublattice of L is meant a distributive sublattice of L which is not properly included in any distributive sublattice of L.

PROOF. The theorem can be resolved into the following two parts:

1. If $d (\in L)$ is non-neutral, L has a maximal distributive sublattice S not including d;
2. If d is neutral, then it is included in every maximal distributive sublattice of L.

If d is non-neutral, then there exists in L a pair of elements x, y such that $\langle d, x, y\rangle$ is non-distributive, whereas $\langle x, y\rangle$ is distributive. Since the set union of any completely ordered set of distributive lattices (completely ordered by set inclusion) is itself a distributive lattice, there exists by the Kuratowski—Zorn lemma a maximal distributive sublattice S including $\langle x, y\rangle$. Clearly, $S \not\ni d$, since otherwise $\langle d, x, y\rangle$ would also be distributive.

Conversely, let S be a maximal distributive sublattice of L and d any neutral element of L. By the foregoing theorem, L can be represented as the subdirect union of certain lattices A, B by assigning d to (i_A, o_B). Hence, the A-component of any element of the sublattice $\bar{S} = \langle S \cup \{d\}\rangle$ is either i_A, or the A-component of some element in S. Since, together with S, the components in A of S constitute a distributive lattice, and i_A is a neutral element in A, the A-components of the elements of $\bar{S}$ constitute a distributive lattice. The same holds for the B-components, and hence $\bar{S}$ is distributive. This implies, however, by the maximality of S, that $\bar{S} = S$ and hence $S \ni d$.

THEOREM 105. *A neutral element has at most one complement which is itself a neutral element (provided it exists).*

PROOF. Let L be a bounded lattice and d some neutral element of L. According to Theorem 103, Proposition (C), consider the subdirect decomposition D^* of L in which (i_A, o_B) is assigned to d. Since in any subdirect union of A and B the elements corresponding to o and i are the elements (o_A, o_B) and (i_A, i_B) hence the element (i_A, o_B) cannot have a complement other than (o_A, i_B). Hence, if this pair of elements occurs in D^*, the element corrresponding to it in L is the (only) complement of d; if not, d is a non-complemented element. Furthermore, if (o_A, i_B) is included in D^*, it is a neutral element of the same, whence the element corresponding to it in L is likewise neutral in L.

By the *centre* of a lattice we mean the set of all complemented neutral elements of the lattice. The elements of the centre are called, briefly, *central elements*. Of course, these terms make sense only in the case of bounded lattices.

THEOREM 106. *The centre of a bounded lattice is a non-void sublattice of the lattice.*

PROOF. The centre Z of the bounded lattice L is non-void since the two bound elements of L are certainly included in Z. Furthermore, if $a, b \in Z$, then by Theorem 104, $a \frown b$ and $a \smile b$ are also neutral and hence the calculation carried out in proving Theorem 54 can be repeated for a and b occurring here. Hence, together with a and b, $a \frown b$ and $a \smile b$ are also complemented elements.

Neutral and central elements play an important role in the study of the congruence relations of lattices. Concerning applications of this nature, see Birkhoff's book [19] Chapter 5, Section 8, and Chapter VIII, Sections 5 and 9. Another important field of application is the theory of continuous geometries. (See, e.g. Maeda's book [133].)

Many interesting properties of the central elements are dealt with by Hájek [86].

For the structural investigations of lattices (and in particular for research into the deeper connections between congruence relations and ideals) a generalization of neutral elements due to Grätzer and Schmidt [82] has proved to be useful.

Exercises to Chapter X

1. Let A be an algebra whose congruence relations are pairwise permutable. Show that A can be represented in the form $A \approx A_1 \otimes \ldots \otimes A_r$ if, and only if, it has congruence relations $\Theta_1, \ldots, \Theta_r$ such that $\Theta_1 \frown \ldots \Theta_r = \mathsf{E}$ and $(\Theta_1 \ldots \frown \Theta_{j-1}) \smile \Theta_j = \mathsf{I}$ $(j = 2, \ldots, r)$.

2. Let $S \approx A \otimes B$ be a direct decomposition of the algebra S; denote the appropriate decomposition congruences by Θ_A and Θ_B. Prove that if $A \approx C \otimes D$, then $S \approx C \otimes D \otimes B$ and $\Theta_C \frown \Theta_D = \Theta_A$.

3. Let A be an algebra whose congruence relations are pairwise permutable and whose congruence lattice satisfies the maximum

condition. Prove that, disregarding the single-element components, every subdirect decomposition of A contains a finite number of components, and that, moreover, any representation of A as an irredundant subdirect union of subdirectly irreducible algebras consists of the same number of components.

4. Let L be a lattice of finite length and let $L \approx A \otimes B$. Prove that the sum of the length of A and B equals the length of L.

5. Show that the direct union of an infinite number of lattices consisting of at least two elements is never of locally finite length.

6. Prove that every chain is directly irreducible.

7. Show that in the direct union of the lattices $L_1, \ldots, L_n$ the set of the elements of the form given under (5) in Section 64 is an ideal if, and only if, every r_j is the least element of L_j. Determine all ideals of $L_1 \otimes \ldots \otimes L_n$.

8. Prove: If $L \approx L_1 \otimes \ldots \otimes L_n$ and L is complete, then each L_j $(j = 1, \ldots, n)$ is complete and each decomposition homomorphism is also complete.

9. Show that the lattice in Fig. 35 (p. 199) is subdirectly irreducible.

10. Prove that in any lattice the bound elements (insofar as any exist) are neutral.

11. Let d and e be elements of a lattice L such that d is neutral in L and $e \leqq d$. Prove that e is neutral in $(d]$ if, and only if, it is neutral in L.

12. Let L be a lattice bounded below. Define the relation Λ on L as follows: let $a \Lambda b$ $(a, b \in L)$ mean that there exists in the lattice L an element x satisfying $a \frown x = b \frown x = o$ and $a \smile x = b \smile x$. Show that if z is a neutral element of L then

a) $$a \Lambda b \Longrightarrow (z \frown a) \Lambda (z \frown b)$$

and

b) $$a \Lambda z \Longrightarrow a \leqq z$$

Show further that if z_1 and z_2 are neutral and $z_1 \Lambda z_2$, then $z_1 = z_2$.

13. Let us call an ideal of a lattice L a *neutral ideal* if it is a neutral element of the ideal lattice $\mathfrak{I}(L)$. Show that an ideal I of a modular lattice is neutral if, and only if, to each element t of L satisfying the condition $t \leqq (x \smile a) \frown (y \smile b)$ $(x, y \in I)$ there can be found a z in I such that $t \leqq z \smile (a \frown b)$.

14. Let I be a neutral ideal of a lattice L bounded below and a any element of I. Show that for any element x of L, $a \Lambda x$ implies $x \in I$ (where Λ is to be understood in the sense of Exercise 12).

15. Show that a principal ideal $(u]$ of a modular lattice is neutral if, and only if, u is a neutral element of the lattice.

16. Let L be a section complemented complete lattice and let Z denote the centre of L. Prove: If $a \in Z$ then

$$a \frown \bigcup_{\beta} b_{\beta} = \bigcup_{\beta} (a \frown b_{\beta})$$

for any subset $\{b_{\beta}\}$ of L.

HINTS TO THE SOLUTION OF THE MORE INVOLVED EXERCISES

Chapter I

11. $A \subseteq B \Longrightarrow \sup_P A \leq \sup_P B$;

$$\sup_P B \in A \Longrightarrow \sup_P B \leq \sup_P A.$$

14. Solve by a slight modification of the argument on p. 42.

15. Show first that $\inf \{a_1, \ldots, a_r\} = \inf \{ \inf \{a_1, \ldots, a_{n-1}\}, a_n\}$ and then apply induction for n.

17. Show that if the partly ordered set P is infinite but every one of its completely unordered subsets is finite, then it has an infinite subchain. For this purpose consider a maximal completely unordered subset $\{x_1, \ldots, x_n\}$ of P; let P_j denote the set of the elements comparable with but differing from x_j. At least one P_j is infinite. Now take a maximal completely unordered subset of P_j and so forth.

18. To (A) $\Longrightarrow$ (B) use the foregoing exercise. To (B) $\Rightarrow$ (A): Every completely unordered subset and every chain of the form $c_0 > c_1 > > c_2 > \ldots$ satisfies the maximum condition.

Chapter II

1. There exists one each of one-, two- and three-element lattices; two four-element, five five-element and fifteen six-element ones; of the latter, seven are self-dual.

5. Consider the meet and the join of all elements of the lattice.

7. They are precisely the chains.

12. To the first statement: If $p' \leq x \leq i$, then $p \cup x \geq p \cup p' = i$. Hence, if $p \leq x$, then $x = i$; if, on the contrary, $p \not\leq x$, then $p \cap x = = o$ also holds, whence $x = p'$.

19. If the lattice L is not a chain, then it has an incomparable pair of elements a, b. Construct the lattice L^* by substituting the chain $a \cap b \prec q^* \prec r^* \prec a \cup b$ in L for $[a \cap b, a \cup b]$. Now define a mapping φ as follows:

$$\varphi(x) = \begin{cases} q^*, & \text{if } a \cap b < x \leq a \\ r^*, & \text{if } a \cap b < x < a \cup b \text{ but } x \not\leq a \\ x, & \text{in every other case} \end{cases}$$

20. If there exists a $\bar{c}(\bar{c} \in L_2)$ such that $\varphi(x) < \bar{c} < \varphi(y)$ and $\varphi(c) = \bar{c}$ $(c \in L_1)$, then $x < (x \cup c) \cap y < y$. An example of the second statement: let φ transform the lattice shown in Fig. 13 onto the chain $o^* \prec d \prec i^*$ so that $\varphi(o) = o^*$, $\varphi(b) = d$, $\varphi(a) = \varphi(c) = \varphi(i) = i^*$

21. If φ is a join-homomorphism then $\varphi(x_0) < \varphi(x_1) < \ldots \varphi(x_r)$, implies $x_0 < x_0 \cup x_1 < \ldots < x_0 \cup x_1 \cup \ldots \cup x_r$. Concerning mappings which are only order preserving, the mapping σ mentioned in the paragraph in small print, of Section 20 is a counter example.

24. To the first proposition: If $\varphi(a) = \varphi(b)$, then $\varphi(a \cap b) = \varphi(a) \cap \varphi(b) = \varphi(a) \cap \varphi(a) = \varphi(a)$, and hence $a \cap b = a$; in a similar manner, $a \cap b = b$. Hence φ is an isomorphism between the two meet-semilattices. Concerning the second statement, the mapping σ mentioned in Section 20 is again a suitable example.

27. For the "if" part of the proposition, to any pair of elements x, y consider the mappings α and β for which $\alpha(x) = x$ and $\beta(x) = y$ (otherwise arbitrarily defined).

Chapter III

1. Let a_1 be any element of R and $a_j (j > 1)$ an element of R such that $a_j \nleqq a_1 \cup \ldots \cup a_{j-1}$.

3. For example, adjoin i as the greatest element to the infinite chain $c_1 < c_2 \ldots$ and consider the mapping $\varphi(c_n) = o^*$ $(n = 1, 2, \ldots)$ $\varphi(i) = i^*$, of the resulting complete chain onto the two-element chain $\{o^*, i^*\}$.

8. If $\sigma^n(o)$ is a fixelement for some non-negative integer n, then σ^n $\sigma^n(o) \leqq \sigma^n(f) = f$ for every fixelement f. In the contrary case, form $u_1 = \bigcup_{n=0}^{\infty} \sigma^n(o)$. Also $u_1 \leqq f$ for every fixelement f. Thus, the preceding consideration can be repeated for u_1 (instead of o) and so on.

9. By the dual of the statement formulated in Exercise 1, in a lattice satisfying the minimum condition every subset has an infimum. See also the proof of Theorem 17.

12. Consider the endomorphisms of the three-element chain.

15. Clearly, $\varphi(x) \in Z_\varphi \cap [x)$. But if $u \in Z_\varphi \cap [x)$, then $u = \varphi(u) \geqq \varphi(x)$.

16. Leave the verification of the idempotence of ψ_U to the end. Since the fixelements of ψ_U are precisely the elements in U, by the hint to the foregoing exercise $U \cap [x) \subseteq U \cap [\psi_U(x))$. The reverse inclusion is trivial.

17. For the "if" part of the proposition see Exercise 15.

18. Obviously $\tau(y)$ is an upper bound for these x. Moreover $\tau(y)$ itself is one of these x, by (4) in Section 28.

Chapter IV

General remark: The sufficiency of modularity and distributivity conditions can be verified in the simplest manner by indirect arguments, making use of Theorems 32, and 33, respectively.

3. To the necessity: $c \frown b = (c \frown a) \smile (c \frown b) = c \frown (a \smile b)$ and similarly $c \smile b = c \smile (a \smile b)$.

6. The statement "if" can also be verified by the substution $t = x \frown y$.

8. To the necessity of the condition: applying I_{12}, for $x = a$ or for $x = b$, $c \smile \big(d \frown (x \smile c)\big) = x \smile c$.

12. Take $x_1 = a$, $x_2 = b$, $y_1 = a \smile b \smile c$, $y_2 = c$.

16. Apply Theorem 36 to the intervals $[o, x_1 \smile \ldots \smile x_n]$ and $[a, x_1 \smile \ldots \smile x_n \smile a]$.

18. In the course of proving Theorem 35, we have already shown that (6) also implies the dual of (8).

22. See Exercise 2 to Chapter III.

Chapter V

1. To the second statement see, for example, Fig. 2a (p. 18).

2. The mapping $\varphi(x) = c \frown x$ maps $[a, b]$ onto $[a \frown c,\ b \frown c]$, since $a \frown c \leqq y \leqq b \frown c (\leqq c)$ implies $a \leqq a \smile y \leqq a \smile (b \frown c) \leqq b$ and $\varphi(a \smile y) = y$. Concerning the rest see Exercise 21 in Chapter II.

5. In this case $p_j \smile p_l = p_k \smile p_k$.

6. For any valuation v of the lattice shown in Fig. 17a (p. 90) $v(a) + v(b) = v(o) + v(i) = v(c) + v(b)$.

7. The equation $\delta(a, b) + \delta(b, c) = \delta(a, c)$ implies $v(b) = v(a \frown b) + v(b \frown c) - v(a \frown c)$. From the latter we get $v(b) \leqq v\big((a \frown b) \smile (b \frown c)\big)$. The reverse inequality is, however, trivial and hence $b = (a \frown b) \smile (b \frown c) \leqq a \smile c$.

9. In the distributive case, show that both a and $a \smile b$ are relative complements of c in $[a \frown c, i]$.

10. To prove $z \frown (x \smile t) = o$ observe that $z = z \frown (x \smile y)$ in both cases; in case b) it must be further taken into consideration that $z = z \frown y$. To prove $z \smile (x \smile t) = i$ in case b) apply the equality $x = (x \frown y) \smile x$.

14. Apply Theorem 49 to the sublattice $[u, v]$.

Chapter VI

1. See, for example, the lattice shown as Fig. 33b. (p. 190).

6a. By the De Morgan formulae, $\big((v \frown u') \smile u\big)' = (v' \smile u) \frown u'$ and $u' \leqq v'$. These imply a). Consequently, $(x \frown a') \smile y = (x \frown a') \smile a \smile y = x \smile y$ in b).

9. Consider the field of sets consisting of all subsets of the lattice and assign to every element S of this field of sets the element $s = \bigcup_{x \in S} x$.

12. In order to prove $(x + y) + z = x + (y + z)$ and $x(y + z) = xy + xz$, consider the Boolean subalgebra $R = [o, x \cup y \cup z]$. If we denote the complement of the element t in R by t', then we get back — after some simple calculation — to the definition of addition given under (2) of Section 44.

17a. For every x, we have $m(a) = 0 \Longrightarrow m(x \cap a) = 0 \Rightarrow m(x) = m((x \cap a) \cup (x \cap a')) \leqq m(x \cap a')$. On the other hand, $m(x) \geqq m(x \cap a')$.

Chapter VII

2. Let $\bar{x}$ denote the Θ-class including x. If $h(a) < m$ and $a \cap b \prec b$ in L then also $\bar{a} \prec \bar{a} \cup \bar{b}$; if $h(a) \geqq m$, then in the new lattice $\bar{a} \cap \bar{b} \prec \bar{b}$ is impossible.

3. If $o = x_0 \prec x_1 \prec \ldots \prec x_r = b$, then $a \cap x_{j-1} \preceq a \cup x_j$ $(j = 1, \ldots, r)$.

7. If L is the equivalence lattice of the set M, then consider the subset lattice $\mathscr{P}(M - \{p\})$, p being an arbitrary but fixed element of M. Construct all subsets T of the form $X \cup \{p\}$ $(X \in \mathscr{P}(M - \{p\}))$ of M and adjoin to each T, as one element equivalence classes, every element of $M - T$.

8. Take for example the partitions (12) (34) . . ., (13) (24) . . ., (12) (3) (4) . . ., where . . . denotes the same partition of the rest of the elements.

11. Let $\cap$, $\prec$ ($\wedge$, $\dashv$) denote the meet and covering in M (respectively in L). The satisfying of the lower covering condition in L requires proof only in the case $x \vee y = o \dashv y$. But if $o \prec y$ does not hold, then y is the join of more than one atom of M, and of these, at least one is not included in $(u]$.

14. By the result of Exercise 3 no inner element of L has a complement.

15. Let $\{p_1, \ldots, p_r\}$ be the set of all atoms of the lattice and consider the chain

$$o < p_1 \leqq p_1 \cup p_2 \leqq \cdots \leqq p_1 \cup \ldots \cup p_r \ (= i).$$

16. Concerning the homomorphic image: Let $\varphi \colon L \sim L^*$ (L and L^* are Birkhoff lattices) and $x^* \neq y^*$, $x^* \succ u^*$, $y^* \succ u^*$ $(x^*, y^*, u^* \in L^*)$, further let $\bar{x}$ and $\bar{y}$ be a pair of elements for which $\varphi(\bar{x}) = x^*$, $\varphi(\bar{y}) = y^*$. Denote by u the greatest element whose φ-image is u^*. Denote the element covering u of the maximal chain between u and $u \cup \bar{x}$ on the one hand and between u and $u \cup \bar{y}$ on the other by x and y, respectively. Then, it is easily shown that $x \cup y \succ x, y$. Hence by Chapter II, Exercise 20, $x^* \cup y^* \succ x^*, y^*$.

17. Assume that $[o, a]$ is not of locally finite length. Let $p(\leq a)$ be an atom, and a_1 one relative complement of p in $[o, a]$. Then, $[o, a_1]$ is not of locally finite length, either, whence the foregoing argument can be repeated for $[o, a_1]$. In this way we get an infinite chain $a > a_1 > > a_2 > \ldots$, which is a contradiction.

18. See, for example, Fig. 20 (p. 102).

20. Observe that in a distributive lattice the join of some semicomplements of an element is itself a semicomplement of the same element.

Chapter VIII

2. Let $\{o^*, i^*\}$ be a two-element chain. If R is an ideal, then the mapping defined by $\varphi(R) = o^*$, $\varphi(L - R) = i^*$ is join-homomorphic.

3. Consider the foregoing φ with $R = I$.

5. If $c_0 > c_1 > \ldots$, then $\bigcap\limits_{n=0}^{\infty} (c_n] = O$.

7. If M is maximal and $a \frown b \in M$, but $a \notin M$, then $(a] \smile M = L \ni b$. Hence, $b \leq a \smile m$ for some m in M. Consequently $b = b \frown (a \smile m) = (b \frown a) \smile (b \frown m) \in M$.

13. See the example given as a hint to Exercise 3 of Chapter III.

Chapter IX

2. Consider the set M of the triplets (0, 0, 0), (0, 0, 1), (0, 1, 0), (0, 1, 2), (1, 0, 0), (1, 0, 2), (1, 1, 1) and the equivalence relations Θ_j ($j = 1, 2, 3$) under which two elements of M are equivalent if, and only if, their j^{th} "components" coincide.

4. The generalization: the equivalence relation Θ defined in the algebra $A = A(\{f_\gamma\}_{\gamma\in\Gamma})$ is a congruence relation if, and only if, for every γ, $x_j \equiv y_j(\Theta)$ $(j = 1, \ldots, n(\gamma))$ implies $f_\gamma(x_1, \ldots, x_{n(\gamma)}) \equiv f_\gamma(x_1, \ldots, x_{j-1}, y_j, x_{j+1}, \ldots, x_{n(\gamma)})(\Theta)$.

6. The number of the atoms of the congruence lattice equals the length of the chain.

7. To transitivity: $[b, b \smile c] \supseteq [(a \smile b) \frown (b \smile c), (b \smile c)]$ and hence, by $b\Theta c$, the latter interval is also of finite length. It follows (see Exercise 2 to Chapter V) that $[a \smile b, a \smile b \smile c]$ is also of finite length. Hence and by the dual consideration, $a\Theta b$ implies also that $[a \frown b \frown c, a \smile b \smile c]$ is of finite length.

To the substitution property: if $a\ \Theta b$, then, similarly to the foregoing, $[(a \frown b) \smile c, (a \smile b) \smile c]$ and, a fortiori, $[(a \smile c) \frown (b \smile c), (a \smile c) \smile (b \smile c)]$ is of finite length.

12. To transitivity: with the notation $u = (a' \frown b) \smile (a \frown b')$ and $v = (b' \frown c) \smile (b \frown c')$, there holds $(a' \frown c) \smile (a \frown c') = (u' \frown v) \smile (u \frown v')$.

18. Let $a \nleq b$ and $a \equiv b(\Theta)$. There exists an atom s such that $s \leq a$ but $s \nleq b$; hence, $s = s \frown a \equiv s \frown b = o(\Theta)$. If now p is any atom other than s, then there exists an atom t such that $p = p \frown (t \smile s) \equiv p \frown t = o(\Theta)$. Hence it is obtained without difficulty that $\Theta = \mathrm{I}$.

Chapter X

3. To the first statement: see Exercise 1 of Chapter III. To the second: in the case under consideration $\mathcal{K}(A)$ is modular, thus Theorem 38 may be applied.

10. See Exercise 1 to Chapter IV.

11. To the "only if" statement: If e is neutral in $(d]$ then L is isomorphic to a subdirect union of $[e]$, $[e, d]$ and $[d)$.

12b. If $a \frown x = z \frown x = o$ and $a \smile x = z \smile x$, then $a \frown z = (a \frown z) \smile (a \frown x) = \ldots = a$.

13. Provided the condition holds, $(I \smile A) \frown (I \smile B) \subseteq I \smile (A \frown B)$ is true for any pair A, B of ideals, and $\mathcal{J}(L)$ is modular; see also Theorem 35. Conversely, if I is a neutral ideal, then, $(I \smile (a]) \frown (I \smile (b]) = I \smile (a \frown b]$ for any pair of elements a, b of L.

14. There exists a y such that $a \frown y = x \frown y = o$ and $a \smile y = x \smile y$ and hence $x \leq (a \smile y) \frown (a \smile x)$. Now apply the condition given in the preceding exercise.

15. The statement "only if" is a consequence of Equations (6) and (7) of Section 54, the statement "if" of the statement of Exercise 13.

16. Let c_β denote some relative complement of $a \frown b_\beta$ in $[o, b_\beta]$ and a' some complement of a. By $c_\beta = c_\beta \frown (a \smile a')$ and $c_\beta = c_\beta \frown b_\beta$, we obtain $c_\beta = c_\beta \frown a'$. Then using $b_\beta = (a \frown b_\beta) \smile c_\beta$ the statement follows by direct calculation.

BIBLIOGRAPHY

I. Lattice Theory

1. S. Abian—A. B. Brown, A theorem on partially ordered sets, with applications to fixed point theorems, *Canadian J. Math.*, **13** (1961), 78—82.
2. Г. Я. Арешкин, Об отношениях конгруенции в дистрибугивных структурах с нулевым елементом. *Доклады Акад. Наук СССР* **90** (1953) 485—486.
3. G. Aumann, Bemerkung über Galois-Verbindungen. *Sitzungsber. Bayer. Akad. Wiss., Math. Nat. Kl.* (1955) 281—284.
4. R. Baer, The significance of the system of subgroups for the structure of the group. *Amer. J. Math.* **61** (1939) 1—44.
5. V. K. Balachandran, On disjunction lattices. *J. Madras Univ.*, Sect. B. **23** (1953) 15—21.
6. V. K. Balachandran, On complete lattices and a problem of Birkhoff and Frink, *Proc. Amer. Math. Soc.* **6** (1955) 548—553.
7. M. Benado, Asupra teoremelor de descompunere al algebrei. *Stud. Cerc. Mat.* **3** (1952) 263—288.
8. M. Benado, Teoria abstractă a relațiilor de normalitate. *Stud. Cerc. Mat.* **4** (1953) 69—120.
9. G. Bergmann, Zur Axiomatik der Elementargeometrie. *Monatshefte Math. Phys.* **36** (1929) 269—284.
10. G. Birkhoff, On the combination of subalgebras. *Proc. Camb. Phil. Soc.* **29** (1933) 441—464.
11. G. Birkhoff, Applications of lattice algebra. *Proc. Camb. Phil. Soc.* **30** (1934) 115—122.
12. G. Birkhoff, On the structure of abstract algebras. *Proc. Camb. Phil. Soc.* **31** (1935) 433—454.
13. G. Birkhoff, Abstract linear dependence and lattices. *Amer. J. Math.* **57** (1935) 800—804.
14. G. Birkhoff, Combinatorial relations in projective geometries. *Annals Math.* **36** (1935) 743—748.
15. G. Birkhoff, Rings of sets. *Duke Math. J.* **3** (1937) 442—454.
16. G. Birkhoff, Neutral elements in general lattices. *Bull. Amer. Math. Soc.* **46** (1940) 702—705.
17. G. Birkhoff, Generalized arithmetic. *Duke Math. J.* **9** (1942) 283—302.
18. G. Birkhoff, Subdirect unions in universal algebras. *Bull. Amer. Math. Soc.* **50** (1944) 764—768.
19. G. Birkhoff, Lattice theory. Amer. Math. Soc. Colloquium Publ. **25**, revised edition, New York 1948.
20. G. Birkhoff—O. Frink, Representations of lattices by sets. *Trans. Amer. Math. Soc.* **64** (1948) 299—316.
21. G. D. Birkhoff—G. Birkhoff, Distributive postulates for systems like Boolean algebras. *Trans. Amer. Math. Soc.* **60** (1946) 3—11.
22. G. Boole, The mathematical analysis of logic. Cambridge 1847.
23. G. Bruns, Distributivität und subdirekte Zerlegbarkeit vollständiger Verbände. *Archiv Math.* **12** (1961) 61—66.
24. L. Byrne, Two brief formulations of Boolean algebra. *Bull. Amer. Math. Soc.* **52** (1946) 269—272.

25. L. Byrne, Short formulations of Boolean algebra, using ring operations. *Canadian J. Math.* **3** (1951) 31—33.
26. A. Châtelet, Algèbre des relations de congruence. *Annales Sci. École Norm. Sup.* **64** (1947) 339—368.
27. A. H. Copeland sr., Implicative Boolean algebra. *Math. Zeitschr.* **53** (1950) 285—290.
28. P. Crawley, The isomorphism theorem in compactly generated lattices. *Bull. Amer. Math. Soc.* **65** (1959) 377—379.
29. P. Crawley, Lattices whose congruences form a Boolean algebra. *Pacific J. Math.* **10** (1960) 787—796.
30. R. Crawley, Decomposition theory for non-semimodular lattices, *Trans. Amer. Math. Soc.* **99** (1961) 246—254.
31. R. Croisot, Condition suffisante pour l'égalité des longueurs de deux chaînes de même extrémités dans une structure. Applications aux relations d'équivalence et aux sous-groupes. *Comptes Rendus Paris* **226** (1948) 767—768.
32. R. Croisot, Axiomatique des treillis semi-modulaires. *Comptes Rendus Paris* **231** (1950) 12—14.
33. R. Croisot, Axiomatique des treillis modulaires. *Comptes Rendus Paris* **231** (1950) 95—97.
34. R. Croisot, Diverses caractérisations des treillis semi-modulaires, modulaires et distributifs. *Comptes Rendus Paris* **231** (1950) 1399—1401.
35. R. Croisot, Axiomatique des lattices distributives. *Canadian J. Math.* **3** (1951) 24—27.
36. R. Croisot, Contribution à l'étude des treillis semi-modulaires de longueur infinie. *Annales Sci. École Norm. Sup.* **68** (1951) 203—265.
37. A. C. Davis, A characterization of complete lattices. *Pacific J. Math.* **5** (1955) 311—319.
38. R. Dedekind, Über Zerlegungen von Zahlen durch ihre größten gemeinsamen Teiler. *Gesammelte Werke* **2,** 103—148.
39. R. Dedekind, Über die von drei Moduln erzeugte Dualgruppe. *Math. Annalen* **53** (1900) 371—403. (*Gesammelte Werke* **2,** 236—271.)
40. A. H. Diamond—J. C. C. McKinsey, Algebras and their subalgebras. *Bull. Amer. Math. Soc.* **53** (1947) 959—962.
41. R. P. Dilworth, On complemented lattices. *Tôhoku Math. J.* **47** (1940) 18—23.
42. R. P. Dilworth, Lattices with unique irreducible decompositions. *Annals Math.* **41** (1940) 771—777.
43. R. P. Dilworth, Ideals in Birkhoff lattices. *Trans. Amer. Math. Soc.* **49** (1941) 325—353.
44. R. P. Dilworth, The arithmetical theory of Birkhoff lattices. *Duke Math. J.* **8** (1941) 286—289.
45. R. P. Dilworth, Lattices with unique complements. *Trans. Amer. Math. Soc.* **57** (1945) 123—154.
46. R. P. Dilworth, Note on the Kurosh—Ore theorem. *Bull. Amer. Math. Soc.* **52** (1946) 659—663.
47. R. P. Dilworth, The structure of relatively complemented lattices. *Annals Math.* **51** (1950) 348—359.
48. R. P. Dillworth, Proof of a conjecture on finite modular lattices. *Annals Math.* **60** (1954) 359—364.
49. R. P. Dilworth—P. Crawley, Decomposition theory for lattices without chain conditions. *Trans. Amer. Math. Soc.* **96** (1960) 1—22.
50. M. L. Dubreil-Jacotin—L. Lesieur—R. Croisot, Leçons sur la théorie des treillis, des structures algébriques ordonnées et des treillis géométriques. Cahiers scientifiques **21,** Gauthiers-Villars, Paris 1953.
51. Ph. Dwinger, On the closure operators of the ordinal product of closed lattices. *Proceedings Amsterdam,* Series A **58** (1955) 36—40.
52. Ph. Dwinger, The closure operators of the cardinal and ordinal sums and products of partially ordered sets and closed lattices. *Proceedings Amsterdam,* Series A, **58** (1955) 341—351.

53. Ph. Dwinger, On the lattices of the closure operators of a complete lattice *Nieuw Archief Wisk.* (3) **4** (1956) 112—117.
54. Ph. Dwinger, Some theorems on universal algebras. *Proceedings Amsterdam,* Series A, **60** (1957), 182—195.
55. Ph. Dwinger, On the axiom of Baer in distributive complete lattices. *Proceedings Amsterdam,* Series A. **60** (1957) 220—226.
56. Ph. Dwinger, Complete homomorphisms of complete lattices. *Proceedings Amsterdam,* Series A, **60** (1957), 412—420.
57. D. Ellis, Notes on the foundations of lattice theory. *Publicationes Math.* **1** (1949—1950) 205—208.
58. D. Ellis, Notes on the foundations of lattice theory, II. *Archiv Math.* **4** (1953) 257—260.
59. C. J. Everett, Closure operators and Galois theory in lattices. *Trans. Amer. Math. Soc.* **55** (1944) 514—525.
60. W. Felscher, Ein unsymmetrisches Assoziativ-Gesetz in der Verbandstheorie. *Archiv Math.* **8** (1957) 171—174.
61. W. Felscher, Jordan—Hölder-Sätze und modular geordnete Mengen. *Math. Zeitschr.* **75** (1961) 83—114.
62. D. T. Finkbeiner, A semi-modular imbedding of lattices. *Canadian J. Math.* **12** (1960) 582—591.
63. D. T. Finkbeiner, Irreducible congruence relations on lattices. *Pacific J. Math.* **10** (1960) 813—822.
64. E. E. Floyd, Boolean algebras with pathological order topologies. *Pacific J. Math.* **5** (1955) 687—689.
65. E. E. Floyd—V. L. Klee, A characterization of reflexivity by the lattice of closed subspaces. *Proc. Amer. Math. Soc.* **5** (1954) 655—661.
66. O. Frink, Representations of Boolean algebras. *Bull. Amer. Math. Soc.* **47** (1941) 755—756.
67. O. Frink, Topology in lattices. *Trans. Amer. Math. Soc.* **51** (1942) 569—582.
68. O. Frink, Complemented modular lattices and projective spaces of infinite dimension. *Trans. Amer. Math. Soc.* **60** (1946) 452—467.
69. L. Fuchs, On quasi-primary ideals. *Acta Sci. Math. Szeged* **11** (1947) 174—183.
70. L. Fuchs, The meet-decomposition of elements in lattice-ordered semigroups. *Acta Sci. Math. Szeged* **12** (1950) 105—111.
71. L. Fuchs, On subdirect unions, I. *Acta Math. Acad. Sci. Hung.* **3** (1952) 103—120.
72. L. Fuchs, A lattice-theoretic discussion of some problems in additive ideal theory. *Acta Math. Acad. Sci. Hung.* **5** (1954) 299—313.
73. T. Fujiwara, Remarks on the Jordan—Hölder—Schreier Theorem. *Proc. Japan Acad.* **31** (1955) 137—140.
74. N. Funayama, On the completion by cuts of distributive lattices. *Proc. Imp. Acad. Tokyo* **20** (1944) 1—2.
75. N. Funayama, Imbedding infinitely distributive lattices completely isomorphically into Boolean algebras *Nagoya Math. J.* **15** (1959), 71—81.
76. N. Funayama—T. Nakayama, On the distributivity of a lattice of lattice-congruences. *Proc. Imp. Acad. Tokyo* **18** (1942) 553—554.
77. A. A. Grau, Ternary Boolean algebra. *Bull. Amer. Math. Soc.* **53** (1947) 567—572.
78. G. Grätzer—E. T. Schmidt, On the Jordan—Dedekind chain condition. *Acta Sci. Math. Szeged* **18** (1957) 52—56.
79. G. Grätzer—E. T. Schmidt, Ideals and congruence relations in lattices. *Acta Math. Acad. Sci. Hung.* **9** (1958) 137—175.
80. G. Grätzer—E. T. Schmidt, Characterizations of relatively complemented distributive lattices. *Publicationes Math.* **5** (1958) 275—287.
81. G. Grätzer—E. T. Schmidt, Two notes on lattice-congruences. *Acta Univ. Sci. Budapestinensis,* Sectio Math. **1** (1958) 83—87.
82. G. Grätzer—E. T. Schmidt, Standard ideals in lattices. *Acta Math. Acad. Sci. Hung.* **12** (1961) 17—86.

83. G. Grätzer—E. T. Schmidt, On congruence lattices of lattices. *Acta Math. Acad. Sci. Hung.* **13** (1962) 179—185.
84. G. Grätzer—E. T. Schmidt, Characterizations of congruence lattices of abstract algebras. *Acta Sci. Math. Szeged*, (to be published).
85. I. Halperin, A Neumann-féle folytonos geometria (The von Neumann continuous geometry). *Matematikai Lapok* **9** (1958) 225—231.
86. O. Hájek, Direct decompositions of lattices, I-II. *Czechosl. Math. J.* **7** (1957) 1—15.
87. J. Hartmanis, Lattice theory of generalized partitions. *Canadian J. Math.* **11** (1959), 97—106.
88. J. Hashimoto, On a lattice with a valuation. *Proc. Amer. Math. Soc.* **3** (1952) 1—2.
89. J. Hashimoto, Ideal theory for lattices. *Math. Japonicae* **2** (1952) 149—186.
90. J. Hashimoto, Direct, subdirect decompositions and congruence relations. *Osaka Math. J.* **9** (1957) 87—112.
91. H. Hermes, Einführung in die Verbandstheorie. Grundlehren der Math. Wissensch. in Einzeldarst. **73**, Springer-Verlag, Berlin—Göttingen—Heidelberg 1955.
92. H. Hermes—G. Köthe, Theorie der Verbände. *Enzyklopädie der math. Wissensch.* I. **1**. 13, Teubner-Verlag, Leipzig—Berlin 1939.
93. E. V. Huntington, Sets of independent postulates for the algebra of logic. *Trans. Amer. Math. Soc.* **5** (1904) 288—309.
94. E. V. Huntington, Postulates for the algebra of logic. *Trans. Amer. Math. Soc.* **35** (1933) 274—304, 357, 971.
95. K. Iséki, Une condition pour qu'une lattice soit distributive. *Comptes Rendus Paris* **230** (1950) 1726—1727.
96. K. Iséki, On lattice theory. *J. Osaka Inst. Sci. Techn.* **3** (1951) 25—31.
97. K. Iséki, A characterization of distributive lattices. *Proceedings Amsterdam*, Series A **54** (1951) 388—389.
98. K. Iséki, A criterion for distributive lattices. *Acta Math. Acad. Sci. Hung.* **3** (1952) 241—242.
99. J. Jakubík, On the Jordan—Dedekind chain condition. *Acta Sci. Math. Szeged* **16** (1955) 266—269.
100. J. Jakubík; Прямые разложення вполне дистрибутивных структур. *Czechosl. Math. J.* **5** (1955) 488—491.
101. J. Jakubík, O zamenitel'ných kongruenciách na svázoch. *Mat.-Fyz. Časopis Slovenskej Akad. Vied* **8** (1958) 155—162.
102. J. Jakubík, O refazcoch v Boolových algebrách. *Mat.-Fyz. Časopis Slovenskej Akad. Vied* **8** (1958) 193—202.
103. B. Jónsson, Modular lattices and Desargues' theorem. *Math. Scand.* **2** (1954) 295—314.
104. B. Jónsson, Distributive sublattices of a modular lattice. *Proc. Amer. Math. Soc.* **6** (1955) 682—688.
105. P. Jordan, Zum Dedekindschen Axiom in der Theorie der Verbände. *Abhandl. Hamburg* **16** (1949) 71—73.
106. P. Jordan, Über nichtkommutative Verbände. *Archiv Math.*, **2** (1949) 56—59.
107. P. Jordan, Zur Theorie der nichtkommutativen Verbände. *Akad. Wiss. Mainz, Abhandl. Mat.-Nat. Kl.*, **12** (1953) 59—64.
108. P. Jordan, Beiträge zur Theorie der Schrägverbände. *Akad. Wiss. Mainz, Abhandl. Mat.-Nat. Kl.*, **15** (1956), 27—42.
109. P. Jordan, Die Theorie der Schrägverbände. *Abhandl. Hamburg*, **21** (1957) 127—138.
110. P. Jordan—W. Böge, Zur Theorie der Schrägverbände II. *Akad. Wiss. Mainz, Abhandl. Mat.-Nat. Kl.* **13** (1954) 79—92.
111. P. Jordan—E. Witt, Zur Theorie der Schrägverbände. *Akad. Wiss. Mainz, Abhandl. Mat.-Nat. Kl.* **12** (1953) 223—232.
112. A. Kertész, On independent sets of elements in algebra. *Acta Sci. Math. Szeged* **21** (1960) 260—269.

113. N. KIMURA, Independency of axioms of lattices. *Kôdai Math. Sem. Rep.* (1950) 14.
114. FR. KLEIN-BARMEN, Über einen Zerlegungssatz in der Theorie der abstrakten Verknüpfungen. *Math. Annalen* **106** (1932) 114—130.
115. FR. KLEIN-BARMEN, Beiträge zur Theorie der Verbände. *Math. Zeitschr.* **39** (1935) 227—239.
116. FR. KLEIN-BARMEN, Birkhoffsche und harmonische Verbände. *Math. Zeitschr.* **42** (1937) 58—81.
117. B. KNASTER, Une théorème sur les fonctions d'ensembles. *Annales Soc. Polonaise Math.* **6** (1927) 133—134.
118. M. KOBAYASI, On the axioms of the theory of lattices. *Proc. Imp. Acad. Tokyo* **19** (1943) 6—9.
119. M. KOLIBIAR, к аксиоматике модулярных структур. *Czechosl. Math. J.* **6** (1956) 381—386.
120. V. KOŘINEK, Der Schreiersche Satz und das Zassenhaussche Verfahren in Verbänden. *Vestn. Kral. České Spol. Nauk* (1941) 1—29.
121. V. S. KRISHNAN, The problem of the last-residue-class in the distributive lattice. *Proc. Ind. Acad. Sci.*, Sect. A **16** (1942) 176—190.
122. V. S. KRISHNAN, Binary relations, congruences and homomorphisms. *J. Madras Univ.*, Sect. B **16** (1944) 8—24.
123. А. Г. Курош, Durchschnittsdarstellungen mit irreduziblen Komponenten in Ringen und in sogenannten Dualgruppen. *Мат. Сборник* **42** (1935) 613—616.
124. L. LESIEUR, Sur les demi-groupes réticulés satisfaisant à une condition de chaîne. *Bull. Soc. Math. France* **83** (1955) 161—193.
125. А. Х. Лившиц, О теореме Жордана — Гельдера. *Мат. оборник* **4** (1938) 31—43.
126. L. H. LOOMIS, On the representation of σ-complete Boolean algebras. *Bull. Amer. Math. Soc.* **53** (1947) 757—760.
127. S. MACLANE, A lattice formulation for transcendence degrees and p-bases. *Duke Math. J.* **4** (1938) 455—468.
128. S. MACLANE, A conjecture of Ore on chains in partially ordered sets. *Bull. Amer. Math. Soc.* **49** (1943) 567—568.
129. H. M. MACNEILLE, Partially ordered sets. *Trans. Amer. Math. Soc.* **42** (1937) 416—460.
130. F. MAEDA, Lattice theoretic characterization of abstract geometries. *J. Sci. Hiroshima Univ.*, Ser. A **15** (1951—1952) 87—96.
131. F. MAEDA, Direct and subdirect factorization of lattices. *J. Sci. Hiroshima Univ.*, Ser. A **15** (1951—1952) 97—102.
132. F. MAEDA, Matroid lattices of infinite length. *J. Sci. Hiroshima Univ.*, Ser. A **15** (1951—1952) 177—182.
133. F. MAEDA, Kontinuierliche Geometrien. Grundlehren der Math. Wissensch. in Einzeldarst. **95,** Springer-Verlag, Berlin — Göttingen — Heidelberg 1958.
134. Y. MATSUSHIMA, Hausdorff interval topology on a partially ordered set, *Proc. Amer. Math. Soc.*, **11** (1960), 233—235.
135. S. MATSUSHITA, Lattices non-commutatifs. *Comptes Rendus Paris* **236** (1953) 1525—1527.
136. S. MATSUSHITA, Zur Theorie der nichtkommutativen Verbände, I., *Math. Annalen* **137** (1959) 1—8.
137. J. E. MCLAUGHLIN, Structured theorems for relatively complemented lattices. *Pacific J. Math.* **3** (1953) 197—208.
138. J. E. MCLAUGHLIN, Atomic lattices with unique comparable complements. *Proc. Amer. Math. Soc.* **7** (1956) 864—866.
139. K. MENGER, New foundations of projective and affine geometry. *Annals Math.* **37** (1936) 456—482.
140. J. MORGADO, Some results on closure operators of partially ordered sets. *Portugaliae Math.* **19** (1960) 101—139.
141. M. L. MOUSINHO, Modular and projective lattices. *Summa Bras. Math.* **2** (1950) 95—112.

142. R. Musti—E. Buttafuoco, Sui subreticoli distributivi dei reticoli modulari. *Boll. Unione Mat. Italiana* **11** (1956) 584—587.
143. L. Nachbin, Une propriété caractéristique des algèbres booléiennes. *Portugaliae Math.* **6** (1947) 115—118.
144. T. Nakayama, Remark on direct product decomposition of a partially ordered system. *Math. Japonicae* **1** (1948) 49—50.
145. J. von Neumann, Continuous geometry. *Proc. Nat. Acad. Sci. U.S.A.* **22** (1936) 92—100.
146. J. von Neumann, Examples of continuous geometries. *Proc. Nat. Acad. Sci. U. S. A.* **22** (1936) 101—108.
147. J. von Neumann, Lectures on continuous geometries. Institute for Advanced Study, Princeton 1936—1937. (New edition: Princeton Math. Series **25**, Princeton Univ. Press, Princeton, 1960.)
148. E. S. Northam, Topology in lattices. *Bull. Amer. Math. Soc.* **59** (1953) 387.
149. T. Ogasawara—U. Sasaki, On a theorem in lattice theory. *J. Sci. Hiroshima Univ.*, Ser. A **14** (1949) 13.
150. O. Ore, On the foundations of abstract algebras, I—II. *Annals Math.* **36** (1935) 406—437 and **37** (1936) 265—292.
151. O. Ore, On the theorem of Jordan—Hölder. *Trans. Amer. Math. Soc.* **41** (1937) 266—275.
152. O. Ore, Structures and group theory, II. *Duke Math. J.* **4** (1938) 247—269.
153. O. Ore, Theory of equivalence relations, *Duke Math. J.* **9** (1942) 573—627.
154. O. Ore, Chains in partially ordered sets. *Bull. Amer. Math. Soc.* **49** (1943) 558—566.
155. O. Ore, Galois connexions. *Trans. Amer. Math. Soc.* **55** (1944) 493—513.
156. C. S. Peirce, On the algebra of logic, I—II. *Amer. J. Math.* **3** (1880) 15—57 and **7** (1884) 180—202.
157. N. Peremans, Embedding of a distributive lattice into a Boolean algebra. *Proc. Amsterdam*, Series A **60** (1957) 73—81.
158. Р. В. Петропавловская, Об определяемости группы структурой ее подсистем. *Мат. Сборник* **29** (1951) 63—78.
159. G. Pickert, Zur Übertragung der Kettensätze. *Math. Annalen* **121** (1949—1950) 100—102.
160. G. Pickert, Bemerkungen über Galois-Verbindungen. *Archiv Math.* **3** (1952) 285—289.
161. Б. И. Плоткин, Некоторые вопросы теории групп без кручения. *Украинский Мат. Ж.* **8** (1956) 325—329.
162. W. Prenowitz, Projective geometries as multigroups. *Amer. J. Math.* **65** (1943) 235—256.
163. W. Prenowitz, Descriptive geometries as multigroups. *Trans. Amer. Mat. Soc.* **59** (1946) 333—380.
164. W. Prenowitz, Total lattices of convex sets and of linear spaces. *Annals Math.* **49** (1948) 659—688.
165. Proceedings of Symposia in Pure Mathematics. 2 Lattice theory. Amer. Math. Soc., Providence, 1961.
166. G. N. Raney, Completely distributive complete lattices. *Proc. Amer. Math. Soc.* **3** (1952) 677—680.
167. G. N. Raney, A subdirect-union representation for completely distributive complete lattices. *Proc. Amer. Math. Soc.* **4** (1953) 518—522.
168. G. N. Raney, Tight Galois connections and complete distributivity, *Trans. Amer. Math. Soc.* **97** (1960) 418—426.
169. S. Rudeanu, Independent systems of axioms in lattice theory, *Bull. Math. Soc. Sci. Math. Phys. RPR* **35** (1959) 475—488.
170, Л. Е. Садовский, О структурных изоморфизмах свободных произведений групп. *Мат. Сборник* **21** (1947) 63—82.
171. U. Sasaki, Lattice theoretic characterization of an affine geometry of arbitrary dimension. *J. Sci. Hiroshima Univ.*. Ser. A **16** (1952—1953) 223—238.

172. U. SASAKI, Semi-modularity in relatively atomic upper continuous lattices. *J. Sci. Hiroshima Univ.*, Ser. A **16** (1952—1953), 409—416.
173. U. SASAKI, Lattice theoretic characterization of geometries satisfying "Axiome der Verknüpfung". *J. Sci. Hiroshima Univ.*, Ser. A **16** (1952—53) 417—423.
174. E. SCHRÖDER, Algebra der Logik. **1**, Teubner-Verlag, Leipzig 1890.
175. K. SHODA, Über die allgemeinen algebraischen Systeme. I—VIII. *Proc. Imp. Acad. Tokyo* **17** (1941) 323—327; **18** (1942) 179—184, 227—232 and 276—279; **19** (1943) 114—118, 259—263 and 515—517; **20** (1944) 584—588.
176. M. SHOLANDER, Postulates for distributive lattices. *Canadian J. Math.* **3** (1951) 28—30.
177. M. SHOLANDER, Postulates for Boolean algebras. *Canadian J. Math.* **5** (1953) 460—464.
178. R. SIKORSKI, On the representation of Boolean algebras as fields of sets. *Fundamenta Math.* **35** (1948) 247—258.
179. R. SIKORSKI, Boolean algebras. Ergebnisse der Math. u. ihrer Grenzgeb. New series **25** Springer-Verlag, Berlin—Göttingen—Heidelberg 1960.
180. R. SIKORSKI, Distributivity and representability. *Fundamenta Math.* **48** (1959) 95—103.
181. E. C. SMITH—A. TARSKI, Higher degrees of distributivity and completeness in Boolean algebras. *Trans. Amer. Math. Soc.* **84** (1957) 230—257.
182. Ю. И. Соркин, Независимые системы аксиом, опеделяющие структур. *Укранискиü мат. ж.* **3.** (1951) 85—97.
183. M. H. STONE, Boolean algebras and their relation to topology. *Proc. Nat. Acad. Sci. U. S. A.* **20** (1934) 197—202.
184. M. H. STONE, Subsumption of Boolean algebras under the theory of rings. *Proc. Nat. Acad. Sci. U.S.A.* **21** (1935) 103—105.
185. M. H. STONE, Postulates for Boolean algebras and generalized Boolean algebras. *Amer. J. Math.* **57** (1935) 703—732.
186. M. H. STONE, The theory of representations for Boolean algebras. *Trans. Amer. Math. Soc.* **40** (1936) 37—111.
187. M. H. STONE, Topological representations of distributive lattices and Browerian Logics. *Časopis Pešt. Mat. Fyz.* **67** (1937—1938) 1—25.
188. M. SUZUKI, Structure of a group and the structure of its lattice of subgroups. Ergebnisse der Math. u. ihrer Grenzgeb. New series **10** Springer-Verlag, Berlin—Göttingen—Heidelberg 1956.
189. G. SZÁSZ, On the structure of semi-modular lattices of infinite length. *Acta Sci. Math. Szeged* **14** (1951—1952) 239—245.
190. G. SZÁSZ, Dense and semi-complemented lattices. *Nieuw Archief Wisk.* (3) **1** (1953) 42—44.
191. G. SZÁSZ, Generalization of a theorem of Birkhoff concerning maximal chains of a certain type of lattices. *Acta Sci. Math. Szeged* **16** (1955) 89—91 and 270.
192. G. SZÁSZ, On relatively complemented lattices. *Acta Sci. Math. Szeged* **18** (1957) 48—51.
193. G. SZÁSZ, Semi-complements and complements in semi-modular lattices. *Publicationes Math.* **5** (1957—1958) 217—221.
194. G. SZÁSZ, On complemented lattices. *Acta Sci. Math. Szeged* **19** (1958) 77—81.
195. G. SZÁSZ, Translationen der Verbände *Acta Fac. Rerum Nat. Univ. Comenianae* **5** (1961), 53—57.
196. G. SZÁSZ, On the valuations of complemented modular lattices of finite length, *Publicationes Math.* **8** (1961) 128—130.
197. G. SZÁSZ, On independent systems of axioms for lattices *Publicationes* Math. (to be published).
198. K. TAKEUCHI, On maximal proper sublattices. *J. Math. Soc. Japan* **2** (1951) 228—230.
199. T. TANAKA, Canonical subdirect factorisations of lattices. *J. Sci. Hiroshima Univ.*, Ser. A **16** (1952—1953) 239—246.
200 A. TARSKI, Zur Grundlegung der Boole'schen Algebra. I. *Fundamenta. Math.* **24** (1935) 177—198.

201. A Tarski, A lattice-theoretical fixpoint theorem and its applications. *Pacific J. Math.* **5** (1955) 285—310.
202. G. Trevisan, Sulla distributività delle strutture che posseggono una valutazione distributiva. *Rendiconti Padova* **20** (1951) 396—400.
203. Y. Utumi, On primary elements of a modular lattice. *Kôdai Math. Sem. Rep.* (1952) 101—103.
204. А. И. Узков, О теореме Жордана — Гельдера. *Мат. Сборник* **4** (1938) 31—43.
205. D. Vaida, Caracterizări ale laticelor distributive. *Comunicările Acad. Rep. Pop. Rom.*, **11** (1961) 797—800.
206. Ph. Vassiliou, A set of postulates for distributive lattices. *Publ. Nat. Techn. Univ. Athen* **5** (1950).
207. V. Vilhelm, Теорема Жордана—Гельдера в структурах без узловия конечности цепей. *Czehosl. Mat. J.* **4** (1954) 28—49.
208. V. Vilhelm, Двойственное себе ядро условий Биргофа в структурах с конечными ценями. *Czehosl. Mat. J.* **5** (1955) 439—450.
209. H. Wallmann, Lattices and topological spaces. *Annals Math.* **39** (1938) 112—126.
210. Wang Shih-chiang, Notes on the permutability of congruence relations. *Acta Math. Sinica* **3** (1953) 133—141.
211. M. Ward, The arithmetical properties of modular lattices. *Revista Ciencias Lima* **41** (1939) 593—603.
212. M. Ward, A characterization of Dedekind structures. *Bull. Amer. Math. Soc.* **45** (1939) 448—451.
213. M. Ward, The closure operators of a lattice. *Annals Math.* **43** (1942) 191—196.
214. Ph. Whitman, Lattices, equivalence relations and subgroups. *Bull. Amer. Math. Soc.* **52** (1946) 507—522.
215. L. R. Wilcox, Modularity in the theory of lattices. *Annals Math.* **40** (1939) 490—505.
216. L. R. Wilcox, Modularity in Birkhoff lattices. *Bull. Amer. Math. Soc.* **50** (1944) 135—138.
217. E. S. Wolk, Dedekind completeness and a fixed-point theorem. *Canadian J. Math.* **9** (1957), 400—405.
218. E. S. Wolk, Order compatible topology on a partially ordered set. *Proc. Amer. Math. Soc.* **9** (1958) 524—529.

II. Other Sources

219. G. Birkhoff—S. MacLane, Survey of modern algebra. MacMillan Company, New York 1941.
220. C. Carathéodory, Über das lineare Maß von Punktmengen — eine Verallgemeinerung des Längenbegriffs. *Nachr. Göttingen* Math.-Phys. Klasse (1914) 404—426.
221. H. S. M. Coxeter, The real projective plane. McGraw-Hill Book Company, Inc., New York—Toronto—London 1949.
(*In German:* Reelle projektive Geometrie der Ebene. Verlag R. Oldenbourg, München 1955.)
222. P. Dubreil, Algèbre, I. Gauthiers-Villars, Paris, 1946.
223. F. Hausdorff, Grundzüge der Mengenlehre. Veit & Co. Leipzig 1914.
224. B. Kerékjártó, Les fondements de la géométrie. II (Géométrie projective). Akadémiai Kiadó, Budapest. (to be publisched).
225. A. N. Kolmogorov, Foundations of the theory of probability. Chelsea Publishing Company, New York 1950.
226. C. Kuratowski, Une méthode d'élimination des nombres transfinis des raisonnements mathématiques. *Fundamenta Math.* **3** (1922) 76—108.
227. А. Г. Курош, Теория групплитературы, Гос. изд. Технико — теоретической. Москва 1953. *(In German:* Gruppentheorie. Akademie-Verlag, Berlin

1953; *in English:* The theory of groups I—II, Chelsea Publishing Company, New York 1956.)

228. L. Rédei, Algebra, I, Akademische Verlagsgesellschaft Geest & Portig K.-G. Leipzig 1959.

229. J. Słomínski, The theory of abstract algebras with infinitary operations, Rozprawy Mat. **18.** Polska Akad. Nauk, Warszawa, 1959.

230. R. Vaidyanathaswamy, Treatise on set topology, I, Indian Math. Soc., Madras 1947. (*Second edition*) Set topology, Chelsea Publishing Co., New York 1960).

231. B. L. van der Waerden, Moderne Algebra, I—II. Springer-Verlag, 1. Auflage, Berlin 1930—1931.

232. M. Zorn, A remark on method in transfinite algebra. *Bull. Amer. Math. Soc.* **41** (1935) 667—670.

INDEX

A

Abian 63
Absorption identities 33
additive valuation 135
affine space 140
algebra 31
— of relations 131
antisymmetric 14
Areshkin 188
atom 45
atomic lattice 45
Aumann 71
automorphism 32

B

Baer 88
Balachandran 49, 51
base 75
Benado 181
Bergmann 36
Birkhoff, G. 5, 6, *18*, 21, 24, 30, 31, 60, 68, 71, 76, 80, 89, 90, 99, *106*, 107, 119, 122, 140, 146, 150, 153, 154, 167, 171, 174, 187, 195, 199, 200, 203, 206, 208
Birkhoff, G. D. 80
Birkhoff lattice 140
Birkhoff's distributivity criterion 90
Boole 5, 79
Boolean algebra 79
— homomorphism 122
— ring 126
— subalgebra 122
bound element 23
bounded set 22
— subset 22
Böge 33
Brown 63
Bruns 86
Buttafuoco 95
Byrne 125, 133

C

Carathéodory 136, 137
central element 208
centre 208
chain 15
— axiom 21
Châtelet 178
classes of an equivalence relation 146
— of a partition 145
— of propositions 134
closed element 68
— subset 64
closure of an element 68
— operation 68
cofinal 76
collinear 62
compact 65
compactly generated 65
comparable elements 16
complement 45
complemented element 46
— lattice 46
complete chain 60
— homomorphism 60
— isomorphism 60
— join homomorphism 60
— lattice 60
— meet homomorphism 60
— sublattice 63
— system of decomposition homomorphisms 192
— system of decomposition congruences 192
completely additive valuation 135
— distributive 85
— join-distributive 85
— join-irreducible 105
— meet-distributive 85
— meet-irreducible 66
— modular 87
— ordered 15, 20
— unordered 15
component of a direct union 191
— of an element 191

component of a meet representation 98
conditionally complete 64
congruence relation 170
— — generated by a homomorphism 171
conjunction 133
continuous geometry 119
convergence topology 76
convergent 75
convex 20
COPELAND 168
covering 17
— conditions 97
CRAWLEY 67, 97, 99, 183
CROISOT 6, 26, 80, 93, 105, 142, 143

D

DAVIS 63
decomposition congruence 192
— homomorphism 192
DEDEKIND 5, 33, 34, 86, 89, 90, 95, 97, 105, 106, 153
Dedekind cut 73
— 's modularity criterion 90
DE MORGAN 123
De Morgan formulae 123
diagram 18
DIAMAND 123
difference of sets 12
DILWORTH 5, 67, 98, 99, 101, 108, 121, 122, 142, 160, 164, 165, 177, 183, 203
dimension 26
— equation 106
— function 26
directed 75
direct decomposition 192
directly decomposable 193
— indecomposable 193
— irreducible 193
— reducible 193
direct union 191, 194
disjoint elements 47
distributive identities 79
— inequalities 79
— lattice 79
— valuation 110
double covering condition 97
down-directed 75
dual atom 45
— ideal 159
— isomorphism 71
— of a lattice 37
— of an ordering relation 16
— of a statement 35
— prime ideal 160
— principal ideal 160
dualization of a proof 36
dualization of a statement 36
dually atomic 45
DUBREIL 175
DUBREIL—JACOTIN 6
DWINGER 70, 77, 86, 175

E

ELLIS 80, 95
endomorphism 32
equality relation 14
equivalence (relation) 14
— lattice 146
equivalent propositions 134
EVERETT 71
extensivity 68

F

factor algebra 170
FELSCHER 56, 181
field of sets 83
FINKBEINER 149, 183
fixelement 62
FLOYD 76
formally false 133
— true 133
FRINK 5, 76, 118, 119, 123, 174
FUCHS 81, 196
FUJIWARA 181
FUNAYAMA 74, 125, 183

G

Galois connection 70
— — corresponding to a relation 71
generalized Boolean algebra 130
— projective spaces 114
GRAU 123
GRÄTZER 105, 106, 107, 130, 175, 177, 183, 184, 188, 208
greatest element 23
— lower bound 23

H

HÁJEK 208
HALPERIN 119
HARTMANIS 149
HASHIMOTO 111, 123, 164, 183, 187, 194
HAUSDORFF 64
Hausdorff space 64
height 26
HERMES 6, 21, 126, 176
homomorphic image 32
— mapping 52
homomorphism 32
HUNTINGTON 39, 123

I

ideal 44
— chain 160
— lattice of a lattice 162
— lattice of a ring 81
idempotency (of a mapping) 68
image set 12
incidence space 62
incomparable elements 16
infimum 23
infinitely distributive 84
— join-distributive 84
— meet-distributive 84
inner element 23
interval 20
— topology 75
inverse of a mapping 12
irreducible meet-representation 98
irredundant meet-representation 98
Iséki 93, 165
isomorphism 32
— theorem for modular lattices 95

J

Jakubík 86, 106, 177, 203
join 33
— -complete sublattice 63
— -homomorphic mapping 52
— homomorphism 52
— -irreducible 49
— -prime 51
— -reducible 49
— semilattice 38
Jónsson 119
Jordan 33, 87
Jordan—Dedekind chain condition 26

K

kernel of a congruence relation 186
— of a homomorphism 53
Kertész 150
Kimura 53
Klee 76
Klein-Barmen 38, 55, 140
Knaster 62
Kobayasi 55
Kolibiar 93
Kořínek 181
Köthe 6
Krishnan *171*, 175, 186
Kuratowski 21
Kuratowski-Zorn lemma 21
Kurosh 87, 98,
Kurosh-Ore theorem 98

L

lattice 33
— axioms 33
— complete with respect to the join (meet) 60
— -ordered semigroup 81
— theoretical duality principle 36
— theoretical proposition 35
least element 23
— upper bound 23
length of a chain 21
— of a partly ordered set 21
Lesieur 6, 81
limit 75
Lindenbaum 125
linear dependence 150
— subspace 62
linearly independent 150
Liwschitz 181
logical value 132
Loomis 167
lower bound 22
— covering condition 97

M

MacLane 5, 26, 140, 142, 143, 169
MacNeille 73
Maeda 119, 142, 143, 200, 208
Matsushima 75
Matsushita 33
maximal chain 20
— element 17
— ideal 168
— proper semicomplement 47
— semicomplement 47
maximum condition 24
McKinsey 123
McLaughlin 205
measurable 136
measure algebra 135
median 89
meet 33
— -complete sublattice 63
— -homomorphic mapping 52
— homomorphism 52
— -irreducible 49
— -prime 51
— -reducible 49
— -representation 98
— semilattice 38
Menger 119, 203
metric lattice 109
minimal congruence relation belonging to a subset 173
— element 17
minimum condition 24
modular identity 86

modular inequality 86
— lattice 86
MORGADO 70
multi-valued operation 30
— — partial operation 30
MUSTI 95

N

NACHBIN 168
NAKAYAMA 182, 200
natural ordering 15
negation 133
neutral element 205
— ideal 209
NEUMANN 5, 95, 112, 119, 124,
non-trivial subchain 44
— sublattice 44
NORTHAM 76

O

OGASAWARA 122
open subset 64
operation 30
order-homomorphic mapping 16
— homomorphism 16
— isomorphism 16
— -preserving mapping 16
— — valuation 109
ordering (relation) 14
— (—) of lattices 39
ORE 5, 26, 52, 71, 82, 98, 146, 173, 175, 176, 181,
orthocomplemented 138
outer measure 136

P

partial operation 30
partition 145
— belonging to an equivalence relation 145
— lattice 147
partly ordered set 15
— — — of finite length 21
— — — of infinite length 21
— — — of locally finite length 22
PEIRCE 15, 42, 123
PEREMANS 169
permutable relations 131
PETROPAVLOVSKAYA 88
PICKERT 71, 101
PLOTKIN 88
positive valuation 109
PRENOWITZ 119
prime ideal 160
principal ideal 160
product of mappings 12
— of relations 132
— of sets 13
projective space 113
— — of finite dimension 117
— — of infinite dimension 117
proper subchain
— sublattice 44
— semicomplement 47

Q

quasimetric lattice 109
— space 111
quasiordering 14

R

RANEY 71, 86
redundant meet-representation 98
refinement of a chain of equivalence relations 178
— of a direct decomposition 200
reflexive 14
relation 13
relative complement 46
relatively atomic 143
— complemented 46
representant 170
ring of sets 83
RUDEANU 56

S

SADOVSKI 88
SASAKI 119, 122, 142
SCHMIDT 105, 106, 130, 175, 177, 183, 184, 188, 208
SCHRÖDER 5, 33, 36, 79
S-covering 137
section complemented 47
self-dual lattice 37
— — statement 36
semicomplement 47
semicomplemented 48
semilattice 38
— axioms 38
semimodular 142
set bounded above (below) 22
set of self-dual statements 36
SHODA 30
SHOLANDER 80, 123
σ-lattice 65
SIKORSKI 122, 125, 167
similar algebras 32
simple algebra 173

SŁOMIŃSKI 30
SMITH 125
SORKIN 56
STONE 5, 123, 127, 130, 160, 162, 163, 164, 165, 167
subalgebra 31
— generated by a set 67
— lattice 68
sub-base 75
subchain 20
subdirect decomposition 195
— union 194
subdirectly decomposable 195
— irreducible 195
— reducible 195
subgroup lattice 35
sublattice 42
subset bounded above (below) 22
— lattice 34
subspace lattice 35, 62
Substitution Property 170
supremum 23
SUZUKI 88
symmetric (relation) 14
symmetrical difference 12
SZÁSZ 55, 56, 77, 104, 105, 112, 113, 120, 121, 153, 154, 155

T

TAKEUCHI 123
TANAKA 183
TARSKI 63, 125
T_1-space 64
topological space 64
transitive 14
transposed 95
TREVISAN 111
trivial congruence relation 173

U

uniquely complemented element 46
— — lattice 46
up-directed 75
upper bound 22
— covering condition 97
UTUMI 81
UZKOV 181

V

valuation 108
VAIDA 111
VAIDYANATASHWAMI 64
VASSILIOU 80
VILHELM 106, 181

W

WALLMANN 76
WANG 183
WARD 68, 69, 93, 97
weakly complemented 48
WHITMAN 149
WILCOX 142
WITT 33
WOLK 63, 75

Z

ZORN 21

Responsible for publication
Gy. Bernát
Director of the Publishing House of the Hungarian Academy of Sciences
and of the
Printing House of the Hungarian Academy of Sciences

Responsible editor
H. F. North

Technical editor
I. Húth